CHURCH HYMNAL

MENNONITE

A Collection of Hymns and Sacred Songs
Suitable for Use in Public Worship,
Worship in the Home, and all
General Occasions

J. D. BRUNK, Musical Editor
S. F. COFFMAN, Hymn Editor

Published by Approval of
MENNONITE GENERAL CONFERENCE

ELEVENTH EDITION
Ninety-sixth Thousand

Mennonite Publishing House
Scottdale, Pennsylvania

1951

Publisher's Note

In the publishing of this Church Hymnal, the Mennonite Publication Board has assumed the task for the Church by request of its constituency. It is in keeping with its policy to serve in any capacity possible for the promotion of the Cause of Christ and His Church. Any publisher serves his interests best as he is able to serve his constituency. In the execution of this work, this fundamental principle has been constantly kept in mind. Its life and usefulness will be determined by the support given to its use by the brotherhood.

At the meeting of the Mennonite General Conference held August 29, 30, 1917, recommendations were adopted authorizing the gathering of material for a book of this kind. At the next General Conference held two years later the following resolution was adopted: "Resolved, that we recommend that the Music Committee with the Publishing Committee take steps in the compiling of a hymn book of Church standard." Two years later the General Conference took further steps in enlarging the personnel of the Music Committee by appointing advisory Hymns and Music Committees. The Committees appointed were as follows:

Music Committee

C. Z. Yoder, Chairman, J. D. Brunk, Secretary and Music Editor, S. F. Coffman, Hymn Editor, Walter E. Yoder, Ed. Miller, S. R. Good, J. B. Smith.

Advisory Hymns Committee

L. J. Heatwole, Noah Mack, John Horsch, J. D. Charles, E. J. Zook, and the Hymn Editor.

Advisory Music Committee

A. B. Kolb, Chauncey J. King, Amos Ebersole, Chester K. Lehman, with the Hymn and Music Editors.

Certain of these members were called by death before the completion of the work and others were unable to serve in their appointments. The vacancies were temporarily filled by others.

No claim is being made for the new productions in this collection. It is rather a compilation of the best of that Church music which has stood the test of past years and which has found a place in the evangelical activities of the Christian Church. That class of hymns and songs most particularly adapted to congregations in their long cherished practice of congregational singing has been selected. Due recognition is given to the owners of copyrighted music. If any songs have been used without the necessary permission, is is unintentional, and will be adjusted upon receipt of the necessary information.

We send it forth with a prayer that its use may bring honor and glory to His name and added spiritual life to the Churches.

The Publishers.

Music Committee's Note

The divine gift of song enables the children of God to express to Him their holy devotion in a manner not otherwise possible. Heaven and earth are full of His praises:—the song of the "Morning Stars" and the melodies in the hearts of His saints. Music and poetry are the language of the soul. The blending of rhythm and harmony in their infinite forms makes possible the endless praise and adoration to God, whose love passeth knowledge, which love is comprehended only in the complete body of Christ gathered together from all parts of the earth and from all ages of time.

The Music Committee appointed by the General Conference has endeavored to fulfill its obligation to the Church in compiling this hymnal. The former Committees, appointed for such duties, undertook and carried out their work faithfully, and with the greatest concern for the spiritual welfare and prosperity of the Church. Your Committee has desired, and endeavored, to serve in the same spirit, keeping in mind the necessity of preserving the purity of doctrine and reverence in worship which has ever promoted the spiritual life and power of the Church and the glory of God in the world.

During the period of ten years, since the appointment of the Committee to undertake the work of compiling this hymnal, there has been a constant outlook and effort to select hymns that are true to the Christian faith, and which give faithful testimony to those principles for which the Church has ever stood. Of necessity the majority of the selections have come from the past centuries, and from authors using the English language. The German language, the language of our forefathers, is rich in hymns and tunes of the highest spiritual value but it was found that generally translations from German have proved unsatisfactory in form and expression of thought.

The Committee made its selection of hymns with a view to the Scriptural teaching rather than to the spiritual emotion expressed in the hymn. The Committee also endeavored to maintain the standards of the Church in the character of the music selected for the hymnal. A limited number of spiritual songs and choruses have been selected which bear the doctrinal message and express the devotional spirit of the worship of Christ. The majority of the selections are hymn tunes which have been used by the Church in the past centuries, many of which have become familiar through use in our congregations. Tunes were selected that were appealing enough in their melodies and simple enough in harmony to encourage congregational singing. It was the impression of the Committee that it was more advisable to encourage the use of the earlier type of Church music, with its richness of devotion and reverence to the holiness and majesty of our God and Savior, than to cultivate the desire for the lighter and more emotional song form of the modern age.

The members of the Committee desire to express their great sorrow in the loss by death, on Feb. 6, 1926, of Brother J. D. Brunk who served in the capacity of Music Editor and Secretary of the Committee for many years. His wide knowledge of music and his conception of the values of hymns and tunes and many years of experience in compiling the music literature of the Church made his services on the Committee invaluable. What has been accomplished in the production of this book has been largely due to his effort and direction.

It was the ardent desire of the Committee to perform a worthy service for the Master, Jesus Christ. Praying that He may use the efforts put forth in compiling this hymnal to His praise, to the edification of saints and the salvation of many souls as the Church continues her testimony in the coming years, we submit these labors to the Lord and to His Church.

The Committee.

Contents

Church Hymnal

MENNONITE

PRAISE TO GOD

Come, Thou Almighty King

Now unto the King—be honor and glory.—I TIM. 1: 17

ITALIAN HYMN 6. 4. 6. 4. 6. 6. 6. 4

CHARLES WESLEY, 1757

FELICE GIARDINI, 1769

1

1. Come, Thou Al - might - y King, Help us Thy name to sing,
2. Come, Thou In - car - nate Word, Gird on Thy might - y sword,
3. Come, Ho - ly Com - fort - er, Thy sa - cred wit - ness bear
4. To the great One in Three E - ter - nal prais - es be

Help us to praise: Fa - ther, all - glo - ri - ous, O'er all vic-
Our prayer at - tend: Come, and Thy peo - ple bless, And give Thy
In this glad hour: Thou who al - might - y art, Now rule in
Hence ev - er - more: His sov'reign maj - es - ty May we in

to - ri - ous, Come, and reign o - ver us, An - cient of Days.
word suc - cess: Spir - it of ho - li - ness, On us de - scend.
ev - 'ry heart, And ne'er from us de - part, Spir - it of pow'r.
glo - ry see, And to e - ter - ni - ty Love and a - dore.

2 Loving Kindness

I will sing of the mercies of the Lord.—Ps. 89: 1

SAMUEL MEDLEY, 1738-1799   L. M.   Western Melody

1. A - wake, my soul, to joy - ful lays, And sing thy great Re-
2. He saw me ru - ined in the fall, Yet loved me not - with-
3. Tho' nu - m'rous hosts of might - y foes, Tho' earth and hell my
4. When troub-le, like a gloom - y cloud, Has gath - ered thick, and

deem - er's praise; He just - ly claims a song from me,
stand - ing all; He saved me from my lost es - tate,
way op - pose, He safe - ly leads my soul a - long,
thun - dered loud, He near my soul has al - ways stood,

His lov - ing - kind - ness, oh, how free! Lov - ing - kind - ness,
His lov - ing - kind - ness, oh, how great! Lov - ing - kind - ness,
His lov - ing - kind - ness, oh, how strong! Lov - ing - kind - ness,
His lov - ing - kind - ness, oh, how good! Lov - ing - kind - ness,

lov - ing - kind - ness, His lov - ing - kind - ness, oh, how free!
lov - ing - kind - ness, His lov - ing - kind - ness, oh, how great!
lov - ing - kind - ness, His lov - ing - kind - ness, oh, how strong!
lov - ing - kind - ness, His lov - ing - kind - ness, oh, how good!

Praise the Lord: Ye Heavens, Adore Him

Praise ye the Lord from the heavens.—Ps. 148: 1

J. KEMPTHORNE, 1775-1838   FABEN 8. 7. 8. 7. D.   JOHN H. WILCOX, 1849

1. Praise the Lord: ye heav'ns, a-dore Him; Praise Him, an - gels, in the height;
2. Praise the Lord, for He is glo - rious; Nev - er shall His prom-ise fail:
4. Wor - ship, hon - or, glo - ry, bless - ing, Lord, we of - fer un - to Thee;

Sun and moon, re - joice be - fore Him; Praise Him, all ye stars and light.
God hath made His saints vic - to - rious; Sin and death shall not pre - vail.
Young and old, Thy praise ex - press - ing, In glad hom - age bend the knee.

Praise the Lord, for He hath spo - ken; Worlds His might-y voice o - beyed:
Praise the God of our sal - va - tion; Hosts on high, His pow'r pro - claim;
All the saints in heav'n a - dore Thee; We would bow be - fore Thy throne:

Laws which nev - er shall be bro - ken For their guid-ance hath He made.
Heav'n and earth and all cre - a - tion, Laud and mag - ni - fy His name.
As Thine an - gels serve be - fore Thee, So on earth Thy will be done.

4 Benedic Anima

Praise and extol and honor the King of heaven.—DAN. 4: 37

HENRY F. LYTE, 1834   8. 7. 8. 7. 8. 7.   SIR JOHN GOSS, 1867

1. Praise, my soul, the King of heav - en; To His feet thy
2. Praise Him for His grace and fa - - vor To our fa - thers
3. Fa - ther - like, He tends and spares us; Well our fee - ble
4. An - gels, help us to a - dore Him; Ye be - hold Him

trib - ute bring; Ran - somed, healed, re - stored, for - giv - en,
in dis - tress; Praise Him, still the same for - ev - er,
frame He knows; In His hands He gen - tly bears us,
face to face; Sun and moon, bow down be - fore Him;

Who, like me, His praise should sing? Praise Him, praise Him,
Slow to chide, and swift to bless; Praise Him, praise Him,
Res - cues us from all our foes; Praise Him, praise Him,
Dwell - ers all in time and space, Praise Him, praise Him,

praise Him, praise Him, Praise the Ev - er - last - ing King.
praise Him, praise Him, Glo - rious in His faith - ful - ness.
praise Him, praise Him, Wide - ly as His mer - cy goes.
praise Him, praise Him, Praise with us the God of grace.

Bless Jehovah

Psalm 103

L. M. D.

S. J. VAIL

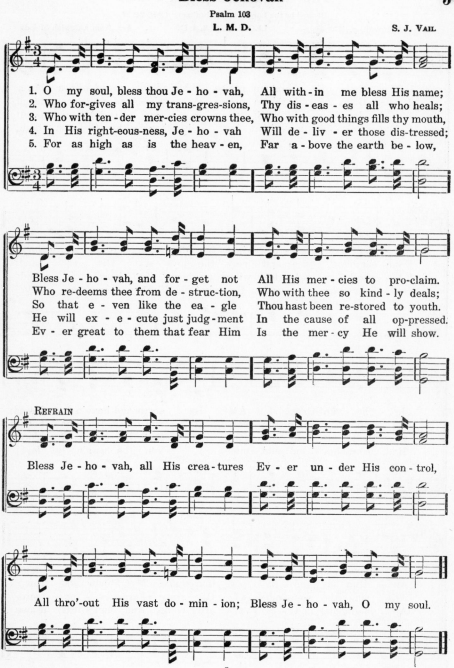

1. O my soul, bless thou Je - ho - vah, All with-in me bless His name;
2. Who for-gives all my trans-gres-sions, Thy dis - eas - es all who heals;
3. Who with ten - der mer-cies crowns thee, Who with good things fills thy mouth,
4. In His right-eous-ness, Je - ho - vah Will de - liv - er those dis-tressed;
5. For as high as is the heav - en, Far a - bove the earth be - low,

Bless Je - ho - vah, and for - get not All His mer - cies to pro-claim.
Who re-deems thee from de - struc-tion, Who with thee so kind - ly deals;
So that e - ven like the ea - gle Thou hast been re-stored to youth.
He will ex - e - cute just judg-ment In the cause of all op-pressed.
Ev - er great to them that fear Him Is the mer - cy He will show.

REFRAIN

Bless Je - ho - vah, all His crea - tures Ev - er un - der His con - trol,

All thro'-out His vast do - min - ion; Bless Je - ho - vah, O my soul.

6 The God of Abraham Praise

Blessed be the Lord God of Abraham.—GEN. 24: 27

THOMAS OLIVER, c. 1770   LEONI 6.6.8.4.D.   Arr. from a Jewish Melody

1. The God of Abraham praise, Who reigns en-throned a - bove,
2. The God of Abraham praise, At whose su - preme com-mand
3. He by Him - self hath sworn, I on His oath de - pend;
4. The whole tri - um - phant host Give thanks to God on high;

An - cient of ev - er - last - ing days, And God of love:
From earth I rise and seek the joys At His right hand:
I shall, on ea - gle's wings up - borne, To heav'n as - cend:
"Hail, Fa - ther, Son, and Ho - ly Ghost!" They ev - er cry:

Je - ho - vah! Great I AM! By earth and heav'n con - fessed;
I all on earth for - sake, Its wis - dom, fame, and pow'r;
I shall be - hold His face, I shall His pow'r a - dore,
Hail, Abraham's God and mine! I join the heav'n - ly lays;

I bow and bless the sa - cred name, For - ev - er blest.
And Him my on - ly por - tion make, My Shield and Tow'r.
And sing the won - ders of His grace For - ev - er - more.
All might and maj - es - ty are Thine, And end - less praise.

I'll Praise My Maker

While I live will I praise the Lord.—Ps. 146: 2

ISAAC WATTS, Alt. NASHVILLE 8s. 6l. Adapted by LOWELL MASON

1. I'll praise my Mak - er while I've breath, And when my voice is lost in death, Praise shall em - ploy my no - bler pow'rs; My days of praise shall ne'er be past, While life, and thought, and be - ing last, Or im - mor - tal - i - ty en - dures.

2. Hap - py the man whose hopes re - ly On Is - rael's God; He made the sky And earth and seas, with all their train: His truth for - ev - er stands se - cure; He saves th' oppressed, He feeds the poor, And none shall find His prom - ise vain.

3. The Lord pours eye - sight on the blind; The Lord sup - ports the faint - ing mind; He sends the la - b'ring con-science peace; He helps the stran - ger in dis - tress, The wid - ow and the fa - ther - less, And grants the pris - 'ner sweet re - lease.

4. I'll praise Him while He lends me breath, And when my voice is lost in death, Praise shall em - ploy my no - bler pow'rs; My days of praise shall ne'er be past, While life, and thought, and be - ing last, Or im - mor - tal - i - ty en - dures.

8

Praise Ye Jehovah

I will praise Thee with my whole heart.—Ps. 138: 1

AUCHINCAIRN 11. 10. 11. 10

MARGARET C. CAMPBELL, 1827-1841

J. K. SCOTT

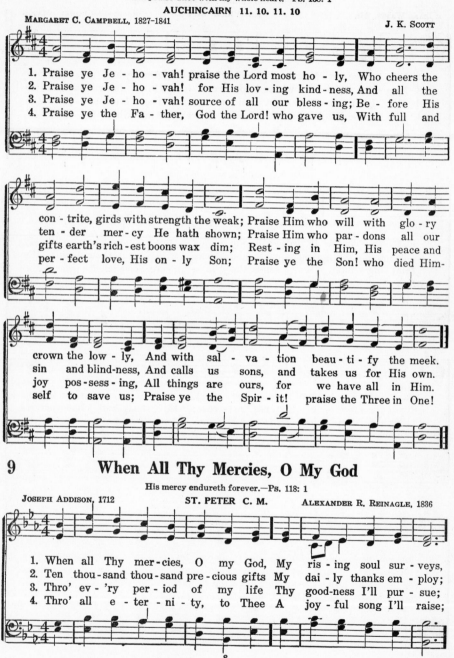

1. Praise ye Je - ho - vah! praise the Lord most ho - ly, Who cheers the
2. Praise ye Je - ho - vah! for His lov - ing kind - ness, And all the
3. Praise ye Je - ho - vah! source of all our bless - ing; Be - fore His
4. Praise ye the Fa - ther, God the Lord! who gave us, With full and

con - trite, girds with strength the weak; Praise Him who will with glo - ry
ten - der mer - cy He hath shown; Praise Him who par - dons all our
gifts earth's rich - est boons wax dim; Rest - ing in Him, His peace and
per - fect love, His on - ly Son; Praise ye the Son! who died Him-

crown the low - ly, And with sal - va - tion beau - ti - fy the meek.
sin and blind-ness, And calls us sons, and takes us for His own.
joy pos - sess - ing, All things are ours, for we have all in Him.
self to save us; Praise ye the Spir - it! praise the Three in One!

9

When All Thy Mercies, O My God

His mercy endureth forever.—Ps. 118: 1

JOSEPH ADDISON, 1712   **ST. PETER C. M.**   ALEXANDER R. REINAGLE, 1836

1. When all Thy mer - cies, O my God, My ris - ing soul sur - veys,
2. Ten thou - sand thou - sand pre - cious gifts My dai - ly thanks em - ploy;
3. Thro' ev - 'ry per - iod of my life Thy good-ness I'll pur - sue;
4. Thro' all e - ter - ni - ty, to Thee A joy - ful song I'll raise;

When All Thy Mercies, O My God—Concluded

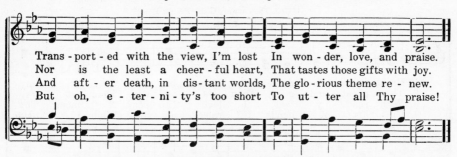

Trans - port - ed with the view, I'm lost In won - der, love, and praise.
Nor is the least a cheer - ful heart, That tastes those gifts with joy.
And aft - er death, in dis - tant worlds, The glo - rious theme re - new.
But oh, e - ter - ni - ty's too short To ut - ter all Thy praise!

From All That Dwell Below the Skies   10

Let all flesh bless His holy name.—Ps. 145: 21

TRURO L. M.

ISAAC WATTS

T. WILLIAMS' "Psalmodia Evangelica," 1789

1. From all that dwell be - low the skies, Let the Cre -
2. E - ter - nal are Thy mer - cies, Lord, E - ter - nal
3. Your loft - y themes, ye mor - tals, bring, In songs of
4. In ev - 'ry land be - gin the song; To ev - 'ry

a - - tor's praise a - rise; Let the Re - deem - er's
truth at - tends Thy word; Thy praise shall sound from
praise di - - vine - ly sing; The great sal - va - tion
land the strains be - long; In cheer - ful sound all

name be sung Thro' ev - 'ry land, by ev - 'ry tongue.
shore to shore, Till suns shall rise and set no more.
loud pro - claim, And shout for joy the Sav - iour's name.
voi - ces raise, And fill the world with loud - est praise.

11

Hagerstown

O God, Thou art my God.—Ps. 63: 1

ISAAC WATTS L. M. J. D. BRUNK, by per.

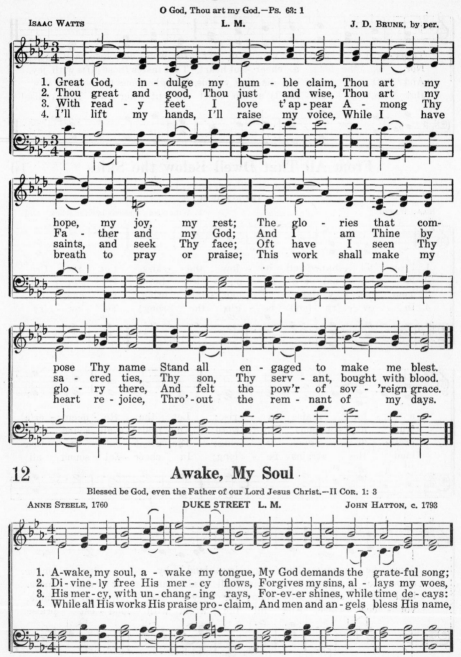

1. Great God, in - dulge my hum - ble claim, Thou art my
2. Thou great and good, Thou just and wise, Thou art my
3. With read - y feet I love t' ap - pear A - mong Thy
4. I'll lift my hands, I'll raise my voice, While I have

hope, my joy, my rest; The glo - ries that com -
Fa - ther and my God; And I am Thine by
saints, and seek Thy face; Oft have I seen Thy
breath to pray or praise; This work shall make my

pose Thy name Stand all en - gaged to make me blest.
sa - cred ties, Thy son, Thy serv - ant, bought with blood.
glo - ry there, And felt the pow'r of sov - 'reign grace.
heart re - joice, Thro'-out the rem - nant of my days.

12

Awake, My Soul

Blessed be God, even the Father of our Lord Jesus Christ.—II Cor. 1: 3

ANNE STEELE, 1760 DUKE STREET L. M. JOHN HATTON, c. 1793

1. A-wake, my soul, a - wake my tongue, My God demands the grate-ful song;
2. Di-vine-ly free His mer - cy flows, Forgives my sins, al - lays my woes,
3. His mer-cy, with un-chang-ing rays, For-ev-er shines, while time de-cays:
4. While all His works His praise pro - claim, And men and an-gels bless His name,

Awake, My Soul—Concluded

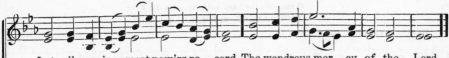

Let all my in - most pow'rs re - cord The wondrous mer - cy of the Lord.
And bids ap-proach-ing death re - move, And crowns me with in - dul-gent love.
And children's children shall re - cord The truth and good-ness of the Lord.
Oh, let my heart, my life, my tongue At-tend, and join the bliss-ful song!

Come, O My Soul, in Sacred Lays   13

Who is like unto Thee, O Lord.—Ex. 15: 11

THOMAS BLACKLOCK, 1721–1791   PARK STREET L. M.   FREDERICK M. A. VENUA, 1810

1. Come, O my soul, in sa - cred lays, At-tempt thy great Cre a -
2. En-throned a - mid the ra - diant spheres, He glo - ry like a
3. In all our Mak - er's grand de - signs, Al-might-y pow'r, with
4. Raised on de - vo - tion's loft - y wing, Do thou, my soul, His

a - tor's praise: But O what tongue can speak His fame? What mor - tal
gar - ment wears; To form a robe of light di - vine, Ten thou-sand
wis - dom, shines; His works, thro' all this won-drous frame, De - clare the
glo - ries sing; And let His praise em - ploy thy tongue, Till lis-t'ning

verse can reach the theme? What mor - tal verse can reach the theme?
suns a - round Him shine, Ten thou-sand suns a - round Him shine.
glo - ry of His name, De - clare the glo - ry of His name.
worlds shall join the song, Till lis-t'ning worlds shall join the song.

11

14 Now Thank We

O magnify the Lord with me. —Ps. 34: 3

NUN DANKET 6. 7. 6. 7. 6. 6. 6. 6.

MARTIN RINKART, c. 1636. Trans. G. JOHANN CRÜGER, 1647

1. Now thank we all our God With heart and hands and voi - ces,
2. O may this boun - teous God Thro' all our life be near us,
3. All praise and thanks to God, The Fa - ther, now be giv - en,

Who won-drous things hath done, In whom His world re - joi - ces;
With ev - er joy - ful hearts And bless - ed peace to cheer us;
The Son, and Him who reigns With them in high - est heav - en,

Who, from our moth - ers' arms, Hath blessed us on our way
And keep us in His grace, And guide us when per - plexed,
The One E - ter - nal God Whom earth and heav'n a - dore;

With count - less gifts of love, And still is ours to - day.
And free us from all ills In this world and the next.
For thus it was, is now, And shall be ev - er - more.

Thank and Praise Jehovah's Name

15

Now therefore, our God, we thank Thee.—I CHR. 29: 13

HORTON 7s.

JAMES MONTGOMERY, 1822

XAVIER SCHNEIDER VON WARTENSEE, 1786

1. Thank and praise Je-ho-vah's name; For His mer - cies, firm and sure,
2. Let the ran-somed thus re - joice, Gath-ered out of ev - 'ry land,
3. Praise Him, ye who know His love; Praise Him from the depths be-neath;
4. For His truth and mer-cy stand, Past, and pres - ent, and to be,

From e - ter - ni - ty the same To e - ter - ni - ty en - dure.
As the peo - ple of His choice, Plucked from the de-stroy-er's hand.
Praise Him in the heights a - bove; Praise your Mak-er all that breathe.
Like the years of His right hand—Like His own e - ter - ni - ty. A - MEN.

Begin, My Tongue, Some Heavenly Theme

16

And my tongue shall speak of Thy righteousness.—PS. 35: 28

MANOAH C. M.

ISAAC WATTS, 1707

Arr. in HENRY W. GREATOREX'S "Collection," Boston, 1851

1. Be - gin, my tongue, some heav'nly theme, And speak some boundless thing,
2. Tell of His won-drous faith-ful - ness, And sound His pow'r a - broad;
3. His ev - 'ry word of grace is strong As that which built the skies;
4. O might I hear Thy heav'n-ly tongue But whis-per, "Thou art Mine,"

The might-y works, or might-ier name Of our E - ter - nal King.
Sing the sweet prom-ise of His grace, And the per-form - ing God.
The voice that rolls the stars a - long Speaks all the prom - is - es.
Those gen - tle words should raise my song To notes al - most di - vine.

17 Around the Throne of God

I heard the voice of many angels round about the throne.—Rev. 5: 11-13

HENRY WARE, 1823   UNITY 6.6.6.6.8.8.   R. HUNTINGTON WOODMAN, 1895: alt.

1. A - round the throne of God / The host an - gel - ic throngs; / They
2. "O ho - ly, ho - ly Lord, / Cre - a - tion's sov-'reign King! / Thy
3. "Who shall not fear Thee, Lord, / And mag - ni - fy Thy name? / Thy
4. While thus the pow'rs on high / Their swell-ing cho - rus raise, / Let

spread their palms a - broad, And shout per - pet - ual songs: Him first they
maj - es - ty a - dored Let all cre - a - tion sing; Who wast, and
judg-ments, sent a - broad, Thy ho - li - ness pro - claim: Na - tions shall
earth and man re - ply, And ech - o back the praise: His glo - ry

own, Him last and best; God ev - er blest, And God a - lone.
art, And art to be; Nor time shall see Thy sway de - part.
throng From ev - 'ry shore, And all a - dore In one loud song."
own, First, last, and best; God ev - er blest, And God a - lone.

18 My God, I Thank Thee

Let them sacrifice the sacrifice of thanksgiving.—Ps. 107· 22

WENTWORTH 8.4.8.4.8.4.

Miss ADELAIDE A. PROCTER, 1825-1864   FREDERICK C. MAKER

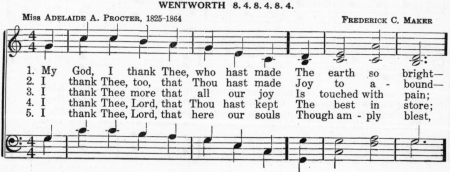

1. My God, I thank Thee, who hast made The earth so bright—
2. I thank Thee, too, that Thou hast made Joy to a - bound—
3. I thank Thee more that all our joy Is touched with pain;
4. I thank Thee, Lord, that Thou hast kept The best in store;
5. I thank Thee, Lord, that here our souls Though am - ply blest,

My God, I Thank Thee—Concluded

So full of splen - dor and of joy, Beau - ty and light—
So man - y gen - tle thoughts and deeds Cir - cling us round;
That shad - ows fall on bright - est hours, That thorns re - main—
We have e - nough, yet not too much, To long for more—
Can nev - er find, al - though they seek, A per - fect rest—

So man - y glo - rious things are here, No - ble and right.
That in the dark - est spot of earth Some love is found.
So that earth's bliss may be our guide, And not our chain.
A yearn-ing for a deep - er peace Not known be - fore.
Nor ev - er shall, un - til they lean On Je - sus' breast. A - MEN.

God is Good   19

Give thanks unto the Lord for He is good.—Ps. 118: 1

ELSIE BYLER   L. M.   SYLVIA BONTRAGER

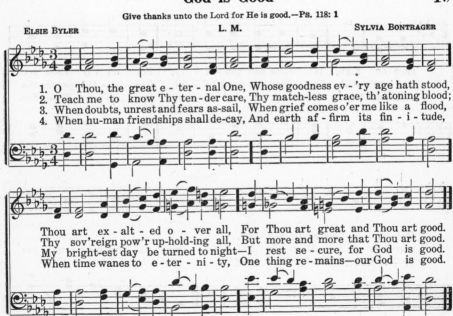

1. O Thou, the great e - ter - nal One, Whose goodness ev - 'ry age hath stood,
2. Teach me to know Thy ten - der care, Thy match-less grace, th'atoning blood;
3. When doubts, unrest and fears as-sail, When grief comes o'er me like a flood,
4. When hu - man friendships shall de-cay, And earth af - firm its fin - i - tude,

Thou art ex - alt - ed o - ver all, For Thou art great and Thou art good.
Thy sov'reign pow'r up-hold-ing all, But more and more that Thou art good.
My bright-est day be turned to night—I rest se - cure, for God is good.
When time wanes to e - ter - ni - ty, One thing re - mains—our God is good.

20

Thine is the Kingdom

EDITH SANFORD TILLOTSON   I. H. MEREDITH

With breadth and dignity

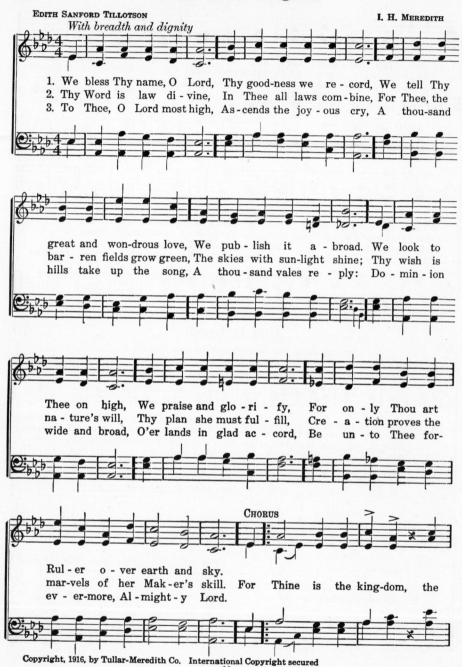

1. We bless Thy name, O Lord, Thy good-ness we re - cord, We tell Thy
2. Thy Word is law di - vine, In Thee all laws com - bine, For Thee, the
3. To Thee, O Lord most high, As - cends the joy - ous cry, A thou-sand

great and won-drous love, We pub - lish it a - broad. We look to
bar - ren fields grow green, The skies with sun-light shine; Thy wish is
hills take up the song, A thou - sand vales re - ply: Do - min - ion

Thee on high, We praise and glo - ri - fy, For on - ly Thou art
na - ture's will, Thy plan she must ful - fill, Cre - a - tion proves the
wide and broad, O'er lands in glad ac - cord, Be un - to Thee for-

CHORUS

Rul - er o - ver earth and sky.
mar-vels of her Mak - er's skill. For Thine is the king-dom, the
ev - er-more, Al - might - y Lord.

Thine is the Kingdom—Concluded

pow - er, the glo - ry, For ev - er and ev - er, Thy prais - es

we will sing, Yes, Thou art al - might-y, and Thou art our King.

will sing,

Great God, How Infinite

21

Thy throne, O God, is forever and ever.—Ps. 45: 6

WINDSOR C. M.

Isaac Watts, 1707   Melody arr. from Christopher Tye, 1533

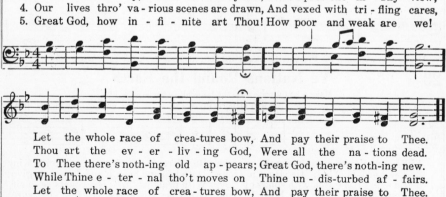

1. Great God, how in - fi - nite art Thou! How poor and weak are we!
2. Thy throne e - ter - nal a - ges stood, Ere seas or stars were made:
3. E - ter - ni - ty, with all its years, Stands pres-ent in Thy view;
4. Our lives thro' va - rious scenes are drawn, And vexed with tri - fling cares,
5. Great God, how in - fi - nite art Thou! How poor and weak are we!

Let the whole race of crea-tures bow, And pay their praise to Thee.
Thou art the ev - er - liv - ing God, Were all the na - tions dead.
To Thee there's noth-ing old ap - pears; Great God, there's noth-ing new.
While Thine e - ter - nal tho't moves on Thine un - dis-turbed af - fairs.
Let the whole race of crea-tures bow, And pay their praise to Thee.

17

22 Lord of the Worlds Above

How amiable are Thy tabernacles, O Lord of hosts.—Ps. 84: 1

ISAAC WATTS, 1719   LAUS DEO 6. 6. 6. 6. 8. 8.   JOHN H. GOWER, 1895

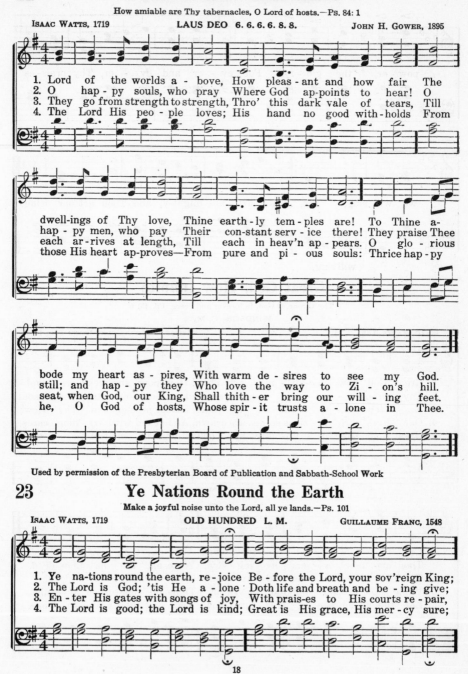

1. Lord of the worlds a - bove, How pleas - ant and how fair The
2. O hap - py souls, who pray Where God ap-points to hear! O
3. They go from strength to strength, Thro' this dark vale of tears, Till
4. The Lord His peo - ple loves; His hand no good with - holds From

dwell-ings of Thy love, Thine earth - ly tem - ples are! To Thine a-
hap - py men, who pay Their con-stant serv - ice there! They praise Thee
each ar - rives at length, Till each in heav'n ap - pears. O glo - rious
those His heart ap-proves—From pure and pi - ous souls: Thrice hap - py

bode my heart as - pires, With warm de - sires to see my God.
still; and hap - py they Who love the way to Zi - on's hill.
seat, when God, our King, Shall thith - er bring our will - ing feet.
he, O God of hosts, Whose spir - it trusts a - lone in Thee.

Used by permission of the Presbyterian Board of Publication and Sabbath-School Work

23 Ye Nations Round the Earth

Make a joyful noise unto the Lord, all ye lands.—Ps. 101

ISAAC WATTS, 1719   OLD HUNDRED L. M.   GUILLAUME FRANC, 1548

1. Ye na-tions round the earth, re - joice Be - fore the Lord, your sov'reign King;
2. The Lord is God; 'tis He a - lone Doth life and breath and be - ing give;
3. En - ter His gates with songs of joy, With prais - es to His courts re - pair,
4. The Lord is good; the Lord is kind; Great is His grace, His mer - cy sure;

Ye Nations Round the Earth—Concluded

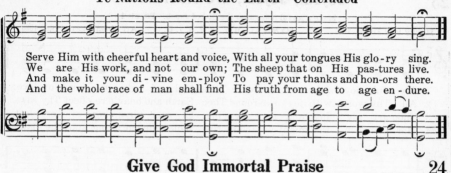

Serve Him with cheerful heart and voice, With all your tongues His glo-ry sing.
We are His work, and not our own; The sheep that on His pas-tures live.
And make it your di-vine em-ploy To pay your thanks and hon-ors there.
And the whole race of man shall find His truth from age to age en-dure.

Give God Immortal Praise

Praise ye the Lord—His mercy endureth forever.—Ps. 106: 1

ISAAC WATTS, 1719   WARRINGTON L. M.   RALPH HARRISON, 1784

24

1. Give to our God im-mor-tal praise; Mer-cy and
2. Give to the Lord of lords re-nown; The King of
3. He built the earth, He spread the sky, And fixed the
4. He fills the sun with morn-ing light; He bids the
5. He sent His Son with pow'r to save From guilt, and

truth are all His ways: Won-ders of grace to
kings with glo-ry crown; His mer-cies ev - - er
star-ry lights on high: Won-ders of grace to
moon di-rect the night: His mer-cies ev - - er
dark-ness, and the grave: Won-ders of grace to

God be-long; Re-peat His mer-cies in your song.
shall en-dure, When lords and kings are known no more.
God be-long; Re-peat His mer-cies in your song.
shall en-dure; When suns and moons shall shine no more.
God be-long; Re-peat His mer-cies in your song.

19

25 Joyful, Joyful, We Adore Thee

Make a joyful noise unto the God of Jacob.—Ps. 81: 1

HENRY VAN DYKE, 1908   HYMN TO JOY 8. 7. 8. 7. D.   ARR. from BEETHOVEN, 1826

1. Joy - ful, joy - ful, we a - dore Thee, God of glo - ry, Lord of love;
2. All Thy works with joy sur-round Thee, Earth and heav'n re - flect Thy rays,
3. Thou art giv - ing and for - giv - ing, Ev - er bless - ing, ev - er blest,
4. Mor-tals, join the might-y cho - rus Which the morn-ing stars be - gan;

Hearts un - fold like flow'rs be - fore Thee, Hail Thee as the sun a - bove.
Stars and an - gels sing a-round Thee, Cen - ter of un - bro-ken praise;
Well-spring of the joy of liv - ing, O - cean-depth of hap - py rest!
Fa - ther - love is reign-ing o'er us, Broth-er - love binds man to man.

Melt the clouds of sin and sad - ness; Drive the dark of doubt a - way;
Field and for - est, vale and moun-tain, Blossoming mead-ow, flash-ing sea,
Thou the Fa - ther, Christ our Broth-er, All who live in love are Thine:
Ev - er sing - ing, march we on - ward, Vic - tors in the midst of strife;

Giv - er of im - mor - tal glad - ness, Fill us with the light of day!
Chant-ing bird and flow - ing foun-tain, Call us to re - joice in Thee.
Teach us how to love each oth - er, Lift us to the Joy Di - vine.
Joy - ful mu - sic lifts us sun-ward In the tri - umph song of life.

Great God! Attend

A day in Thy courts is better than a thousand.—Ps. 84: 10, 11

ISAAC WATTS, 1719   UXBRIDGE L. M.   LOWELL MASON, 1830

1. Great God! at-tend while Zi - on sings The joy that from Thy pres-ence springs;
2. Might I en - joy the mean-est place With-in Thy house, O God of grace!
3. All need-ful grace will God be - stow, And crown that grace with glory too;
4. O God, our King, whose sov'reign sway The glorious hosts of heav'n o - bey,

To spend one day with Thee on earth, Ex-ceeds a thou-sand days of mirth.
Not tents of ease, nor thrones of pow'r, Should tempt my feet to leave Thy door.
He gives us all things, and with-holds No re - al good from up - right souls.
And dev - ils at Thy pres-ence flee; Blest is the man that trusts in Thee.

My God, How Endless is Thy Love

They are new every morning, great is Thy faithfulness.—LAM. 3: 22, 23

ALSACE L. M.

ISAAC WATTS, 1709   Arr. from LUDWIG VAN BEETHOVEN, 1770-1827

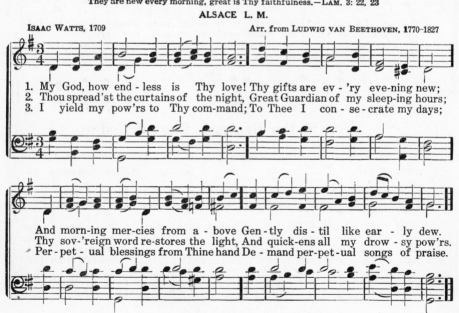

1. My God, how end - less is Thy love! Thy gifts are ev - 'ry eve-ning new;
2. Thou spread'st the curtains of the night, Great Guardian of my sleep-ing hours;
3. I yield my pow'rs to Thy com-mand; To Thee I con - se - crate my days;

And morn-ing mer-cies from a - bove Gen-tly dis - til like ear - ly dew.
Thy sov-'reign word re-stores the light, And quick-ens all my drow - sy pow'rs.
Per - pet - ual blessings from Thine hand De - mand per-pet-ual songs of praise.

28 Holy, Holy, Holy

They rest not day and night saying Holy, holy, holy.—Rev. 4: 8

REGINALD HEBER, 1783-1826   12. 13. 12. 10. P. M.   J. B. DYKES

1. Ho-ly, ho-ly, ho-ly, Lord God Al-might-y! Ear-ly in the morn-ing our song shall rise to Thee; Ho-ly, ho-ly, ho-ly, mer-ci-ful and might-y, God in Three Per-sons, bless-ed Trin-i-ty!
2. Ho-ly, ho-ly, ho-ly, all the saints a-dore Thee, Cast-ing down their gold-en crowns a-round the glass-y sea; Cher-u-bim and ser-a-phim, fall-ing down be-side Thee, Which wert, and art, and ev-er-more shalt be.
3. Ho-ly, ho-ly, ho-ly, tho' the dark-ness hide Thee, Tho' the eye of sin-ful man Thy glo-ry may not see; On-ly Thou art ho-ly! there is none be-side Thee, Per-fect in pow'r, in love, in pu-ri-ty.
4. Ho-ly, ho-ly, ho-ly, Lord God Al-might-y! All Thy works shall praise Thy name, in earth, and sky, and sea; Ho-ly, ho-ly, ho-ly, mer-ci-ful and might-y, God in Three Per-sons, bless-ed Trin-i-ty!

29 High in the Heavens, Eternal God

Thy mercy, O Lord, is in the heavens.—Ps. 36: 5

TRURO L. M.

ISAAC WATTS, 1719   T. WILLIAMS' "Psalmodia Evangelica," 1789

1. High in the heav'ns, E-ter-nal God, Thy good-ness
2. For ev-er firm Thy jus-tice stands, As moun-tains
3. My God, how ex-cel-lent Thy grace, Whence all our
4. Life, like a foun-tain, rich and free, Springs from the

High in the Heavens, Eternal God—Concluded

in full glo - ry shines; Thy truth shall break through
their foun - da - tions keep; Wise are the won - ders
hope and com - fort spring! The sons of Ad - am
pres - ence of our Lord; And in Thy light our

ev - 'ry cloud That veils and dark - ens Thy de - signs.
of Thy hands; Thy judg-ments are a might - y deep.
in dis - tress Fly to the shad - ow of Thy wing.
souls shall see The glo - ries prom - ised in Thy Word.

Before Jehovah's Awful Throne

30

Thou art worthy, O Lord, to receive glory, honor and power.—Rev. 4: 10, 11

ISAAC WATTS, 1719   **WATTS L. M.**   J. D. BRUNK, 1910

1. Be - fore Je - ho-vah's aw - ful throne, Ye na-tions, bow with sa-cred joy:
2. His sov-'reign pow'r, without our aid, Made us of clay, and formed us men;
3. We are His peo - ple, we His care, Our souls, and all our mor-tal frame;
4. We'll crowd Thy gates with thankful songs, High as the heav'ns our voi-ces raise;
5. Wide as the world is Thy com-mand, Vast as e - ter - ni - ty Thy love;

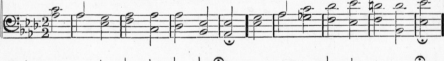

Know that the Lord is God a - lone: He can cre - ate, and He de - stroy.
And when like wand'ring sheep we strayed, He bro't us to His fold a - gain.
What last - ing hon - ors shall we rear, Al - might - y Mak - er, to Thy name?
And earth, with her ten thousand tongues, Shall fill Thy courts with sounding praise.
Firm as a rock Thy truth must stand, When roll - ing years shall cease to move.

31 The Spacious Firmament On High

The heavens declare the glory of God.—Ps. 19: 1-6

CREATION L. M. D.

JOSEPH ADDISON, 1712   Arr. from F. JOSEPH HAYDN, 1798

1. The spa - cious fir - ma - ment on high, With all the blue e-
2. Soon as the eve-ning shades pre - vail, The moon takes up the
3. What tho' in sol-emn si - lence all Move round this dark ter-

the - real sky, And span-gled heav'ns, a shin - ing frame, Their
won - drous tale, And night-ly to the lis - t'ning earth Re-
res - trial ball? What tho' no re - al voice nor sound A-

great O - rig - i - nal pro - claim. Th' un-wea-ried sun, from day to day,
peats the sto - ry of her birth; Whilst all the stars that round her burn,
midst their ra - diant orbs be found? In rea - son's ear they all re - joice,

Does his Cre - a - tor's pow'r dis - play, And pub - lish - es to
And all the plan - ets in their turn, Con-firm the ti - dings
And ut - ter forth a glo - rious voice; For - ev - er sing - ing,

The Spacious Firmament On High—Concluded

ev - - 'ry land The work.... of an...... al-might - y hand.
as they roll, And spread .. the truth... from pole to pole.
as they shine, "The hand.... that made... us is Di - vine."

Eternal Father

32

I dwell in the high and holy place.—Isa. 57: 15

HERVEY D. GANSE, 1872　　　WAREHAM L. M.　　　WILLIAM KNAPP, 1738

1. E - ter - nal Fa - ther, when to Thee, Be - yond all
2. But, Sav - iour, Thou art by my side; Thy voice I
3. And Thou, great Spir - it, in my heart Dost make Thy
4. Blest Trin - i - ty, in whom a - lone All things cre-

worlds, by faith I soar, Be - fore Thy bound - less
hear, Thy face I see: Thou art my Friend, my
tem - ple day by day; The Ho - ly Ghost of
a - - ted move or rest, High in the heav'ns Thou

maj - es - ty I stand in si - lence, and a - dore.
dai - ly Guide; God o - ver all, yet God with me.
God Thou art, Yet dwell - est in this house of clay.
hast Thy throne; Thou hast Thy throne with - in my breast.

33 God is Love

God is love.— I Jno. 4: 8

Anon.   E. S. Lorenz

1. Come, let us all u - nite to sing, God is love; Let heav'n and
2. Oh, tell to earth's re - mot - est bound, God is love; In Christ we
3. How hap-py is our por - tion here, God is love; His prom - is-

earth their prais - es bring, God is love; Let ev - 'ry soul from
have re - demp-tion found, God is love; His blood has washed our
es our spir - its cheer, God is love; He is our sun and

sin a - wake, Each in his heart sweet mu - sic make, And sing with
sins a - way, His Spir - it turned our night to day, And now we
shield by day, Our help, our hope, our strength and stay, He will be

REFRAIN

us for Je - sus' sake, For God is love. God is love! God is
can re-joice to say, That God is love.
with us all the way, Our God is love. God is love!

love! Come, let us all u - nite to sing That God is love.
God is love!

Mighty God, While Angels Bless Thee

And all the angels stood round about the throne.—REV. 7: 11, 12

AUTUMN 8. 7. D.

ROBERT ROBINSON, 1774. Alt.

LOUIS VON ESCH, c., 1810
Arr. by GEORGE F. ROOT

34

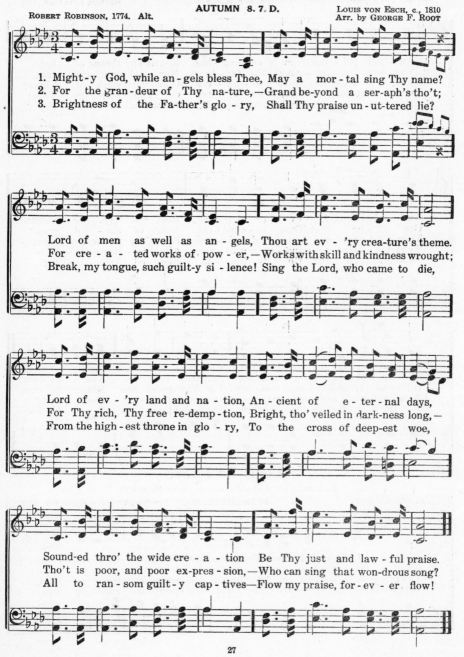

1. Might-y God, while an-gels bless Thee, May a mor-tal sing Thy name?
2. For the gran-deur of Thy na-ture,—Grand be-yond a ser-aph's tho't;
3. Brightness of the Fa-ther's glo-ry, Shall Thy praise un-ut-tered lie?

Lord of men as well as an-gels, Thou art ev-'ry crea-ture's theme.
For cre-a-ted works of pow-er,—Works with skill and kindness wrought;
Break, my tongue, such guilt-y si-lence! Sing the Lord, who came to die,

Lord of ev-'ry land and na-tion, An-cient of e-ter-nal days,
For Thy rich, Thy free re-demp-tion, Bright, tho' veiled in dark-ness long,—
From the high-est throne in glo-ry, To the cross of deep-est woe,

Sound-ed thro' the wide cre-a-tion Be Thy just and law-ful praise.
Tho't is poor, and poor ex-pres-sion,—Who can sing that won-drous song?
All to ran-som guilt-y cap-tives—Flow my praise, for-ev-er flow!

35 Angel Voices

I heard the voice of many angels round about the throne.—Rev. 5: 11

FRANCIS POTT, 1861   **8. 5. 8. 5. 8. 4. 3.**   ARTHUR SULLIVAN, 1872

1. An - gel voi - ces, ev - er sing - ing Round Thy throne of light,
2. Thou who art be - yond the far - thest Mor - tal eye can scan,
3. Yea, we know Thy love re - joi - ces O'er each work of Thine;
4. Here, great God, to - day we of - fer Of Thine own to Thee;
5. Hon - or, glo - ry, might, and mer - it, Thine shall ev - er be,

An - gel harps, for - ev - er ring - ing, Rest not day nor night;
Can it be that Thou re - gard - est Songs of sin - ful man?
Thou didst ears and hands and voi - ces For Thy praise com - bine;
And for Thine ac - cept - ance prof - fer, All un - wor - thi - ly,
Fa - ther, Son, and Ho - ly Spir - it, Bless - ed Trin - i - ty:

Thou-sands on - ly live to bless Thee, And con - fess Thee Lord of might.
Can we feel that Thou art near us, And wilt hear us? Yea, we can.
Craftsman's art and mu-sic's meas-ure For Thy pleas - ure Didst de - sign.
Hearts and minds, and hands and voi-ces, In our choic - est Mel - o - dy.
Of the best that Thou hast giv - en Earth and heav - en Ren - der Thee.

36 Long As I Live

I will sing unto the Lord as long as I live.—Ps. 104: 33

ISAAC WATTS, 1707   **BELMONT C. M.**   Arr. from WILLIAM GARDINER, 1812

1. Long as I live I'll bless Thy name, My King, my God, my love;
2. Great is the Lord, His pow'r unknown, And let His praise be great;
3. Thy grace shall dwell up - on my tongue, And while my lips re - joice,
4. The world is gov-erned by Thy hand; The saints are ruled by love;

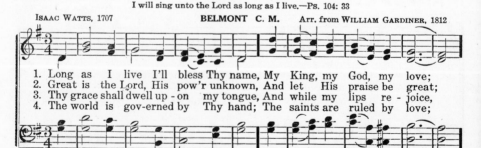

Long As I Live—Concluded

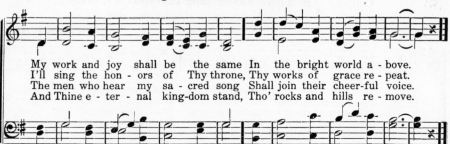

My work and joy shall be the same In the bright world a-bove.
I'll sing the hon-ors of Thy throne, Thy works of grace re-peat.
The men who hear my sa-cred song Shall join their cheer-ful voice.
And Thine e-ter-nal king-dom stand, Tho' rocks and hills re-move.

Let All On Earth Their Voices Raise 37

Sing unto the Lord, all the earth.—Ps. 96: 1

ISAAC WATTS   ARIEL 8. 8. 6. D.   Arr. by LOWELL MASON

1. Let all on earth their voi-ces raise, To sing the great Je-ho-vah's praise,
2. He framed the globe; He built the sky; He made the shining worlds on high,
3. Come the great day, the glo-rious hour, When earth shall feel His saving pow'r,

And bless His ho-ly name: His glo-ry let the heathen know, His won-ders
And reigns in glo-ry there: His beams are maj-es-ty and light; His beau-ties
All na-tions fear His name: Then shall the race of men con-fess The beau-ty

to the na-tions show, His saving grace proclaim, His saving grace pro-claim.
how di-vine-ly bright! His dwelling place, how fair! His dwelling place, how fair!
of His ho-li-ness, His saving grace proclaim, His saving grace pro-claim.

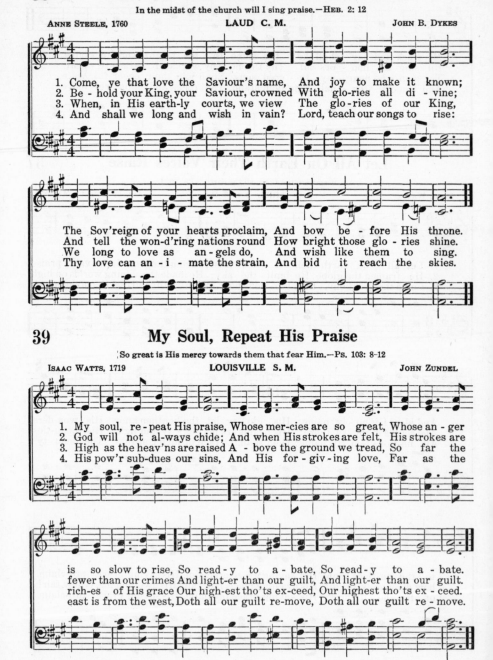

38 Come, Ye That Love the Saviour's Name

In the midst of the church will I sing praise.—Heb. 2: 12

Anne Steele, 1760 — LAUD C. M. — John B. Dykes

1. Come, ye that love the Saviour's name, And joy to make it known;
2. Be - hold your King, your Saviour, crowned With glo-ries all di - vine;
3. When, in His earth-ly courts, we view The glo-ries of our King,
4. And shall we long and wish in vain? Lord, teach our songs to rise:

The Sov'reign of your hearts proclaim, And bow be - fore His throne.
And tell the won-d'ring nations round How bright those glo - ries shine.
We long to love as an - gels do, And wish like them to sing.
Thy love can an - i - mate the strain, And bid it reach the skies.

39 My Soul, Repeat His Praise

So great is His mercy towards them that fear Him.—Ps. 103: 8-12

Isaac Watts, 1719 — LOUISVILLE S. M. — John Zundel

1. My soul, re - peat His praise, Whose mer-cies are so great, Whose an - ger
2. God will not al-ways chide; And when His strokes are felt, His strokes are
3. High as the heav'ns are raised A - bove the ground we tread, So far the
4. His pow'r sub-dues our sins, And His for - giv - ing love, Far as the

is so slow to rise, So read - y to a - bate, So read - y to a - bate.
fewer than our crimes And light-er than our guilt, And light-er than our guilt.
rich-es of His grace Our high-est tho'ts ex-ceed, Our highest tho'ts ex - ceed.
east is from the west, Doth all our guilt re-move, Doth all our guilt re - move.

Bless, O My Soul, the Living God

40

Forget not all His benefits.—Ps. 103: 1-4

ISAAC WATTS, 1719   MILLER L. M.   EDWARD MILLER

1. Bless, O my soul, the liv - ing God; Call home thy tho'ts that rove a - broad:
2. Bless, O my soul, the God of grace; His fa - vors claim thy high-est praise;
3. 'Tis He, my soul, that sent His Son To die for crimes which thou hast done;
4. Let ev - 'ry land His pow'r con-fess; Let all the earth a - dore His grace:

Let all the pow'rs with-in me join In work and wor-ship so di-vine.
Why should the wonders He hath wrought Be lost in si - lence, and for-got?
He owns the ran - som, and for-gives The hour - ly fol - lies of our lives.
My heart and tongue with rap-ture join In work and wor-ship so di-vine.

O Love of God, How Strong and True

41

Yet, I have loved thee with an everlasting love.— JER. 31: 3

HORATIUS BONAR, 1861   BROOKFIELD L. M.   THOMAS B. SOUTHGATE, 1855

1. O love of God, how strong and true! E - ter - nal, and yet ev - er new;
2. O wide-em - brac-ing, won - drous love! We read thee in the sky a - bove,
3. We read thee best in Him who came To bear for us the cross of shame,
4. We read thy pow'r to bless and save, E'en in the dark-ness of the grave;
5. O love of God, our shield and stay Thro' all the per - ils of our way!

Un - com-pre - hend-ed and un-bought, Be - yond all knowledge and all thought.
We read thee in the earth be - low, In seas that swell, and streams that flow.
Sent by the Fa-ther from on high, Our life to live, our death to die.
Still more in res - ur - rec-tion light We read the full - ness of thy might.
E - ter - nal love, in thee we rest, For-ev - er safe, for-ev - er blest.

42 There's a Wideness in God's Mercy

His tender mercies are over all His works.—Ps. 145: 9

FREDERICK W. FABER, 1814-1863   WELLESLEY 8. 7. 8. 7.   LIZZIE S. TOURJEE

1. There's a wide-ness in God's mer - cy, Like the wide-ness of the sea;
2. There is wel-come for the sin - ner, And more grac - es for the good;
3. For the love of God is broad - er Than the meas-ure of man's mind;
4. If our love were but more sim - ple, We should take Him at His word;

There's a kind-ness in His jus-tice, Which is more than lib - er - ty.
There is mer-cy with the Sav-iour; There is heal - ing in His blood.
And the heart of the E - ter-nal Is most won - der - ful - ly kind.
And our lives would be all sun-shine In the sweet-ness of our Lord.

43 God is Love, His Mercy Brightens

The mercy of the Lord is from everlasting to everlasting to them that fear Him.—Ps. 103: 17

J. ALLEN   EFFIE 8. 7. 8. 7.   D. M. CLICK

1. God is love, His mer - cy bright-ens All the path in which we move;
2. Chance and change are bus - y ev - er; Worlds de-cay, and a - ges move;
3. E'en the hour that dark - est seem - eth Will His changeless good-ness prove;
4. He with earth-ly cares en - twin - eth Hope and com - fort from a - bove;

Bliss He forms, and woe He light - ens; God is light, and God is love.
But His mer - cy wan - eth nev - er; God is light, and God is love.
From the mist His bright-ness streameth; God is light, and God is love.
Ev - 'ry-where His glo - ry shin - eth; God is light, and God is love.

The King of Love

The good shepherd giveth His life for the sheep.—JNO. 10: 11

44

HENRY W. BAKER, 1868   DOMINUS REGIT ME 8. 7. 8. 7.   JOHN B. DYKES, 1868

1. The King of love my Shep-herd is, Whose good-ness fail-eth nev-er;
2. Where streams of liv-ing wa-ter flow My ran-somed soul He lead-eth,
3. In death's dark vale I fear no ill With Thee, dear Lord, be-side me;
4. Thou spread'st a ta-ble in my sight; Thy unc-tion grace be-stow-eth;
5. And so through all the length of days Thy good-ness fail-eth nev-er:

I noth-ing lack if I am His And He is mine for-ev-er.
And, where the ver-dant pas-tures grow, With food ce-les-tial feed-eth.
Thy rod and staff my com-fort still, Thy cross be-fore to guide me.
And O what trans-port of de-light From Thy pure chal-ice flow-eth.
Good Shepherd, may I sing Thy praise With-in Thy house for-ev-er.

Lord, Thou Hast Searched

45

O Lord, Thou hast searched and known me. —PS. 139: 1-12

ISAAC WATTS, 1719   BERA L. M.   JOHN E. GOULD, 1849

1. Lord, Thou hast searched and seen me thro': Thine eye commands, with piercing view,
2. My tho'ts, be-fore they are my own Are to my God dis-tinct-ly known;
3. With-in Thy cir-cling pow'r I stand; On ev-'ry side I find Thy hand:
4. O may these tho'ts pos-sess my breast, Where'er I rove, wher-e'er I rest;

My ris-ing and my rest-ing hours, My heart and flesh with all their pow'rs.
He knows the words I mean to speak, Ere from my ope-ning lips they break.
A-wake, a-sleep, at home, a-broad, I am sur-round-ed still with God.
Nor let my weak-er pas-sions dare Con-sent to sin, for God is there. A-MEN.

46 The Lord is My Shepherd

Psalm 23

GOOD SHEPHERD 11. 11. 11. 11.

JAMES MONTGOMERY, 1822

JOSEPH BARNBY

1. The Lord is my Shep - herd, no want shall I know;
2. Thro' the val - ley and shad - ow of death though I stray,
3. In the midst of af - flic - tion my ta - ble is spread;
4. Let good - ness and mer - cy, my boun - ti - ful God,

I feed in green pas - tures, safe - fold - ed I rest;
Since Thou art my guard - ian, no e - vil I fear;
With bless - ings un - meas - ured my cup run - neth o'er;
Still fol - low my steps till I meet Thee a - bove;

He lead - eth my soul where the still wa - ters flow,
Thy rod shall de - fend me, Thy staff be my stay;
With per - fume and oil Thou a - noint - est my head;
I seek— by the path which my fore - fa - thers trod,

Re - stores me when wan - d'ring, re - deems when op - pressed.
No harm can be - fall, with my Com - fort - er near.
O what shall I ask of Thy prov - i - dence more?
Thro' the land of their so - journ—Thy king - dom of love.

With Songs and Honors Sounding

47

Great is the Lord and of great power.—Ps. 147: 5, 8-18

ISAAC WATTS, 1719   ST. LEONARD (Smart) C. M.   HENRY SMART, 1867

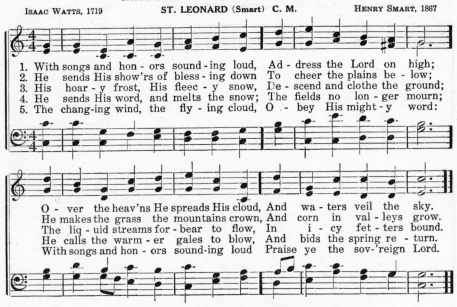

1. With songs and hon - ors sound-ing loud, Ad - dress the Lord on high;
2. He sends His show'rs of bless-ing down To cheer the plains be - low;
3. His hoar - y frost, His fleec - y snow, De - scend and clothe the ground;
4. He sends His word, and melts the snow; The fields no lon - ger mourn;
5. The chang-ing wind, the fly - ing cloud, O - bey His might - y word:

O - ver the heav'ns He spreads His cloud, And wa - ters veil the sky.
He makes the grass the mountains crown, And corn in val - leys grow.
The liq - uid streams for - bear to flow, In i - cy fet - ters bound.
He calls the warm - er gales to blow, And bids the spring re - turn.
With songs and hon - ors sound-ing loud Praise ye the sov-'reign Lord.

Jehovah, God, Thy Gracious Power

48

Thou openest Thine hand and satisfiest the desire of every living thing.—Ps. 145: 15, 16

JOHN THOMSON, 1810   TEMPLE C. M.   MARO L. BARTLETT

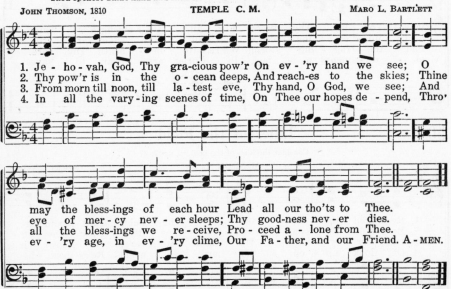

1. Je - ho - vah, God, Thy gra-cious pow'r On ev - 'ry hand we see; O
2. Thy pow'r is in the o - cean deeps, And reach-es to the skies; Thine
3. From morn till noon, till la - test eve, Thy hand, O God, we see; And
4. In all the vary - ing scenes of time, On Thee our hopes de - pend, Thro'

may the bless-ings of each hour Lead all our tho'ts to Thee.
eye of mer - cy nev - er sleeps; Thy good-ness nev - er dies.
all the bless-ings we re - ceive, Pro - ceed a - lone from Thee.
ev - 'ry age, in ev - 'ry clime, Our Fa - ther, and our Friend. A - MEN.

49 Maker of All Things

God created the heaven and the earth.—GEN. 1: 1

PHILIP DODDRIDGE, 1837, alt.　　　LANESBORO C. M. 51.　　　WILLIAM DIXON, 1790

1. Ma - ker of all things, might -y Lord! We own Thy pow'r di-
2. Wide as the win - try tem-pests sweep, They work Thy sov - 'reign
3. When dan-gers threat in ev - 'ry form, And death it - self is
4. With cheer-ful hope on Thee we stay, To res - cue from the

vine; The winds and waves o - bey Thy Word, The winds and
will; Thy voice is heard up - on the deep, Thy voice is
near; O God, a - mid the rag - ing storm, O God, a-
grave; Thou, whom the el - e - ments o - - bey, Thou, whom the

waves o - bey Thy Word, For all their strength is Thine.
heard up - on the deep, And all its waves are still.
mid the rag - ing storm, We're safe be - neath Thy care.
el - e - ments o - bey, In Christ art near to save.

50 Lilies of the Field

Consider the lilies of the field.—LK. 12: 27

MENDON L. M.　　　German Melody

1. Be - hold the lil - - ies of the field, That bloom a-
2. Be - hold the spar - rows as they fly; They come at
3. Our ver - y hairs He counts with care; He knows our
4. Oh, look up - on the Lord so near! Re - pose be-

Lilies of the Field—Concluded

round the Mas-ter's feet; Their droop-ing leaves new
His com-mand and call; They seem but specks up-
dai--ly hopes and fears; When griefs as-sail and
neath the shel-tered rock; The cross He light-ens

fra-grance yield, By Her-mon's dew and grate-ful heat.
on the sky, And yet He notes them when they fall.
tem-pests scare, He notes the mourn-er's se-cret tears.
by His cheer; The wind He temp-ers to His flock.

The Lord My Shepherd Is 51

Psalm 23

ISAAC WATTS, 1719   SWEET DAY S. M.   B. C. UNSELD

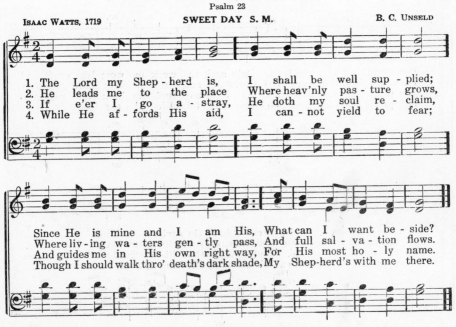

1. The Lord my Shep-herd is, I shall be well sup-plied;
2. He leads me to the place Where heav'nly pas-ture grows,
3. If e'er I go a-stray, He doth my soul re-claim,
4. While He af-fords His aid, I can-not yield to fear;

Since He is mine and I am His, What can I want be-side?
Where liv-ing wa-ters gen-tly pass, And full sal-va-tion flows.
And guides me in His own right way, For His most ho-ly name.
Though I should walk thro' death's dark shade, My Shep-herd's with me there.

52 A Mighty Fortress

The Lord is my Rock and my Fortress.—Ps. 18: 2

MARTIN LUTHER, 1529   **EIN FESTE BURG P. M.**   MARTIN LUTHER, 1529

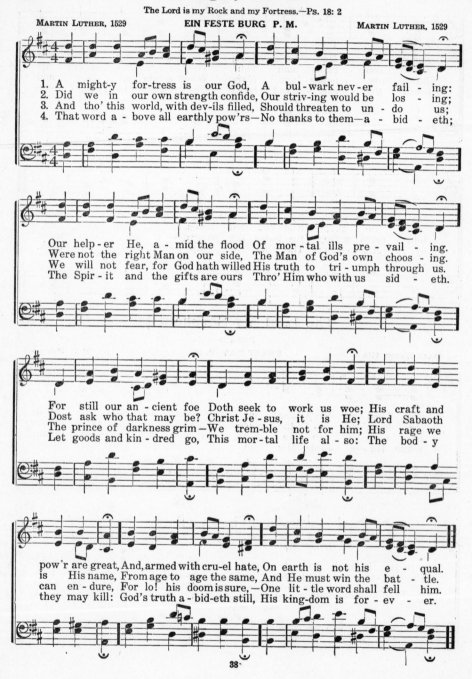

1. A might-y for-tress is our God, A bul-wark nev-er fail - ing:
2. Did we in our own strength confide, Our striv-ing would be los - ing;
3. And tho' this world, with dev-ils filled, Should threaten to un - do us;
4. That word a - bove all earthly pow'rs—No thanks to them—a - bid - eth;

Our help - er He, a - mid the flood Of mor - tal ills pre - vail - ing.
Were not the right Man on our side, The Man of God's own choos - ing.
We will not fear, for God hath willed His truth to tri - umph through us.
The Spir - it and the gifts are ours Thro' Him who with us sid - eth.

For still our an - cient foe Doth seek to work us woe; His craft and
Dost ask who that may be? Christ Je - sus, it is He; Lord Sabaoth
The prince of darkness grim—We trem-ble not for him; His rage we
Let goods and kin - dred go, This mor - tal life al - so: The bod - y

pow'r are great, And, armed with cru-el hate, On earth is not his e - qual.
is His name, From age to age the same, And He must win the bat - tle.
can en - dure, For lo! his doom is sure,—One lit - tle word shall fell him.
they may kill: God's truth a - bid-eth still, His king-dom is for - ev - er.

38

O God, Thy Power is Wonderful

Power belongeth unto God.—Ps. 62: 11, 12

53

FREDERICK W. FABER, 1814–1863   **BEATITUDO C. M.**   JOHN B. DYKES, 1875

1. O God, Thy pow'r is won - der - ful, Thy glo - ry pass - ing bright;
2. I see Thee in th' e - ter - nal years In glo - ry all a - lone,
3. I see Thee walk in E - den's shade, I see Thee all thro' time;
4. I see Thee when the doom is o'er, And out - worn time is done,
5. O lit - tle heart of mine! shall pain Or sor - row make thee moan,

Thy wis-dom, with its deep on deep, A rap - ture to the sight.
Ere round Thine un - cre - a - ted fires Cre - a - ted light had shone.
Thy pa-tience and com - pas - sion seem New at - tri - butes sub-lime.
When all this God is all for thee, O God, yet not a - lone.
    A Fa - ther all thine own?

God, My King

I will extol Thee, O God, my King.—Ps. 145: 1–12

54

STUTTGART 8. 7. 8. 7.

RICHARD MANT, 1824   Arr. from "Psalmodia Sacra" Gotha, 1715

1. God, my King, Thy might con - fess - ing, Ev - er will I bless Thy name;
2. Hon - or great our God be - fit - teth; Who His maj - es - ty can reach?
3. They shall talk of all Thy glo - ry, On Thy might and great-ness dwell,
4. All Thy works, O Lord, shall bless Thee; Thee shall all Thy saints a - dore:

Day by day Thy throne ad - dress - ing, Still will I Thy praise pro-claim.
Age to age His works trans-mit - teth, Age to age His pow'r shall teach.
Speak of Thy dread acts the sto - ry, And Thy deeds of won - der tell.
King su-preme shall they con - fess Thee, And pro-claim Thy sov-'reign pow'r.

55 Shepherd of Tender Youth

He shall feed His flock like a shepherd.—Isa. 40: 11

BRAUN 6. 6. 4. 6. 6. 6. 4.

Ascribed to CLEMENT OF ALEXANDRIA, c., 220

JOHANN G. BRAUN, 1675

1. Shep - herd of ten - der youth, Guid - ing in love and truth
2. Thou art our Ho - ly Lord, The all - sub - du - ing Word,
3. Thou art the Great High Priest, Thou hast pre - pared the feast
4. Ev - er be Thou our Guide, Our Shep - herd and our Pride,
5. So now and till we die, Sound we Thy prais - es high,

Thro' de - vious ways: Christ, our tri - um - phant King, We come Thy
Heal - er of strife: Thou didst Thy - self a - base, That from sin's
Of heav'n - ly love: While in our mor - tal pain, None calls on
Our Staff and Song: Je - sus, Thou Christ of God, By Thy per -
And joy - ful sing: In - fants, and the glad throng Who to Thy

name to sing; Hith - er our chil - dren bring, To shout Thy praise.
deep dis - grace Thou might-est save our race, And give us life.
Thee in vain: Help Thou dost not dis - dain, Help from a - bove.
en - nial Word, Lead us where Thou hast trod; Make our faith strong.
Church be-long, U - nite to swell the song To Christ our King.

56 Jesus Shall Reign

And He shall reign forever and ever.—Rev. 11: 15

ISAAC WATTS, 1719

DUKE STREET L. M.

JOHN HATTON, c., 1793

1. Je - sus shall reign wher - e'er the sun Does his suc-
2. For Him shall end - less prayer be made, And prais - es
3. Bless - ings a - bound wher - e'er He reigns; The pris - 'ner
4. Let ev - 'ry crea - ture rise and bring Pe - cul - iar

40

Jesus Shall Reign—Concluded

ces - sive jour - neys run; His king - dom stretch from
throng to crown His head; His name, like sweet per-
leaps to lose his chains, The wea - ry find e-
hon - ors to our King, An - gels de - scend with

shore to shore, Till moons shall wax and wane no more.
fume, shall rise With ev - 'ry morn - ing sac - ri - fice;
ter - nal rest, And all the sons of want are blest.
songs a - gain, And earth re - peat the loud A - men.

Behold the Glories of the Lamb 57

Worthy is the Lamb that was slain.—Rev. 5: 6, 9, 10, 12

Isaac Watts, 1706　　　ST. MARTIN'S C. M.　　　William Tans'ur, 1735

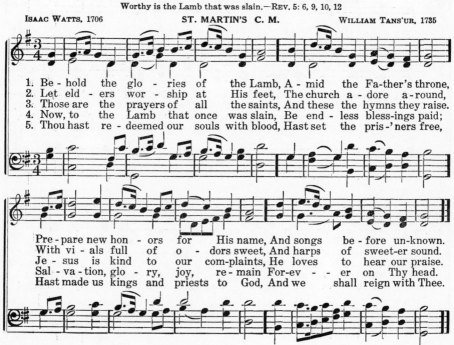

1. Be - hold the glo - ries of the Lamb, A - mid the Fa-ther's throne,
2. Let eld - ers wor - ship at His feet, The church a - dore a - round,
3. Those are the prayers of all the saints, And these the hymns they raise.
4. Now, to the Lamb that once was slain, Be end - less bless-ings paid;
5. Thou hast re - deemed our souls with blood, Hast set the pris -'ners free,

Pre - pare new hon - ors for His name, And songs be - fore un-known.
With vi - als full of o - dors sweet, And harps of sweet-er sound.
Je - sus is kind to our com-plaints, He loves to hear our praise.
Sal - va - tion, glo - ry, joy, re - main For-ev - - er on Thy head.
Hast made us kings and priests to God, And we shall reign with Thee.

41

58 Alleluia! Sing to Jesus

To Him be glory and dominion forever.—Rev. 1: 5, 6

Wm. C. Dix, 1866   ALLELUIA (Wesley) 8. 7. 8. 7. D.   Samuel S. Wesley, 1868

1. Al - le - lu - ia! sing to Je - sus! His the scep - ter, His the throne;
2. Al - le - lu - ia! not as or - phans, Are we left in sor - row now;
3. Al - le - lu - ia! Bread of an - gels, Thou on earth our Food, our Stay;
4. Al - le - lu - ia! sing to Je - sus! His the scep - ter, His the throne;

Al - le - lu - ia! His the tri - umph, His the vic - to - ry a - lone:
Al - le - lu - ia! He is near us, Faith be - lieves, nor ques - tions how:
Al - le - lu - ia! here the sin - ful Flee to Thee from day to day;
Al - le - lu - ia! His the tri - umph, His the vic - to - ry a - lone:

Hark! the songs of peace - ful Zi - on Thun - der like a might - y flood;
Tho' the cloud from sight re - ceived Him, When the for - ty days were o'er,
In - ter - ces - sor, Friend of sin - ners, Earth's Re - deem - er, plead for me,
Hark! the songs of peace - ful Zi - on Thun - der like a might - y flood;

Je - sus, out of ev - 'ry na - tion, Hath re - deemed us by His blood.
Shall our hearts for - get His prom - ise, "I am with you ev - er - more"?
Where the songs of all the sin - less Sweep a - cross the crys - tal sea.
Je - sus, out of ev - 'ry na - tion, Hath re - deemed us by His blood.

Oh, Bless the Lord, My Soul

Forget not all His benefits.—Ps. 103: 1

ISAAC WATTS, 1719   **ST. THOMAS S. M.**   AARON WILLIAMS' Coll.

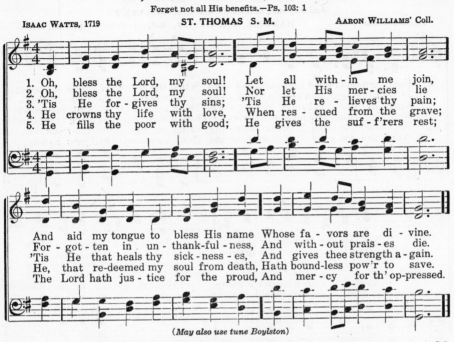

1. Oh, bless the Lord, my soul! Let all with-in me join,
2. Oh, bless the Lord, my soul! Nor let His mer-cies lie
3. 'Tis He for-gives thy sins; 'Tis He re-lieves thy pain;
4. He crowns thy life with love, When res-cued from the grave;
5. He fills the poor with good; He gives the suf-f'rers rest;

And aid my tongue to bless His name Whose fa-vors are di-vine.
For-got-ten in un-thank-ful-ness, And with-out prais-es die.
'Tis He that heals thy sick-ness-es, And gives thee strength a-gain.
He, that re-deemed my soul from death, Hath bound-less pow'r to save.
The Lord hath jus-tice for the proud, And mer-cy for th' op-pressed.

(May also use tune Boylston)

Oh, For a Thousand Tongues to Sing   60

My tongue shall speak of Thy righteousness and of Thy praise all the day long.—Ps. 35: 28

CHARLES WESLEY, 1739   **NATIVITY C. M.**   HENRY LAHEE, 1855

1. Oh, for a thou-sand tongues to sing My dear Re-deem-er's praise,
2. My gra-cious Mas-ter, and my God, As-sist me to pro-claim,
3. Je-sus! the name that calms our fears, That bids our sor-rows cease—
4. He breaks the pow'r of reign-ing sin, He sets the pris-'ner free;

The glo-ries of my God and King, The tri-umphs of His grace!
To spread thro' all the earth a-broad The hon-ors of Thy name.
'Tis mu-sic to my rav-ished ears, 'Tis life, and health, and peace.
His blood can make the foul-est clean: His blood a-vailed for me!

(May also use tune Dundee)

61 **Hark! Ten Thousand Harps and Voices**

And they sung as it were a new song.—Rev. 14: 2, 3

Thomas Kelly, 1804   HARWELL 8. 7. 8. 7. 7. 7. Ref.   Lowell Mason

1. {Hark! ten thou-sand harps and voi - ces Sound the notes of praise a - bove;
{Je - sus reigns, and heav'n re-joi - ces; Je - sus reigns, the God of love.
2. {King of glo - ry! reign for - ev - er—Thine an ev - er - last-ing crown;
{Noth-ing, from Thy love, shall sev - er Those whom Thou hast made Thine own;
3. {Sav - iour! has - ten Thine ap-pear - ing; Bring, oh, bring the glo-rious day,
{When, the aw - ful sum-mons hear-ing, Heav'n and earth shall pass a-way;—

See, He sits on yon-der throne;   Je-sus rules the world a - lone.
See, He sits   on yon-der throne;   Je - sus rules   the world a - lone.
Hap-py ob-jects of Thy grace   Des-tined to be-hold Thy face.
Hap-py ob - - jects of Thy grace   Des-tined to   be-hold Thy face.
Then, with golden harps we'll sing,   "Glo - ry, glo-ry to our King!"
Then, with gold - en harps we'll sing,   "Glo-ry, glo - - ry to our King!"

Al - le - lu - ia, Al - le - lu - ia, Al - le - lu - ia! A - men.

62 **Come, Let Us Join Our Cheerful Song**

And every creature . . . Heard I saying, . . . blessing, and honor, and glory . . .
unto the Lamb.—Rev. 5: 11-13

Isaac Watts, 1707   NEWBOLD C. M. 51.   George Kingsley, 1811-1884

1. Come, let us join our cheerful songs With an - gels round the throne; Ten thousand
2. "Worthy the Lamb that died," they cry, "To be ex - alt - ed thus!" "Wor-thy the
3. Je - sus is wor-thy to re-ceive Hon - or and pow'r di - vine; And blessings
4. The whole cre - a - tion join in one, To bless the sa - cred name Of Him that

44

Come, Let Us Join Our Cheerful Song—Concluded

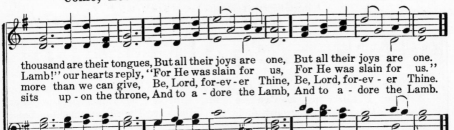

thousand are their tongues, But all their joys are one, But all their joys are one.
Lamb!" our hearts reply, "For He was slain for us, For He was slain for us."
more than we can give, Be, Lord, for-ev-er Thine, Be, Lord, for-ev-er Thine.
sits up-on the throne, And to a-dore the Lamb, And to a-dore the Lamb.

The Lord is King 63

The Lord God Omnipotent reigneth.—REV. 19: 6

CREATION L. M.

JOSIAH CONDER, 1824   Arr. from F. JOSEPH HAYDN

1. The Lord is King! lift up your voice, O earth; and
2. The Lord is King! who then shall dare Re-sist His
3. The Lord is King! Child of the dust, The Judge of
4. One Lord, one em-pire, all se-cures; He reigns, and

all ye heav'ns, re-joice: From world to world.... the
will, dis-trust His care, Or mur-mur at....... His
all the earth is just; Ho-ly and true..... are
life and death are yours: Thro' earth and heav'n .. one

joy...... shall ring, "The Lord.... Om-nip-o-tent is King!"
wise..... de-crees, Or doubt... His roy-al prom-is-es?
all...... His ways: Let ev-'ry crea-ture speak His praise.
song .... shall ring, "The Lord.... Om-nip-o-tent is King!"

64 Come, Thou Fount of Every Blessing

Hitherto hath the Lord helped us.—I SAM. 7: 12

ROBERT ROBINSON, 1758   NETTLETON 8. 7. 8. 7. D.   ASAHEL NETTLETON, 1825

1. Come, Thou Fount of ev - 'ry bless - ing, Tune my heart to sing Thy grace:
2. Here I raise my Eb - en - e - zer, Hith - er by Thine help I'm come;
3. Oh, to grace how great a debt - or Dai - ly I'm con-strained to be!

Streams of mer - cy, nev - er ceas - ing, Call for songs of loud - est praise.
And I hope, by Thy good pleas - ure, Safe-ly to ar - rive at home.
Let Thy grace, Lord, like a fet - ter, Bind my wan-d'ring heart to Thee.

Teach me some me - lo - dious son - net, Sung by flam - ing tongues a-bove;
Je - sus sought me when a stran-ger, Wan-d'ring from the fold of God,
Prone to wan - der, Lord, I feel it; Prone to leave the God I love—

Praise the mount—I'm fixed up - on it—Mount of Thy re - deem-ing love!
He, to res - cue me from dan - ger, In - ter-posed His pre-cious blood.
Here's my heart, oh, take and seal it, Seal it for Thy courts a - bove.

Hail, Thou Once Despised Jesus

Thou wast slain, and hast redeemed us to God by Thy blood.—REV. 5: 8-12

JOHN BAKEWELL, 1757. Alt.　　ST. HILDA 8. 7. 8. 7. D.　　JOSEPH BARNBY, 1861

1. Hail, Thou once de - spis - ed Je - sus, Hail, Thou Gal - i - le - an King!
2. Pas - chal Lamb, by God ap-point-ed, All our sins were on Thee laid;
3. Je - sus, hail! en-throned in glo - ry, There for - ev - er to a - bide;
4. Wor-ship, hon - or, pow'r, and bless-ing Thou art wor-thy to re - ceive:

Thou didst suf - fer to re - lease us: Thou didst free sal - va - tion bring.
By Al - might - y Love a - noint-ed, Thou hast full a - tone-ment made:
All the heav'n-ly hosts a - dore Thee, Seat - ed at Thy Fa-ther's side:
Loud-est prais - es with - out ceas-ing, Meet it is for us to give.

Hail, Thou ag - o - niz - ing Sav - iour, Bear - er of our sin and shame!
All Thy peo - ple are for - giv - en Thro' the vir - tue of Thy blood;
There for sin - ners Thou art plead-ing; There Thou dost our place pre - pare;
Help, ye bright an - gel - ic spir - its, Bring your sweetest, no - blest lays;

By Thy mer - its we find fa - vor; Life is giv - en through Thy name.
O - pened is the gate of heav - en, Peace is made 'twixt man and God.
Ev - er for us in - ter - ced - ing, Till in glo - ry we ap-pear.
Help to sing our Sav-iour's mer-its, Help to chant Em - man-uel's praise.

47

66   All Hail the Power of Jesus' Name

At the name of Jesus every knee should bow.—PHIL. 2: 10, 11

E. PERRONET, 1780   CORONATION C. M. 6 l.   O. HOLDEN

1. All hail the pow'r of Je - sus' name! Let an - gels pros-trate fall;
2. Ye cho - sen seed of Is - rael's race, A rem - nant weak and small,
3. Ye Gen - tile sin - ners, ne'er for - get The worm-wood and the gall;
4. Let ev - 'ry kin - dred, ev - 'ry tribe On this ter - res - trial ball,
5. O that, with yon - der sa - cred throng, We at His feet may fall,

Bring forth the roy - al di - a - dem, And crown Him Lord of all;
Hail Him who saves you by His grace, And crown Him Lord of all;
Go, spread your tro - phies at His feet, And crown Him Lord of all;
To Him all maj - es - ty as - cribe, And crown Him Lord of all;
We'll join the ev - er - last-ing song, And crown Him Lord of all;

Bring forth the roy - al di - a - dem, And crown Him Lord.... of all.
Hail Him who saves you by His grace, And crown Him Lord.... of all.
Go, spread your tro - phies at His feet, And crown Him Lord.... of all.
To Him all maj - es - ty as - cribe, And crown Him Lord ... of all.
We'll join the ev - er - last-ing song, And crown Him Lord ... of all.

67   All Praise to Him

Wherefore God hath highly exalted Him.—PHIL. 2: 9

W. H. CLARK   CHESTERFIELD C. M.   THOMAS HAWEIS

1. All praise to Him who reigns a - bove, In maj - es - ty su-preme,
2. His name a - bove all names shall stand, Ex - alt - ed more and more,
3. Re - deem - er, Sav - iour, Friend of man, Once ru - ined by the fall,
4. His name shall be the Coun - sel - lor, The might - y Prince of Peace,

48

All Praise to Him—Concluded

Who gave His Son for man to die, That He might man re-deem.
At God the Fa - ther's own right hand, Where an - gel hosts a - dore.
Thou hast de - vised sal - va - tion's plan, For Thou hast died for all.
Of all earth's king-doms con - quer - or, Whose reign shall nev - er cease.

Come, Let Us Tune Our Loftiest Song   68

Of Him, and through Him, and to Him are all things, . . to whom be glory forever.—ROM. 11: 36

ROBERT A. WEST   MOZART L. M.   Attributed to MOZART

1. Come, let us tune our loft - iest song, And raise to
2. His sov - 'reign pow'r our bod - ies made; Our souls are
3. Burn ev - 'ry breast with Je - - sus' love; Bound ev - 'ry
4. Ex - tol the Lamb with loft - iest song; As - cend for

Christ our joy - ful strain; Wor - ship and thanks to
His im - mor - tal breath; And when His crea - tures
heart with rap - turous joy; And saints on earth, with
Him our cheer - ful strain; Wor - ship and thanks to

Him be - long, Who reigns, and shall for - ev - er reign.
sinned, He bled, To save us from e - ter - nal death.
saints a - bove, Your voi - ces in His praise em - ploy.
Him be - long, Who reigns, and shall for - ev - er reign.

69 Hark, the Glad Sound!

The Lord hath anointed me to preach good tidings.—Isa. 61: 1

PHILIP DODDRIDGE, 1735   HENRY C. M.   S. B. POND, 1792–1871

1. Hark, the glad sound! the Sav-iour comes, The Sav-iour prom-ised long;
2. On Him the Spir - it, large-ly poured, Ex-erts its sa - cred fire;
3. He comes, the pris - 'ners to re-lease, In Sa-tan's bond - age held;
4. He comes, the bro - ken heart to bind, The bleed-ing soul to cure;
5. Our glad ho - san - nas, Prince of Peace, Thy wel-come shall pro-claim;

Let ev - 'ry heart pre-pare a throne, And ev - 'ry voice a song.
Wis-dom and might, and zeal and love, His ho - ly breast in-spire.
The gates of brass be - fore Him burst, The i - - ron fet - ters yield.
And with the treas - ures of His grace To en-rich the hum - ble poor.
And heav'n's e - ter - nal arch-es ring With Thy be-lov - ed name.

70 Oh, Worship the King

O worship the Lord in the beauty of holiness.—Ps. 96: 9

R. H. GRANT, 1833   LYONS 10. 10. 11. 11.   Arr. from MICHAEL HAYDN

1. Oh, wor-ship the King all - glo-rious a - bove, And grate-ful - ly
2. Oh, tell of His might and sing of His grace, Whose robe is the
3. Thy boun - ti - ful care what tongue can re - cite? It breathes in the
4. Frail chil - dren of dust, and fee - ble as frail, In Thee do we

sing His won - der - ful love; Our Shield and De - fend - er, the
light, whose can - o - py space; His char - iots of wrath the deep
air, it shines in the light, It streams from the hills, it de-
trust, nor find Thee to fail; Thy mer - cies how ten - der, how

Oh, Worship the King—Concluded

An - cient of days, Pa - vil - ioned in splen-dor, and gird - ed with praise.
thun-der-clouds form, And dark is His path on the wings of the storm.
scends to the plain, And sweet-ly dis - tils in the dew and the rain.
firm to the end! Our Mak - er, De - fend - er, Re - deem-er and Friend.

Glory to God On High 71

Thou art worthy, O Lord, to receive glory and honor.—REV. 4: 11

JAMES ALLEN   ITALIAN HYMN 6. 6. 4. 6. 6. 6. 4.   GIARDINI, 1769

1. Glo - ry to God on high! Let heav'n and earth re - ply,
2. While they a - round the throne Cheer-ful - ly join in one,
3. Join, all ye ran - somed race, Our Lord and God to bless:
4. Soon must we change our place, Yet will we nev - er cease

"Praise ye His name!" His love and grace a - dore, Who all our
Prais - ing His name— Ye who have felt His blood Seal - ing your
Praise ye His name! In Him we will re - joice, And make a
Prais - ing His name: To Him our songs we bring; Hail Him our

sor - rows bore; Sing loud for - ev - er - more, "Wor - thy the Lamb!"
peace with God, Sound His dear name a - broad, "Wor - thy the Lamb!"
joy - ful noise, Shout-ing with heart and voice, "Wor - thy the Lamb!"
gra - cious King; And thro' all a - ges sing, "Wor - thy the Lamb!"

72 Thou Art the Way

I am the way, the truth, and the life.—JN. 14: 6

LAMBETH C. M.

GEORGE W. DOANE, 1824

S. WEBBE, 1740-1818
WILHELM F. A. SCHULTHES, 1871

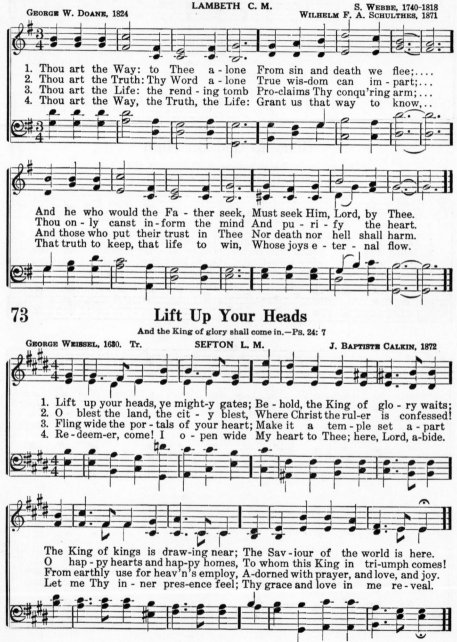

1. Thou art the Way: to Thee a-lone From sin and death we flee;....
2. Thou art the Truth: Thy Word a-lone True wis-dom can im-part;...
3. Thou art the Life: the rend-ing tomb Pro-claims Thy conqu'ring arm;...
4. Thou art the Way, the Truth, the Life: Grant us that way to know,..

And he who would the Fa-ther seek, Must seek Him, Lord, by Thee.
Thou on-ly canst in-form the mind And pu-ri-fy the heart.
And those who put their trust in Thee Nor death nor hell shall harm.
That truth to keep, that life to win, Whose joys e-ter-nal flow.

73 Lift Up Your Heads

And the King of glory shall come in.—Ps. 24: 7

GEORGE WEISSEL, 1630. Tr.

SEFTON L. M.

J. BAPTISTE CALKIN, 1872

1. Lift up your heads, ye might-y gates; Be-hold, the King of glo-ry waits;
2. O blest the land, the cit-y blest, Where Christ the rul-er is confessed!
3. Fling wide the por-tals of your heart; Make it a tem-ple set a-part
4. Re-deem-er, come! I o-pen wide My heart to Thee; here, Lord, a-bide.

The King of kings is draw-ing near; The Sav-iour of the world is here.
O hap-py hearts and hap-py homes, To whom this King in tri-umph comes!
From earthly use for heav'n's employ, A-dorned with prayer, and love, and joy.
Let me Thy in-ner pres-ence feel; Thy grace and love in me re-veal.

O Saviour, Precious Saviour

Whom having not seen, ye love.—I PET. 1: 8, 9

JESU DILECTISSIME 7. 6. 7. 6. D.

FRANCES R. HAVERGAL

R. H. McCARTNEY, 1844-1895

74

1. O Sav-iour, pre-cious Sav-iour, Whom yet un-seen we love!
2. O Bring-er of sal-va-tion, Who won-drous-ly hast wrought,
3. O grant the con-sum-ma-tion Of this our song a-bove,

O name of might and fa-vor, All oth-er names a-bove!
Thy-self the rev-e-la-tion Of love be-yond our thought;
In end-less ad-o-ra-tion And ev-er-last-ing love.

We wor-ship Thee, we bless Thee, To Thee, O Christ, we sing;
In Thee all full-ness dwell-eth, All grace and pow'r di-vine;
Then shall we praise and bless Thee, Where per-fect prais-es ring,

We praise Thee, and con-fess Thee Our ho-ly Lord and King.
The glo-ry that ex-cel-leth, O Son of God, is Thine.
And ev-er-more con-fess Thee Our Sav-iour and our King.

75   Oh, Could I Speak the Matchless Worth

I will declare what He hath done for my soul.—Ps. 66: 16

ARIEL   8. 8. 6. 8. 8. 6. 6.

SAMUEL MEDLEY, 1789

Arr. from MOZART, by L. MASON, 1836

1. Oh, could I speak the match-less worth, Oh, could I sound the glo-ries forth, Which in my Sav-iour shine! I'd soar and touch the heav'n-ly strings, And vie with Ga-briel while he sings In tones al-most di-vine, In tones al-most di-vine.

2. I'd sing the pre-cious blood He spilt, My ran-som from the dread-ful guilt, Of sin, and wrath di-vine: I'd sing His glo-rious right-eous-ness, In which all-per-fect heav'n-ly dress My soul shall ev-er shine, My soul shall ev-er shine.

3. I'd sing the char-ac-ters He bears, And all the forms of love He wears, Ex-alt-ed on His throne; In loft-iest songs of sweet-est praise, I would to ev-er-last-ing days Make all His glo-ries known, Make all His glo-ries known.

4. Well—the de-light-ful day will come When my dear Lord will bring me home, And I shall see His face; Then with my Sav-iour, Broth-er, Friend, A blest e-ter-ni-ty I'll spend, Tri-um-phant in His grace, Tri-um-phant in His grace.

At the Name of Jesus

Every knee shall bow to me, and every tongue shall confess.—ROM. 14: 11

CAROLINE M. NOEL, 1870   ST. CEPHAS 6. 5. 6. 5. D.   HOWARD A. CROSBY, 1875

1. At the name of Je - sus Ev - 'ry knee shall bow,
2. At His voice cre - a - tion Sprang at once to sight,
3. Hum - bled for a sea - son, To re - ceive a name,
4. In your hearts en - throne Him; There let Him sub - due
5. Broth-ers, this Lord Je - sus Shall re - turn a - gain,

Ev - 'ry tongue con - fess Him King of glo - ry now.
All the an - gel fa - ces, All the hosts of light,
From the lips of sin - ners Un - to whom He came,
All that is not ho - ly, All that is not true:
With His Fa - ther's glo - ry, With His an - gel train;

'Tis the Fa - ther's pleas - ure We should call Him Lord,
Thrones and dom - i - na - tions, Stars up - on their way,
Faith - ful - ly He bore it Spot - less to the last,
Crown Him as your Cap - tain In temp - ta - tion's hour:
For all wreaths of em - pire Meet up - on His brow,

Who from the be - gin - ning Was the might - y Word.
All the heav'n - ly or - ders In their great ar - ray.
Brought it back vic - to - rious, When from death He passed.
Let His will en - fold you In its light and pow'r.
And our hearts con - fess Him King of glo - ry now.

77 **Majestic Sweetness Sits Enthroned**

And set Him at His own right hand.—EPH. 1: 20

SAMUEL STENNETT, c., 1787   ORTONVILLE C. M. 5 l.   THOMAS HASTINGS, 1837

1. Ma - jes - tic sweet - ness sits en - throned, Up - on the
2. No mor - tal can with Him com - pare, A - mong the
3. To Him I owe my life and breath, And all the
4. Since from His boun - ty I re - ceive Such proofs of

Sav - iour's brow; His head with ra - diant glo - ries crowned,
sons of men; Fair - er is He than all the fair
joys I have; He makes me tri - umph o - ver death,
love di - vine, Had I a thou - sand hearts to give,

His lips with grace o'er - flow, His lips with grace o'er - flow.
That fill the heav'n - ly train, That fill the heav'n - ly train.
And saves me from the grave, And saves me from the grave.
Lord, they should all be Thine, Lord, they should all be Thine.

78 **Jesus, the Very Thought of Thee**

Christ is all, and in all.—COL. 3: 11

BERNARD OF CLAIRVAUX, 1091-1153   ST. AGNES C. M.   JOHN B. DYKES

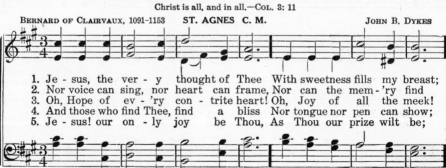

1. Je - sus, the ver - y thought of Thee With sweetness fills my breast;
2. Nor voice can sing, nor heart can frame, Nor can the mem - 'ry find
3. Oh, Hope of ev - 'ry con - trite heart! Oh, Joy of all the meek!
4. And those who find Thee, find a bliss Nor tongue nor pen can show;
5. Je - sus! our on - ly joy be Thou, As Thou our prize wilt be;

56

Jesus, the Very Thought of Thee—Concluded

But sweet-er far Thy face to see, And in Thy pres - ence rest.
A sweet-er sound than Thy blest name, O Sav - iour of man-kind!
To those who fall, how kind Thou art! How good to those who seek!
The love of Je - sus, what it is, None but His loved ones know.
Je - sus! be Thou our glo - ry now, And thro' e - ter - ni - ty.

My Jesus, I Love Thee 79

We love Him, because He first loved us.—I Jn. 4: 19

London Hymn book, 1864   11. 11. 11. 11.   A. J. GORDON

1. My Je - sus, I love Thee, I know Thou art mine; For Thee all the
2. I love Thee be - cause Thou hast first lov - ed me, And pur-chased my
3. I will love Thee in life, I will love Thee in death, And praise Thee as
4. In man-sions of glo - ry and end - less de - light, I'll ev - er a-

fol - lies of sin I re - sign; My gra - cious Re - deem - er, my
par - don on Cal - va - ry's tree; I love Thee for wear - ing the
long as Thou lend - est me breath; And say when the death - dew lies
dore Thee in heav - en so bright; I'll sing with the glit - ter - ing

Sav - iour art Thou, If ev - er I loved Thee, my Je - sus, 'tis now.
thorns on Thy brow; If ev - er I loved Thee, my Je - sus, 'tis now.
cold on my brow, If ev - er I loved Thee, my Je - sus, 'tis now.
crown on my brow, If ev - er I loved Thee, my Je - sus, 'tis now.

3

80 Ye Servants of God

Salvation to our God, . . and to the Lamb.—Rev. 7: 10

CHARLES WESLEY, 1744   LYONS 10. 10. 11. 11.   Arr. from J. MICHAEL HAYDN

1. Ye serv-ants of God, your Mas-ter pro-claim, And pub-lish a-
2. God rul-eth on high, al-might-y to save; And still He is
3. Sal-va-tion to God who sits on the throne! Let all cry a-
4. Then let us a-dore, and give Him His right, All glo-ry and

broad His won-der-ful name; The name, all-vic-to-rious, of
nigh— His pres-ence we have: The great con-gre-ga-tion His
loud and hon-or the Son: The prais-es of Je-sus the
pow'r, and wis-dom and might, All hon-or and bless-ing, with

Je-sus ex-tol; His king-dom is glo-rious, and rules o-ver all.
tri-umph shall sing, As-crib-ing sal-va-tion to Je-sus, our King.
an-gels pro-claim, Fall down on their fa-ces and wor-ship the Lamb.
an-gels a-bove, And thanks nev-er ceas-ing, and in-fi-nite love.

81 How Sweet the Name of Jesus

Unto you therefore which believe He is precious.—I Pet. 2: 7

JOHN NEWTON, 1779   ORTONVILLE C. M. 5 l.   THOMAS HASTINGS, 1837

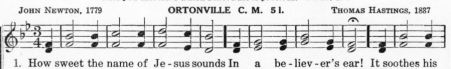

1. How sweet the name of Je-sus sounds In a be-liev-er's ear! It soothes his
2. It makes the wounded spir-it whole, And calms the troubled breast; 'Tis man-na
3. Dear name! the rock on which I build, My shield and hid-ing place; My nev-er-
4. Weak is the ef-fort of my heart, And cold my warmest tho't; But when I
5. Till then I would Thy love pro-claim With ev-'ry fleeting breath; And may the

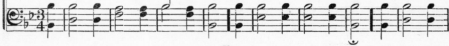

How Sweet the Name—Concluded

sorrows, heals his wounds, And drives a - way his fear, And drives a - way his fear.
to   the hun - gry soul, And to   the wea - ry rest, And to   the wea - ry rest.
fail - ing treasury filled With boundless stores of grace, With boundless stores of grace.
see Thee as Thou art, I'll praise Thee as   I ought, I'll praise Thee as   I ought.
mu - sic of Thy name Re - fresh my soul in death, Re - fresh my soul in death!

Jesus, Thou Mighty Lord   82

And His name shall be called, Wonderful, Counsellor, the mighty God.—Isa. 9: 6

JAMES MILLER, 1782   6. 4. 6. 4. D.   W. H. DOANE

1. Je - sus, Thou might - y Lord, Great is   Thy name;   Still thro' e-
2. Je - sus, Thou might - y Lord, Je - sus, our King,   Praise for Thy
3. Sought by Thy mer - cy, Lord, Saved by Thy pow'r,   Led by Thy

ter - nal years, Thou art   the same; Change-less Thy ho - ly Word,
won-drous love Glad - ly   we sing. Love   in   Thy di - a - dem
gra - cious hand, Kept ev - 'ry hour. Thine shall the hon - or be,

True   ev - er - more; Thy name we glo - ri - fy, Thy name a - dore.
Shines ev - er - more; Thy name we glo - ri - fy, Thy name a - dore.
Thine ev - er - more; Thy name we glo - ri - fy, Thy name a - dore.

83 There Is No Name So Sweet On Earth

And Thou shalt call His name Jesus.—MATT. 1: 21

THE BLESSED NAME 8. 7. 8. 7. D.

GEORGE W. BETHUNE   WILLIAM B. BRADBURY

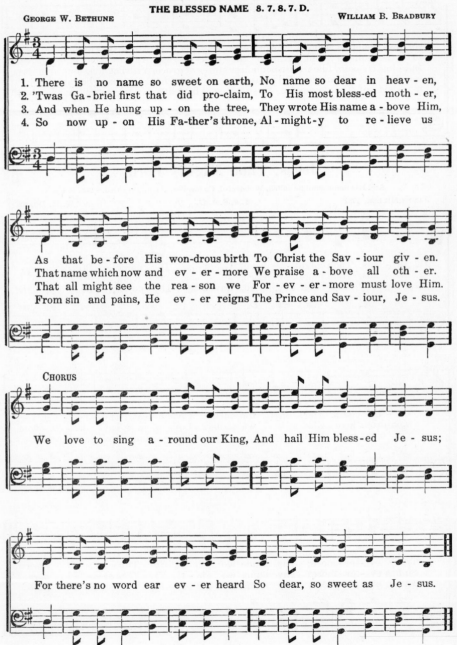

1. There is no name so sweet on earth, No name so dear in heav-en,
2. 'Twas Ga-briel first that did pro-claim, To His most bless-ed moth-er,
3. And when He hung up-on the tree, They wrote His name a-bove Him,
4. So now up-on His Fa-ther's throne, Al-might-y to re-lieve us

As that be-fore His won-drous birth To Christ the Sav-iour giv-en.
That name which now and ev-er-more We praise a-bove all oth-er.
That all might see the rea-son we For-ev-er-more must love Him.
From sin and pains, He ev-er reigns The Prince and Sav-iour, Je-sus.

CHORUS

We love to sing a-round our King, And hail Him bless-ed Je-sus;

For there's no word ear ev-er heard So dear, so sweet as Je-sus.

60

Love Divine

84

Behold what manner of love the Father hath bestowed upon us.—I Jn. 3: 1, 2

CHARLES WESLEY, 1741   BEECHER 8. 7. 8. 7. D.   J. ZUNDEL, 1870

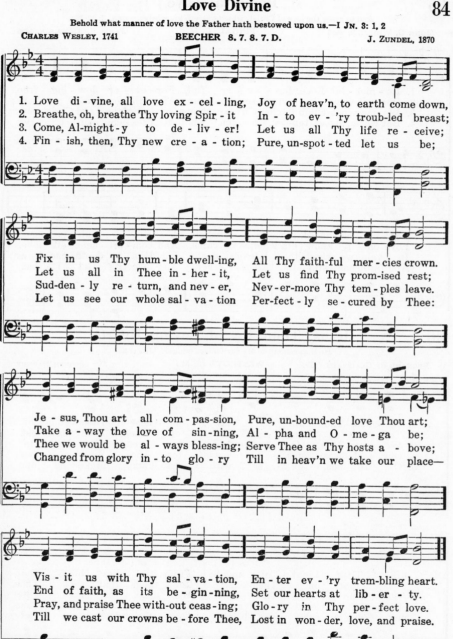

1. Love di - vine, all love ex - cel - ling, Joy of heav'n, to earth come down,
2. Breathe, oh, breathe Thy loving Spir - it In - to ev - 'ry troub-led breast;
3. Come, Al-might - y to de - liv - er! Let us all Thy life re - ceive;
4. Fin - ish, then, Thy new cre - a - tion; Pure, un-spot - ted let us be;

Fix in us Thy hum - ble dwell-ing, All Thy faith-ful mer - cies crown.
Let us all in Thee in - her - it, Let us find Thy prom-ised rest;
Sud-den - ly re - turn, and nev - er, Nev - er-more Thy tem - ples leave.
Let us see our whole sal - va - tion Per-fect - ly se - cured by Thee:

Je - sus, Thou art all com - pas-sion, Pure, un-bound-ed love Thou art;
Take a - way the love of sin - ning, Al - pha and O - me - ga be;
Thee we would be al - ways bless-ing; Serve Thee as Thy hosts a - bove;
Changed from glory in - to glo - ry Till in heav'n we take our place—

Vis - it us with Thy sal - va - tion, En - ter ev - 'ry trem-bling heart.
End of faith, as its be - gin-ning, Set our hearts at lib - er - ty.
Pray, and praise Thee with-out ceas-ing; Glo - ry in Thy per - fect love.
Till we cast our crowns be - fore Thee, Lost in won - der, love, and praise.

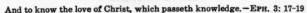

85   Immortal Love

And to know the love of Christ, which passeth knowledge.—EPH. 3: 17-19

JOHN G. WHITTIER, 1866   FINGAL C. M.   JAMES S. ANDERSON, 1885

1. Im - mor - tal Love, for - ev - er full, For - ev - er flow - ing free,
2. Our out-ward lips con - fess the name All oth - er names a - bove;
3. We may not climb the heav'n - ly steeps To bring the Lord Christ down;
4. But warm, sweet, ten - der, e - ven yet A pres - ent help is He;

For - ev - er shared, for - ev - er whole, A nev - er - ebb - ing sea!
Love on - ly know - eth whence it came, And com - pre - hend - eth love.
In vain we search the low - est deeps, For Him no depths can drown:
And faith has still its Ol - i - vet, And love its Gal - i - lee.

86   Jesus, Thou Joy of Loving Hearts

He that cometh to Me shall never hunger.—JN. 6: 35

BERNARD OF CLAIRVAUX. Tr.   WESTCOTT L. M.   JOSEPH BARNBY

1. Je - sus, Thou Joy of lov - ing hearts! Thou Fount of
2. Thy truth un - changed hath ev - - er stood; Thou sav - est
3. We taste Thee, O Thou Liv - - ing Bread, And long to
4. Our rest - less spir - its yearn for Thee, Wher - e'er our
5. O Je - sus, ev - er with us stay; Make all our

life! Thou Light of men! From the best bliss that
those that on Thee call; To them that seek Thee,
feast up - on Thee still; We drink of Thee, the
change - ful lot is cast; Glad, when Thy gra - cious
mo - ments calm and bright; Chase the dark night of

Jesus, Thou Joy of Loving Hearts—Concluded

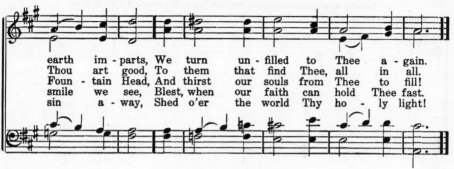

earth im - parts, We turn un - filled to Thee a - gain.
Thou art good, To them that find Thee, all in all.
Foun - tain Head, And thirst our souls from Thee to fill!
smile we see, Blest, when our faith can hold Thee fast.
sin a - way, Shed o'er the world Thy ho - ly light!

My Dear Redeemer 87

Let this mind be in you, which was also in Christ Jesus.—PHIL. 2: 4-8

ISAAC WATTS, 1709　　　　MISSIONARY CHANT L. M.　　　　HEINRICH C. ZEUNER

1. My dear Re - deem - er and my Lord, I read my
2. Such was Thy truth, and such Thy zeal, Such def - 'rence
3. Cold moun - tains and the mid - night air Wit-nessed the
4. Be Thou my pat - tern; make me bear More of Thy

du - ty in Thy Word; But in Thy life the
to Thy Fa - ther's will, Such love, and meek - ness
fer - vor of Thy prayer; The des - ert Thy temp-
gra - cious im - age here: Then God the Judge shall

law ap - pears Re - vealed in liv - ing char - ac - ters.
so di - vine, I would trans - cribe and make them mine.
ta - tions knew, Thy con - flict and Thy vic - t'ry too.
own my name A - mongst the fol - l'wers of the Lamb.

88 How Beauteous Were the Marks Divine

Leaving us an example that we should follow in His steps.—I Pet. 2: 21-24

ARTHUR C. COX, 1840   **MAYTON L. M.**   H. PERCY SMITH, 1874

1. How beau-teous were the marks di-vine That in Thy meek-ness used to shine; That lit Thy lone-ly path-way, trod In won-drous love, O Son of God!
2. O who like Thee so hum-bly bore The scorn, the scoffs of men be-fore? So meek, for-giv-ing, God-like, high, So glo-rious in hu-mil-i-ty!
3. And all Thy life's un-chang-ing years, A man of sor-rows and of tears, The cross, where all our sins were laid, Up-on Thy bend-ing shoul-ders weighed.
4. And death, that sets the pris-'ner free, Was pang and scoff and scorn to Thee; Yet love through all Thy tor-ture glowed, And mer-cy with Thy life-blood flowed.
5. O in Thy light be mine to go, Il-lum-ing all this way of woe; And give me ev-er on the road To trace Thy foot-steps, Son of God!

89 Holy and Reverend is the Name

Holy and reverend is His name.—Ps. 111: 9

J. NEEDHAM, 1768   **EAGLEY C. M.**   JAMES WALCH, 1860

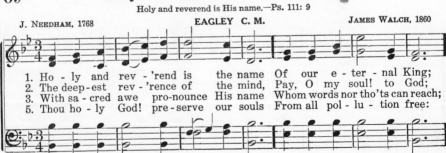

1. Ho-ly and rev-'rend is the name Of our e-ter-nal King;
2. The deep-est rev-'rence of the mind, Pay, O my soul! to God;
3. With sa-cred awe pro-nounce His name Whom words nor tho'ts can reach;
5. Thou ho-ly God! pre-serve our souls From all pol-lu-tion free:

Holy and Reverend is the Name—Concluded

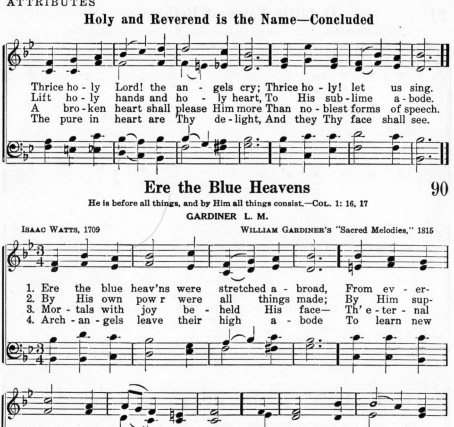

Thrice ho - ly Lord! the an - gels cry; Thrice ho - ly! let us sing.
Lift ho - ly hands and ho - ly heart, To His sub - lime a - bode.
A bro - ken heart shall please Him more Than no - blest forms of speech.
The pure in heart are Thy de - light, And they Thy face shall see.

Ere the Blue Heavens

90

He is before all things, and by Him all things consist.—COL. 1: 16, 17

GARDINER L. M.

ISAAC WATTS, 1709

WILLIAM GARDINER'S "Sacred Melodies," 1815

1. Ere the blue heav'ns were stretched a - broad, From ev - er -
2. By His own pow'r were all things made; By Him sup -
3. Mor - tals with joy be - held His face— Th' e - ter - nal
4. Arch - an - gels leave their high a - bode To learn new

last - ing was the Word; With God He was; the
port - ed, all things stand; He is the whole cre -
Fa - ther's on - ly Son; How full of truth! how
mys - t'ries here, and tell The love of our de -

Word was God, And must di - vine - ly be a - dored.
a - tion's head, And an - gels fly at His com - mand.
full of grace! When thro' His eyes the God - head shone.
scend - ing God, The glo - ries of Em - man - u - el.

91 O Little Town of Bethlehem

And thou Bethlehem, . . . art not the least among the princes of Judah.—MATT. 2: 6

PHILLIPS BROOKS, 1868   ST. LOUIS 8. 6. 8. 6. 7. 6. 8. 6.   L. H. REDNER

1. O lit - tle town of Beth - le - hem! How still we see thee lie;
2. For Christ is born of Ma - - ry, And gath - ered all a - bove,
3. How si - lent - ly, how si - lent - ly, The won - drous gift is giv'n!
4. O ho - ly Child of Beth - le - hem! De - scend to us, we pray;

A - bove thy deep and dream-less sleep The si - lent stars go by;
While mor-tals sleep, the an - gels keep Their watch of won-d'ring love.
So God im - parts to hu - man hearts The bless - ings of His heav'n.
Cast out our sin, and en - ter in, Be born in us to - day.

Yet in thy dark streets shin - eth The ev - er - last - ing Light;
O morn - ing stars, to - geth - er Pro - claim the ho - ly birth!
No ear may hear His com - ing, But in this world of sin,
We hear the Christ-mas an - gels, The great glad ti - dings tell;

The hopes and fears of all the years Are met in thee to - night.
And prais - es sing to God the King, And peace to men on earth.
Where meek souls will re - ceive Him still, The dear Christ en - ters in.
O come to us, a - bide with us, Our Lord Em - man - u - el!

Calm On the Listening Ear of Night

92

The glory of the Lord shone round about them.—LK. 2: 8, 9

EDMUND H. SEARS, 1810-1865   NOEL C. M. D.   A. S. SULLIVAN

1. Calm on the lis - t'ning ear of night Come heav'n's me-lo-dious strains,
2. The an-sw'ring hills of Pal - es - tine Send back the glad re - ply;
3. "Glo - ry to God!" the sound-ing skies Loud with their an-thems ring,

Where wild Ju - de - a stretch-es far Her sil - ver - man-tled plains.
And greet, from all their ho - ly heights, The Day-Spring from on high.
"Peace to the earth, good-will to men, From heav'n's e - ter - nal King!"

Ce - les - tial choirs from courts a - bove Shed sa - cred glo - ries there;
O'er the blue depths of Gal - i - lee There comes a ho - lier calm,
Light on thy hills, Je - ru - sa - lem! The Sav - iour now is born;

And an - gels with their spar-kling lyres, Make mu - sic on the air.
And Shar - on waves, in sol - emn praise, Her si - lent groves of palm.
More bright on Beth-l'hem's joy - ous plains Breaks the first Christ-mas morn.

93 O Come, All Ye Faithful

Let us now go . . . and see this thing which is come to pass.—LK. 2: 15

From Lat. F. OAKLEY, 1802-1880   **ADESTE FIDELES P. M.**   J. READING
WILLIAM MERCER, v. 2   WARD'S Cantus Diversa, 1751

1. O come, all ye faith-ful, Joy-ful and tri-um-phant,
2. True God of true God, Light of light e-ter-nal,
3. Sing, choirs of an-gels, Sing in ex-ul-ta-tion,
4. Yea, Lord, we greet Thee, Born this hap-py morn-ing,

O come ye, O come ye to Beth-le-hem;
Our low-ly na-ture He hath not ab-horred;
Sing, all ye cit-i-zens of heav'n a-bove:
Je-sus, to Thee be glo-ry giv'n;

Come and be-hold Him Born, the King of an-gels;
Son of the Fa-ther, Be-got-ten, not cre-a-ted;
Glo-ry to God In the high-est;
Word of the Fa-ther, Now in flesh ap-pear-ing;

After each verse

O come, let us a-dore Him, O come, let us a-dore Him,

O Come, All Ye Faithful—Concluded

O come, let us a - dore Him, Christ, the Lord.

Angels From the Realms of Glory

94

A multitude of the heavenly host praising God.—Lk. 2: 13

JAMES MONTGOMERY, 1816   REGENT SQUARE 8. 7. 8. 7. 8. 7.   HENRY SMART, 1866

1. An - gels, from the realms of glo - ry, Wing your flight o'er all the earth,
2. Shep-herds, in the field a - bid - ing, Watch-ing o'er your flocks by night,
3. Saints, be - fore the al - tar bend - ing, Watch-ing long in hope and fear,
4. Sin-ners, wrung with true re - pent-ance, Doomed for guilt to end - less pains,

Ye who sang cre - a - tion's sto - ry, Now pro - claim Mes - si - ah's birth:
God with man is now re - sid - ing; Yon - der shines the in - fant light:
Sud - den - ly the Lord, de - scend - ing, In His tem - ple shall ap - pear:
Jus - tice now re - vokes the sen - tence, Mer - cy calls you, break your chains:

Come and wor - ship, Come and wor - ship, Wor - ship Christ, the new - born King.

95 Hark! the Herald Angels

Glory to God in the highest, and on earth peace, good will to men.—Lk. 2: 14

MENDELSSOHN 7s. 10 l.

CHARLES WESLEY, 1739

FELIX MENDELSSOHN-BARTHOLDY, 1840

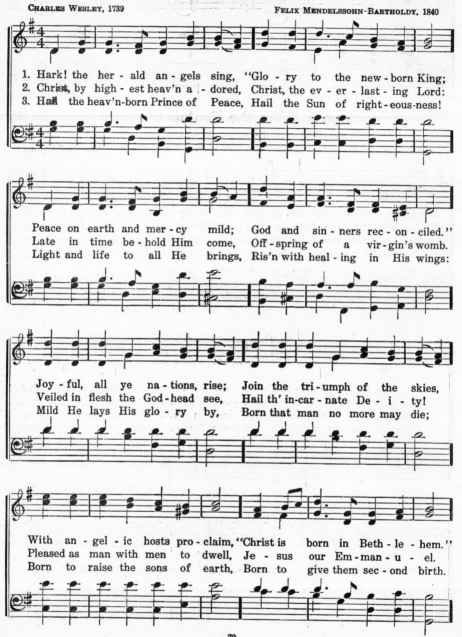

1. Hark! the her - ald an - gels sing, "Glo - ry to the new - born King;
2. Christ, by high - est heav'n a - dored, Christ, the ev - er - last - ing Lord:
3. Hail the heav'n-born Prince of Peace, Hail the Sun of right - eous-ness!

Peace on earth and mer - cy mild; God and sin - ners rec - on - ciled."
Late in time be - hold Him come, Off - spring of a vir - gin's womb.
Light and life to all He brings, Ris'n with heal - ing in His wings:

Joy - ful, all ye na - tions, rise; Join the tri - umph of the skies,
Veiled in flesh the God - head see, Hail th' in - car - nate De - i - ty!
Mild He lays His glo - ry by, Born that man no more may die;

With an - gel - ic hosts pro - claim, "Christ is born in Beth - le - hem."
Pleased as man with men to dwell, Je - sus our Em - man - u - el.
Born to raise the sons of earth, Born to give them sec - ond birth.

Hark! the Herald Angels—Concluded

Hark! the her - ald an - gels sing, "Glo - ry to the new - born King!"

Joy to the World   96

Rejoice greatly, O daughter of Zion.—ZECH. 9: 9

ANTIOCH C. M.

ISAAC WATTS, 1719

Arr. from G. F. HANDEL
By LOWELL MASON, 1830

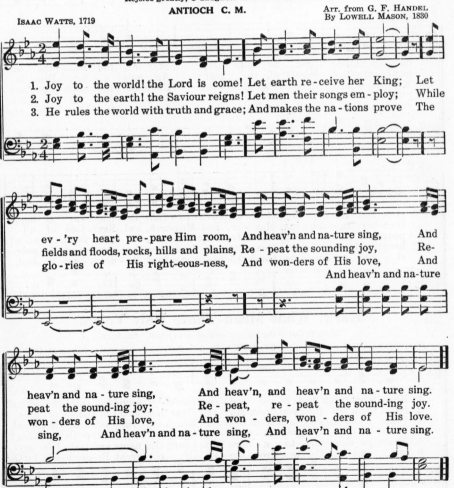

1. Joy to the world! the Lord is come! Let earth re - ceive her King; Let
2. Joy to the earth! the Saviour reigns! Let men their songs em - ploy; While
3. He rules the world with truth and grace; And makes the na - tions prove The

ev - 'ry heart pre - pare Him room, And heav'n and na - ture sing, And
fields and floods, rocks, hills and plains, Re - peat the sounding joy, Re-
glo - ries of His right-eous-ness, And won-ders of His love, And
And heav'n and na-ture

heav'n and na - ture sing, And heav'n, and heav'n and na - ture sing.
peat the sound-ing joy; Re - peat, re - peat the sound-ing joy.
won - ders of His love, And won - ders, won - ders of His love.
sing, And heav'n and na-ture sing, And heav'n and na - ture sing.

97 Brightest and Best

We have seen His star in the east.—MATT. 2: 2

REGINALD HEBER, 1811   MORNING STAR 11. 10. 11. 10.   J. P. HARDING

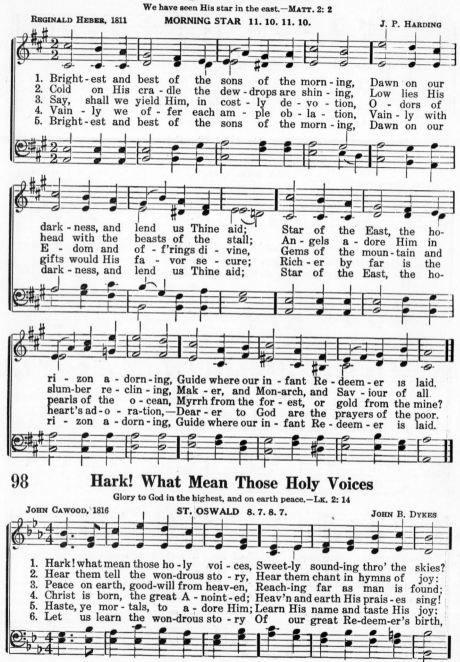

1. Bright-est and best of the sons of the morn-ing, Dawn on our
2. Cold on His cra-dle the dew-drops are shin-ing, Low lies His
3. Say, shall we yield Him, in cost-ly de-vo-tion, O-dors of
4. Vain-ly we of-fer each am-ple ob-la-tion, Vain-ly with
5. Bright-est and best of the sons of the morn-ing, Dawn on our

dark-ness, and lend us Thine aid; Star of the East, the ho-
head with the beasts of the stall; An-gels a-dore Him in
E-dom and of-f'rings di-vine, Gems of the moun-tain and
gifts would His fa-vor se-cure; Rich-er by far is the
dark-ness, and lend us Thine aid; Star of the East, the ho-

ri-zon a-dorn-ing, Guide where our in-fant Re-deem-er is laid.
slum-ber re-clin-ing, Mak-er, and Mon-arch, and Sav-iour of all.
pearls of the o-cean, Myrrh from the for-est, or gold from the mine?
heart's ad-o-ra-tion,—Dear-er to God are the prayers of the poor.
ri-zon a-dorn-ing, Guide where our in-fant Re-deem-er is laid.

98 Hark! What Mean Those Holy Voices

Glory to God in the highest, and on earth peace.—LK. 2: 14

JOHN CAWOOD, 1816   ST. OSWALD 8. 7. 8. 7.   JOHN B. DYKES

1. Hark! what mean those ho-ly voi-ces, Sweet-ly sound-ing thro' the skies?
2. Hear them tell the won-drous sto-ry, Hear them chant in hymns of joy:
3. Peace on earth, good-will from heav-en, Reach-ing far as man is found;
4. Christ is born, the great A-noint-ed; Heav'n and earth His prais-es sing!
5. Haste, ye mor-tals, to a-dore Him; Learn His name and taste His joy:
6. Let us learn the won-drous sto-ry Of our great Re-deem-er's birth,

Hark! What Mean Those Holy Voices—Concluded

Lo! th' an-gel-ic host re-joi-ces; Heav'n-ly hal-le-lu-jahs rise.
"Glo-ry, in the high-est, glo-ry! Glo-ry be to God most high!"
Souls redeemed, and sins for-giv-en, Loud our gold-en harps shall sound.
Oh, re-ceive whom God ap-point-ed For your Proph-et, Priest, and King!
Till in heav'n ye sing be-fore Him, "Glo-ry be to God most high!"
Spread the brightness of His glo-ry, Till it cov-er all the earth.

Zion's Glad Morning 99

They saw the young child with Mary His mother, and fell down and worshipped Him.—MATT. 2: 11

REGINALD HEBER, 1811   11. 10. 11. 10.   Arr. from Harmonia Sacra

1. Hail the blest morn when the great Me-di-a-tor Down from the
2. Bright-est and best of the sons of the morn-ing, Dawn on our
3. Cold on His cra-dle the dew-drops are shin-ing, Low lies His
4. Say, shall we yield Him, in cost-ly de-vo-tion, O-dors of
5. Vain-ly we of-fer each am-ple ob-la-tion, Vain-ly with

re-gions of glo-ry de-scends; Shep-herds, go wor-ship the
dark-ness, and lend us Thine aid; Star of the East, the ho-
head with the beasts of the stall; An-gels a-dore Him in
E-dom and of-f'rings di-vine, Gems of the moun-tain and
gifts would His fa-vor se-cure; Rich-er by far is the

Babe in the man-ger; Lo! for His guard the bright an-gels at-tend.
ri-zon a-dorn-ing, Guide where our in-fant Re-deem-er is laid.
slum-ber re-clin-ing, Mak-er, and Mon-arch, and Sav-iour of all.
pearls of the o-cean, Myrrh from the for-est, or gold from the mine?
heart's ad-o-ra-tion,—Dear-er to God are the prayers of the poor.

100 Glory Be to God On High

GLORIA IN EXCELSIS

Old Scottish Chant

Glory be to God on high: and on earth peace, good will towards men.
We praise Thee, wor-ship Thee: we glorify Thee, Thee for Thy great glory.
we bless Thee, we | we give thanks to |

O Lord God, heaven-ly King: God the Fa - ther Al - - mighty.
O Lord, the only- Je - sus Christ: O Lord God, Lamb Son — of the Father,
begotten Son | of God, |

That takest away the sins of the world: have mercy up-on — us.
Thou that takest away the sins of the world: receive — our prayer.
Thou that sittest at the | God the Father: have mercy up-on — us.
right hand of |

For Thou only art — holy: Thou on - ly art the Lord.
Thou only, O | Ho - ly Ghost: art most high glory of God the Father. A-MEN.
Christ, with the | in the |

It Came Upon the Midnight Clear

Lord, Thou wilt ordain peace for us.—ISA. 26: 12

EDMUND H. SEARS, 1850　　　　CAROL C. M. D.　　　　RICHARD S. WILLIS, 1850

1. It came up-on the mid-night clear, That glo-rious song of old,
2. Still thro' the clov-en skies they come, With peace-ful wings un-furled,
3. And ye, be-neath life's crush-ing load, Whose forms are bend-ing low,
4. For lo, the days are has-t'ning on, By proph-et bards fore-told,

From an-gels bend-ing near the earth To touch their harps of gold:
And still their heav'n-ly mu-sic floats O'er all the wea-ry world:
Who toil a-long the climb-ing way With pain-ful steps and slow,—
When with the ev-er-cir-cling years Comes round the age of gold;

"Peace on the earth, good will to men, From heav'n's all-gra-cious King."
A-bove its sad and low-ly plains They bend on hov-'ring wing,
Look now! for glad and gold-en hours Come swift-ly on the wing:
When peace shall o-ver all the earth Its an-cient splen-dors fling,

The world in sol-emn still-ness lay, To hear the an-gels sing.
And ev-er o'er its Ba-bel-sounds The bless-ed an-gels sing.
O rest be-side the wea-ry road, And hear the an-gels sing.
And the whole world give back the song Which now the an-gels sing.

102 While Shepherds Watched

Fear not; for behold I bring you good tidings of great joy.—LK. 2: 10

NAHUM TATE, 1762   CHRISTMAS C. M. 5 l.   From GEORGE F. HANDEL

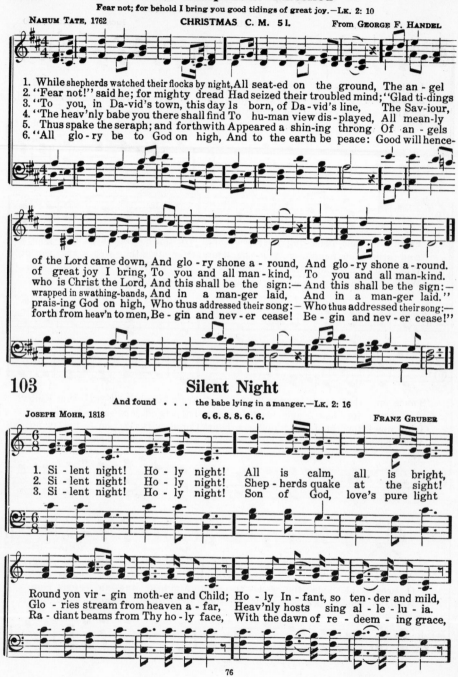

1. While shepherds watched their flocks by night, All seat-ed on the ground, The an - gel
2. "Fear not!" said he; for mighty dread Had seized their troubled mind; "Glad ti-dings
3. "To you, in Da-vid's town, this day ls born, of Da-vid's line, The Sav-iour,
4. "The heav'nly babe you there shall find To hu-man view dis-played, All mean-ly
5. Thus spake the seraph; and forthwith Appeared a shin-ing throng Of an - gels
6. "All glo - ry be to God on high, And to the earth be peace: Good will hence-

of the Lord came down, And glo - ry shone a - round, And glo - ry shone a - round.
of great joy I bring, To you and all man - kind, To you and all man-kind.
who is Christ the Lord, And this shall be the sign:— And this shall be the sign:—
wrapped in swathing-bands, And in a man-ger laid, And in a man-ger laid."
prais-ing God on high, Who thus addressed their song:— Who thus addressed their song:—
forth from heav'n to men, Be - gin and nev - er cease! Be - gin and nev - er cease!"

103 Silent Night

And found . . . the babe lying in a manger.—LK. 2: 16

JOSEPH MOHR, 1818   6. 6. 8. 8. 6. 6.   FRANZ GRUBER

1. Si - lent night! Ho - ly night! All is calm, all is bright,
2. Si - lent night! Ho - ly night! Shep - herds quake at the sight!
3. Si - lent night! Ho - ly night! Son of God, love's pure light

Round yon vir - gin moth-er and Child; Ho - ly In - fant, so ten - der and mild,
Glo - ries stream from heaven a - far, Heav'nly hosts sing al - le - lu - ia.
Ra - diant beams from Thy ho - ly face, With the dawn of re - deem - ing grace,

Silent Night—Concluded

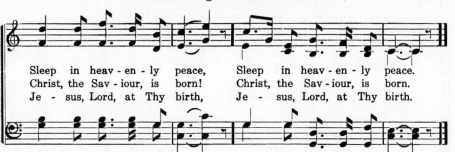

Sleep in heav - en - ly peace,
Christ, the Sav - iour, is born!
Je - sus, Lord, at Thy birth,

Sleep in heav - en - ly peace.
Christ, the Sav - iour, is born.
Je - sus, Lord, at Thy birth.

From the Eastern Mountains 104

There came wise men from the east.—MATT. 2: 1

GODFREY THRING, 1879   PRINCETHORPE 6. 5. 6. 5. D.   WILLIAM PITTS

1. From the east-ern moun-tains Press-ing on they come, Wise men in their
2. There the Lord and Sav - iour Meek and low - ly lay, Won-drous light that
3. Thou who in a man - ger Once hast low - ly lain, Who dost now in

wis - dom, To His hum - ble home, Stirred by deep de - vo - tion, Hast-ing
led them On - ward on their way, Ev - er now to light - en Na - tions
glo - ry O'er all kingdoms reign, Gath - er in the hea - then, Who in

from a - far, Ev - er jour-n'ying on - ward, Guid-ed by a star.
from a - far, As they jour - ney home-ward, By that guid-ing star.
lands a - far, Ne'er have seen the bright-ness Of Thy guid-ing star.

105 Throned Upon the Awful Tree

And sitting down they watched Him there.—MATT. 27: 36

JOHN ELLERTON, 1871   SPANISH HYMN 7s. 6 l.   Arr. by BENJAMIN CARR, 1824

1. Throned up - on the aw - ful tree, King of grief, I watch with Thee:
2. Si - lent thro' those three dead hours, Wres-tling with the e - vil pow'rs,
3. Hark that cry that peals a - loud Up - ward thro' the whelm-ing cloud!
4. Lord, should fear and an - guish roll Dark - ly o'er my sin - ful soul,

Dark - ness veils Thine an-guished face, None its lines of woe can trace,
Left a - lone with hu - man sin, Gloom a - round Thee and with - in,
Thou, the Fa - ther's on - ly Son, Thou, His own A - noint - ed One,
Thou, who once was thus be - reft That Thine own might ne'er be left,

None can tell what pangs un-known Hold Thee si - lent and a - lone.
Till th' ap-point-ed time is nigh, Till the Lamb of God may die.
Thou dost ask Him— can it be? "Why hast Thou for - sak - en Me?''
Teach me by that bit - ter cry In the gloom to know Thee nigh.

106 There is a Green Hill Far Away

And they brought Him unto the place Golgotha.— MK. 15: 22

Mrs. CECIL F. ALEXANDER, 1848   MEDITATION C. M.   JOHN H. GOWER, 1890

1. There is a green hill far a - way, With - out a cit - y wall,
2. We may not know, we can - not tell, What pains He had to bear;
3. He died that we might be for - giv'n, He died to make us good,
4. There was no oth - er good e - nough To pay the price of sin;
5. O dear - ly, dear - ly has He loved, And we must love Him too,

There is a Green Hill Far Away—Concluded

Where the dear Lord was cru - ci - fied, Who died to save us all.
But we be - lieve it was for us He hung and suf-fered there.
That we might go at last to heav'n, Saved by His pre-cious blood.
He on - ly could un - lock the gate Of heav'n, and let us in.
And trust in His re - deem-ing blood, And try His works to do.

Go to Dark Gethsemane 107

Though He were a Son, yet learned He obedience by the things which He suffered.—HEB. 5: 8

JAMES MONTGOMERY, 1820   AJALON 7s. 6 l.   RICHARD REDHEAD, 1853

1. Go to dark Geth-sem - a - ne, Ye that feel the tempt-er's pow'r,
2. Fol - low to the judg-ment hall; View the Lord of life ar-raigned.
3. Cal-v'ry's mourn-ful moun-tain climb; There, a - dor - ing at His feet,
4. Ear - ly has - ten to the tomb Where they laid His breath-less clay:

Your Re - deem-er's con - flict see; Watch with Him one bit - ter hour:
O the worm-wood and the gall! O the pangs His soul sus-tained!
Mark that mir - a - cle of time, God's own sac - ri - fice com-plete:
All is sol - i - tude and gloom; Who hath tak - en Him a - way?

Turn not from His griefs a - way; Learn of Je - sus Christ to pray.
Shun not suf-f'ring, shame, or loss; Learn of Him to bear the cross.
"It is fin-ished!"—hear the cry; Learn of Je - sus Christ to die.
Christ is ris'n! He meets our eyes. Sav - iour, teach us so to rise.

108 Beneath the Cross of Jesus

God forbid that I should glory, save in the cross of our Lord Jesus Christ.—GAL. 6: 14

ST. CHRISTOPHER 7. 6. 8. 6. 8. 6. 8. 6.

ELIZABETH C. CLEPHANE, 1867

FREDERICK C. MAKER, 1881

1. Be - neath the cross of Je - sus I fain would take my stand,—
2. Up - on that cross of Je - sus Mine eye at times can see
3. I take, O cross, thy shad - ow For my a - bid - ing place;

The shad - ow of a might - y rock With - in a wea - ry land;
The ver - y dy - ing form of One Who suf - fered there for me;
I ask no oth - er sun - shine than The sun - shine of His face,—

A home with - in the wil - der - ness, A rest up - on the way,
And from my smit - ten heart with tears Two won - ders I con - fess,—
Con - tent to let the world go by, To know no gain nor loss,

From the burn - ing of the noon - tide heat, And the bur - den of the day.
The won - ders of His glo - rious love And my un - wor - thi - ness.
My sin - ful self my on - ly shame, My glo - ry all the cross.

Behold the Man

109

Behold the man!—Behold your King!—Jn. 19: 5. 14

JOHN W. WAYLAND

JOHN D. BRUNK, 1926

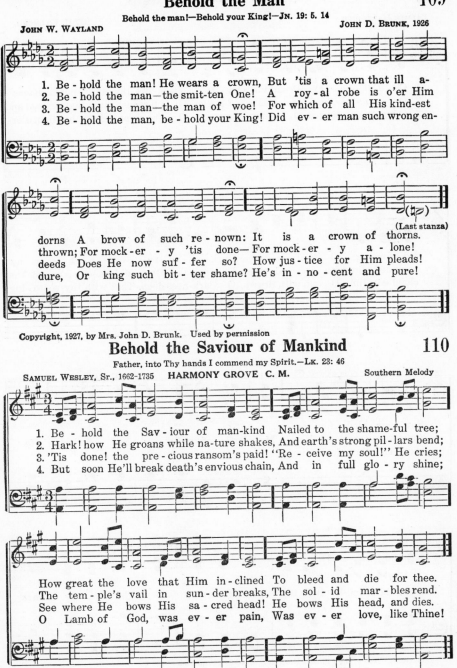

1. Be - hold the man! He wears a crown, But 'tis a crown that ill a-
2. Be - hold the man—the smit-ten One! A roy - al robe is o'er Him
3. Be - hold the man—the man of woe! For which of all His kind-est
4. Be - hold the man, be - hold your King! Did ev - er man such wrong en-

(Last stanza)

dorns A brow of such re - nown: It is a crown of thorns.
thrown; For mock - er - y 'tis done— For mock-er - y a - lone!
deeds Does He now suf - fer so? How jus - tice for Him pleads!
dure, Or king such bit - ter shame? He's in - no - cent and pure!

Copyright, 1927, by Mrs. John D. Brunk. Used by permission

Behold the Saviour of Mankind

110

Father, into Thy hands I commend my Spirit.—Lk. 23: 46

SAMUEL WESLEY, Sr., 1662-1735   HARMONY GROVE C. M.   Southern Melody

1. Be - hold the Sav - iour of man-kind Nailed to the shame-ful tree;
2. Hark! how He groans while na-ture shakes, And earth's strong pil - lars bend;
3. 'Tis done! the pre - cious ransom's paid! "Re - ceive my soul!" He cries;
4. But soon He'll break death's envious chain, And in full glo - ry shine;

How great the love that Him in - clined To bleed and die for thee.
The tem - ple's vail in sun - der breaks, The sol - id mar - bles rend.
See where He bows His sa - cred head! He bows His head, and dies.
O Lamb of God, was ev - er pain, Was ev - er love, like Thine!

111 O Calvary

PALMER HARTSOUGH

J. H. FILLMORE

Andante

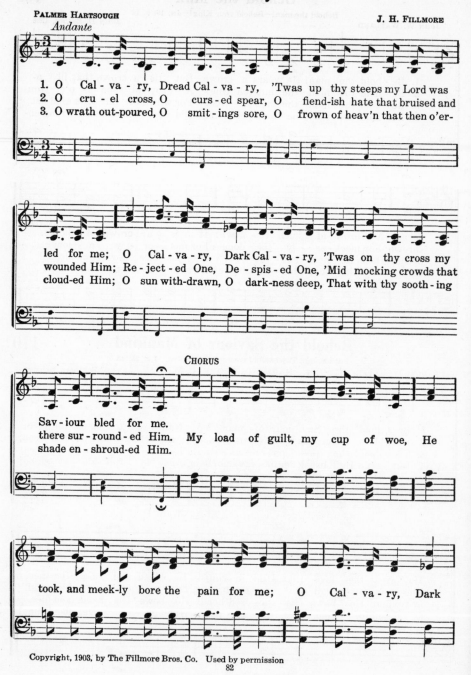

1. O Cal - va - ry, Dread Cal - va - ry, 'Twas up thy steeps my Lord was
2. O cru - el cross, O curs - ed spear, O fiend-ish hate that bruised and
3. O wrath out-poured, O smit - ings sore, O frown of heav'n that then o'er-

led for me; O Cal - va - ry, Dark Cal - va - ry, 'Twas on thy cross my
wounded Him; Re - ject - ed One, De - spis - ed One, 'Mid mocking crowds that
cloud-ed Him; O sun with-drawn, O dark-ness deep, That with thy sooth - ing

CHORUS

Sav - iour bled for me.
there sur - round - ed Him. My load of guilt, my cup of woe, He
shade en - shroud-ed Him.

took, and meek-ly bore the pain for me; O Cal - va - ry, Dark

O Calvary—Concluded

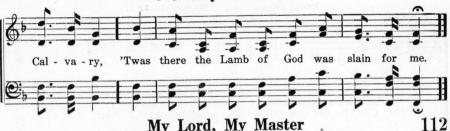

Cal - va - ry, 'Twas there the Lamb of God was slain for me.

My Lord, My Master

112

And He that saw it bare record, and His record is true.—JN. 19: 35

STRENGTH AND STAY 11. 10. 11. 10.

JAQUES BRIDANE, 1701–1767

JOHN B. DYKES, 1875

1. My Lord, my Mas - ter, at Thy feet a - dor - ing, I   see Thee
2. Thine own dis - ci - ple to the Jews has sold Thee; With friendship's
3. With taunts and scoffs they mock what seems Thy weak-ness, With blows and
4. My Lord, my Sav - iour, when I see Thee wear - ing Up - on Thy
5. O   Vic - tim of   Thy love! O pangs most heal - ing! O   sav - ing

bowed be-neath Thy load of woe: For me, a   sin - ner, is Thy life-blood
kiss   and loy - al word he came: How oft of   faith - ful   love my lips have
out - rage add-ing pain to pain: Thou art un - moved and stead-fast in Thy
bleed - ing brow the crown of thorn, Shall I for pleas - ure live, or shrink from
death! O wounds that I a - dore! O shame most glo - rious! Christ, before Thee

pour - ing;   For Thee, my Sav-iour, scarce my tears will   flow.
told   Thee, While Thou hast seen my false-hood and   my   shame.
meek - ness; When I am wronged how quick-ly   I   com - plain.
bear - ing What-e'er my lot may be of pain or   scorn?
kneel - ing,   I   pray Thee keep me Thine for - ev - er - more. A-MEN.

83

113 Arise, My Soul, Arise

Behold My hands, . . . My side.—Jn. 20: 27

C. Wesley   LENOX 6. 6. 6. 6. 8. 8. 8.   Lewis Edson, 1782

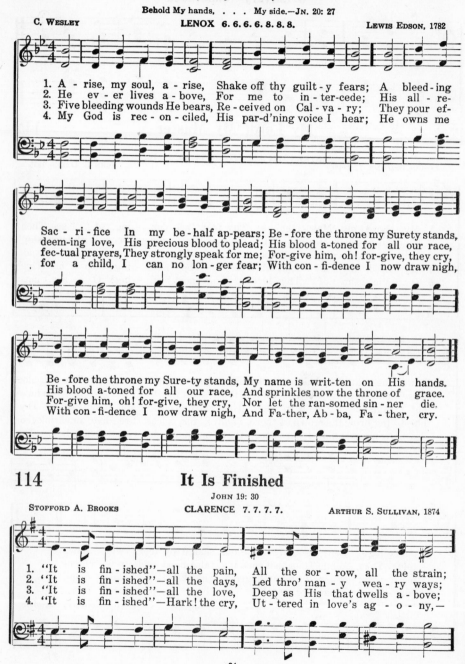

1. A - rise, my soul, a - rise, Shake off thy guilt - y fears; A bleed - ing
2. He ev - er lives a - bove, For me to in - ter - cede; His all - re -
3. Five bleeding wounds He bears, Re - ceived on Cal - va - ry; They pour ef -
4. My God is rec - on - ciled, His par-d'ning voice I hear; He owns me

Sac - ri - fice In my be - half ap-pears; Be - fore the throne my Surety stands,
deem-ing love, His precious blood to plead; His blood a-toned for all our race,
fec-tual prayers, They strongly speak for me; For-give him, oh! for-give, they cry,
for a child, I can no lon - ger fear; With con - fi-dence I now draw nigh,

Be - fore the throne my Sure-ty stands, My name is writ-ten on His hands.
His blood a-toned for all our race, And sprinkles now the throne of grace.
For-give him, oh! for-give, they cry, Nor let the ran-somed sin - ner die.
With con - fi-dence I now draw nigh, And Fa-ther, Ab - ba, Fa - ther, cry.

114 It Is Finished

John 19: 30

Stopford A. Brooks   CLARENCE 7. 7. 7. 7.   Arthur S. Sullivan, 1874

1. "It is fin - ished"—all the pain, All the sor - row, all the strain;
2. "It is fin - ished"—all the days, Led thro' man - y wea - ry ways;
3. "It is fin - ished"—all the love, Deep as His that dwells a - bove,
4. "It is fin - ished"—Hark! the cry, Ut - tered in love's ag - o - ny,—

It Is Finished—Concluded

Death has freed the Lord of life | From the bur-den of His strife.
Now at last His eye-lids close | On the ha-tred of His foes.
Sav-ing oth-ers, all He gave, | But Him-self He would not save.
Is the seal, be-low, a-bove, | Of the vic-to-ry of love.

'Tis Finished 115

Ought not Christ to have suffered these things?—LK. 24: 26

SAMUEL STENNETT, 1727-1796. Alt.   WESTCOTT L. M.   JOSEPH BARNBY

1. "'Tis fin-ished!" so the Sav-iour cried, And meek-ly
2. 'Tis fin-ished! all that heav'n fore-told By proph-ets
3. 'Tis fin-ished! Son of God, Thy pow'r Hath tri-umphed
4. 'Tis fin-ished! let the joy-ful sound Be heard through

bowed His head and died: 'Tis fin-ished! yes, the
in the days of old; And truths are o-pened
in this aw--ful hour; And yet our eyes with
all the na--tions round; 'Tis fin-ished! let the

race is run, The bat-tle fought, the vic-t'ry won.
to our view, That kings and proph-ets nev-er knew.
sor-row see That life to us was death to Thee.
tri-umph rise And swell the cho-rus of the skies!

116 The Words of the Cross

Father, forgive them.—Lk. 23: 34

THOMAS B. POLLOCK, 1870. Alt.　　7. 7. 7. 6.　　WILLIAM H. MONK, 1889

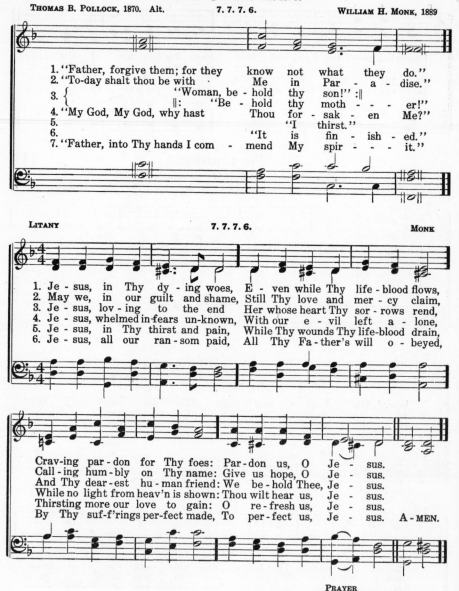

7 Jesus, all Thy labor vast,
　All Thy woe and conflict past,
　Yielding up Thy soul at last,
　For our life, O Jesus.

8 May Thy life and death supply
　Grace to live and grace to die,
　Grace to reach the home on high:
　Hear us, Holy Jesus. Amen.

Jesus, in Thy Dying Woes

THE SEVEN WORDS 7. 7. 7. 6.

THOMAS B. POLLOCK, 1870. Alt.

W. S. HOYTE, 1866

1. Je - sus, in Thy dy - ing woes, E - ven while Thy life-blood flows,
2. May we, in our guilt and shame, Still Thy love and mer - cy claim,
3. Je - sus, lov - ing to the end Her whose heart Thy sor - rows rend,
4. Je - sus, whelmed in fears un-known, With our e - vil left a - lone,

Crav - ing par - don for Thy foes: Par - don us, O Je - sus.
Call - ing hum - bly on Thy name: Give us hope, O Je - sus.
And Thy dear - est hu - man friend: We be - hold Thee, Je - sus.
While no light from heav'n is shown: Thou wilt hear us, Je - sus. A - MEN.

5 Jesus, in Thy thirst and pain,
  While Thy wounds Thy life-blood drain,
  Thirsting more our love to gain:
  O refresh us, Jesus.

6 Jesus, all our ransom paid,
  All Thy Father's will obeyed;
  By Thy sufferings perfect made,
  To perfect us, Jesus.

7 Jesus, all Thy labor vast,
  All Thy woe and conflict past,
  Yielding up Thy soul at last,
  For our life, O Jesus.

PRAYER

8 May Thy life and death supply
  Grace to live and grace to die,
  Grace to reach the home on high;
  Hear us, Holy Jesus. Amen.

Second Tune

LITANY 7. 7. 7. 6.

C. C. SCHOLEFIELD

118 Stricken, Smitten and Afflicted

We did esteem Him stricken, smitten of God and afflicted.—Isa. 53: 4

O MEIN JESU, ICH MUSS STERBEN 8. 7. 8. 7. D.

THOMAS KELLY, 1804

PADERBORN MELODY, 1850

1. { Strick-en, smit-ten and af - flict - ed, See Him dy - ing on the tree!
{ 'Tis the Christ by man re - ject - ed; Yes, my soul, 'tis He, 'tis He!
2. { Ye who think of sin but light - ly, Nor sup - pose the e - vil great,
{ Here may view its na - ture right - ly, Here its guilt may es - ti - mate.
3. { Here we have a firm foun - da - tion; Here the ref - uge of the lost;
{ Christ's the Rock of our sal - va - tion: His the name of which we boast;

'Tis the long ex - pect - ed Proph - et, Da-vid's Son, yet Da-vid's Lord;
Mark the Sac - ri - fice ap-point-ed! See who bears the aw - ful load;
Lamb of God, for sin-ners wound-ed! Sac - ri - fice to can-cel guilt!

Proofs I see suf - fi - cient of it: 'Tis the true and faith-ful Word.
'Tis the Word, the Lord's A - noint-ed, Son of man, and Son of God.
None shall ev - er be con-found-ed Who on Him their hope have built.

119 O the Agonizing Prayer

My soul is exceeding sorrowful, even unto death.—MATT. 26: 38

THOS. MacKELLER, 1812

GETHSEMANE 7s. 5 l.

C. H. BRUNK, 1890

1. O the ag - o - niz-ing prayer Ris-ing on the mid-night air! "Let this cup pass
2. O the tears and blood-y sweat Fall-ing fast on Ol - i - vet! In Thy lone-ly
3. O what wrath of earth and hell On Thy head un-pity-ing fell, When Thy passion
4. Wak-en me from sin-ful sleep; Faithful, loving, make me keep, Watching ev-'ry

O the Agonizing Prayer—Concluded

from thy Son: Not my will, but Thine be done!" Je-sus in Geth-sem-a-ne!
ag - o - y, Shed-ding crimson tears for me, Je-sus in Geth-sem-a-ne!
time be-gan, Bear-er of the sin of man, Je-sus in Geth-sem-a-ne!
hour with Thee Who didst ag-o-nize for me, Je-sus in Geth-sem-a-ne!

'Tis Midnight 120

And He went forward a little farther, and fell on the ground and prayed.—MK. 14: 35

WM. BINGHAM TAPPAN, 1744-1849   OLIVE'S BROW L. M.   WM. B. BRADBURY

1. 'Tis mid-night, and on Ol - ive's brow The star is
2. 'Tis mid-night, and from all re - moved The Sav - iour
3. 'Tis mid-night, and for oth - ers' guilt The Man of
4. 'Tis mid-night, and from e - ther - plains Is borne the

dimmed that late - ly shone; 'Tis mid - night, in the
wres - tles lone with fears; E'en that dis - ci - ple
Sor - rows weeps in blood; Yet He who hath in
song that an - gels know; Un - heard by mor - tals

gar - den now The suf - f'ring Sav - iour prays a - lone.
whom He loved Heeds not his Mas - ter's grief and tears.
an - guish knelt Is not for - sak - en by His God.
are the strains That sweet - ly soothe the Sav - iour's woe.

89

4

121

Passion Chorale

And platted a crown of thorns, and put it about His head.—Mk. 15: 17

BERNARD OF CLAIRVAUX, 1091–1153
Tr. J. W. ALEXANDER, 1804–1859

7. 6. 7. 6. D.

HANS LEO HASSLER, 1601
Harmonized by J. S. BACH, 1729

1. O   sa - cred Head, now wound - ed,   With grief and shame weighed down!
2. O   no - blest brow and   dear - est,   In   oth - er   days the   world
3. What Thou, my Lord, hast   suf - fered   Was   all   for   sin - ners'   gain:
4. What lan-guage shall I   bor - row   To thank Thee, dear-est   Friend,
5. Be   near when I   am   dy - ing,   O   show Thy   cross to   me;

Now   scorn-ful - ly   sur - round - ed   With thorns, Thine on - ly   crown:
All   feared when Thou ap - pear - edst;   What shame on   Thee is   hurled!
Mine,   mine was the   trans - gres - sion,   But   Thine the   dead - ly   pain.
For   this Thy   dy - ing   sor - row,   Thy   pit - y   with - out   end?
And   for   my   suc - cor   fly - ing,   Come, Lord, to   set   me   free;

O   sa - cred Head, what glo - ry,   What bliss till   now was   Thine!
How   art Thou pale with   an - guish, With sore a - buse and   scorn;
Lo,   here I   fall, my   Sav - iour!   'Tis   I   de - serve Thy   place;
O   make me Thine for - ev - er;   And should I   faint-ing   be,
These eyes, new faith re - ceiv - ing,   From Je - sus shall not   move;

Yet,   tho' de - spised and   gor - y,   I   joy   to   call Thee mine.
How   does that vis - age   lan - guish   Which once was bright as   morn!
Look   on   me with Thy   fa - vor,   Vouch-safe to   me Thy   grace.
Lord, let   me nev - er,   nev - er   Out - live my   love to   Thee.
For   he who dies be - liev - ing,   Dies safe - ly, thro' Thy   love.

90

Cross of Jesus

Truly this man was the Son of God.—MK. 15: 39

JAMES S. SIMPSON, 1886   8. 7. 8. 7.   JOHN STAINER, 1887

122

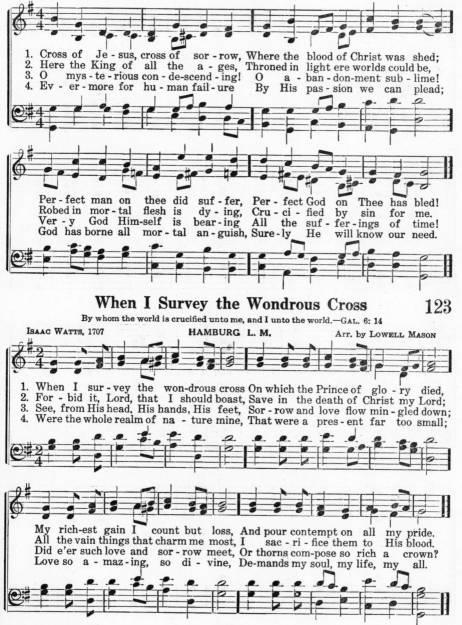

1. Cross of Je - sus, cross of sor - row, Where the blood of Christ was shed;
2. Here the King of all the a - ges, Throned in light ere worlds could be,
3. O mys - te - rious con - de - scend - ing! O a - ban - don - ment sub - lime!
4. Ev - er - more for hu - man fail - ure By His pas - sion we can plead;

Per - fect man on thee did suf - fer, Per - fect God on Thee has bled!
Robed in mor - tal flesh is dy - ing, Cru - ci - fied by sin for me.
Ver - y God Him-self is bear-ing All the suf - fer - ings of time!
God has borne all mor - tal an - guish, Sure - ly He will know our need.

When I Survey the Wondrous Cross

123

By whom the world is crucified unto me, and I unto the world.—GAL. 6: 14

ISAAC WATTS, 1707   HAMBURG. L. M.   Arr. by LOWELL MASON

1. When I sur - vey the won-drous cross On which the Prince of glo - ry died,
2. For - bid it, Lord, that I should boast, Save in the death of Christ my Lord;
3. See, from His head, His hands, His feet, Sor - row and love flow min - gled down;
4. Were the whole realm of na - ture mine, That were a pres - ent far too small;

My rich-est gain I count but loss, And pour contempt on all my pride.
All the vain things that charm me most, I sac - ri - fice them to His blood.
Did e'er such love and sor - row meet, Or thorns com-pose so rich a crown?
Love so a - maz - ing, so di - vine, De-mands my soul, my life, my all.

124 The Day of Resurrection

Jesus met them, saying, "All hail."—MATT. 28: 9

LANCASHIRE 7. 6. 7. 6. D.

JOHN OF DAMASCUS, 8th Century

HENRY SMART, 1836

1. The day of res - ur - rec - tion! Earth, tell it out a - broad;
2. Our hearts be pure from e - vil, That we may see a - right
3. Now let the heav'ns be joy - ful, Let earth her song be - gin;

The Pass - o - ver of glad - ness, The Pass - o - ver of God.
The Lord in rays e - ter - nal Of res - ur - rec - tion-light;
Let the round world keep tri - umph, And all that is there - in;

From death to life e - ter - nal, From this world to the sky,
And, lis - t'ning to His ac - cents, May hear, so calm and plain,
In - vis - i - ble and vis - i - ble, Their notes let all things blend,

Our Christ hath brought us o - ver With hymns of vic - to - ry.
His own "All hail!" and hear - ing, May raise the vic - tor strain.
For Christ the Lord hath ris - en, Our Joy that hath no end.

Awake, O Earth

I am the resurrection and the life.—Jn. 11: 25

LUCY RANDOLPH FLEMING   6s. 8 l.   J. HENRY SHOWALTER

1. A-wake, a-wake, O earth! Thy man-y voi-ces raise, And let the echo-ing
2. A-wake, a-wake, O earth! For-get the hour of gloom, When in thy shudd'ring
3. Bring treasures of the field, Bring leaf and blossom sweet, Thy choic-est and thy
4. Lift up thy gates with praise, And robes of joy put on, The Lord of life and

hills Re-peat the note of praise. Let all the isles re-joice, Let seas take
breast Thy Maker claimed a tomb. Put off thy win-try robes For garb of
best, Be-fore His pierc-ed feet. While all thy sons are glad, And tears are
death Hath ris-en to His throne. He hath gone up on high, And giv-eth

up the strain, Christ from the dead hath come, He lives, He lives a-gain.
joy-ous spring, Crown thee with lil-ies fair, To greet the ris-en King.
put a-way, Let youth and age a-like Sing "Christ is ris'n to-day."
gifts to men; He lives, no more to die, He lives, He lives a-gain.

D. S.—*from the dead hath come, He lives, He lives a-gain.*

REFRAIN

D. S.

He lives...... a-gain!...... Our ris-en Lord, to-day! Christ
He lives! Christ lives! He lives a-gain!

126 Christ is Risen

He is risen, as He said.—MATT. 28: 6

A. B. KOLB, 1896

8. 7. 8. 7. Ref.

A. B. KOLB

Joyfully

1. Christ who left His home in glo - ry, And up - on the cross was slain,
2. While the world in peace was sleep-ing, Ear - ly on that Eas - ter day,
3. Christ, our lov - ing Me - di - a - tor, Now with God for you and me

Now is ris'n! Oh, tell the sto - ry That the Sav - iour lives a - gain.
Came the faith - ful wom-en, weep-ing, But the stone was rolled a - way.
In - ter-cedes, and our Cre - a - tor Hears and an - swers ev - 'ry plea.

REFRAIN

Hail Him! Hail Him! Tell the sto - - ry;
Hail to the King, the mighty Redeemer! Hail Him who robbed the grave of its pow'r!

Hail! all hail!........ Je - sus lives for - ev - er - more.
Tell ev - 'ry na - tion, all is well,

Copyright by A. B. Kolb. By permission

127 The Strife is O'er

Having spoiled principalities and powers.—COL. 2: 15

FRANCIS POTT, 1859. Tr. Latin   VICTORY 8. 8. 8. 4.   From PALESTRINA, 1591

Al - le - lu - ia! Al - le - lu - ia! Al - le - lu - ia!

The Strife is O'er—Concluded

1. The strife is o'er, the bat - tle done; The vic - to - ry of life is won;
2. The pow'rs of death have done their worst, But Christ their legions hath dis-persed:
3. The three sad days are quick - ly sped; He ris - es glo-rious from the dead:
4. He closed the yawn-ing gates of hell; The bars from heav'n's high portals fell;
5. Lord, by the stripes that wound-ed Thee, From death's dread sting Thy servants free,

The song of tri - umph has be - gun.   Al - le - lu - ia!
Let shout of ho - ly joy out-burst,   Al - le - lu - ia!
All glo - ry to our ris - en Head!   Al - le - lu - ia!
Let hymns of praise His tri - umphs tell!   Al - le - lu - ia!
That we may live and sing to Thee,   Al - le - lu - ia! A - MEN.

The Lord is Risen Indeed   128

LUKE 24: 34

THOMAS KELLY, 1809   BENJAMIN S. M. 51.   FRANZ J. HAYDN

1. "The Lord is ris'n in - deed," And are the ti - dings true? Yes, we be - held
2. "The Lord is ris'n in - deed," Then Jus - tice asks no more; Mer - cy and Truth
3. "The Lord is ris'n in - deed," Then is His work performed; The cap - tive sure-
4. "The Lord is ris'n in - deed," At - tend - ing an - gels hear; Up to the courts
5. While on their gold-en lyres, They strike each cheerful chord, We join the bright

the Sav - iour bleed, And saw Him liv - ing too, And saw Him liv - ing too.
are now a - greed, Who stood opposed be - fore, Who stood op - posed be - fore.
ly now is freed, And death, our foe, disarmed, And death, our foe, dis-armed.
of heav'n, with speed, The joy - ful ti - dings bear, The joy - ful ti - dings bear.
ce - les - tial choirs, To sing our ris - en Lord, To sing our ris - en Lord.

129 Look, Ye Saints, the Sight is Glorious

On His head were many crowns.—REV. 19: 12

THOMAS KELLY, 1809   REGENT SQUARE 8. 7. 8. 7. 8. 7.   HENRY SMART

1. Look, ye saints, the sight is glo-rious, See the Man of sor-rows now;
2. Crown the Sav-iour, an - gels crown Him: Rich the tro-phies Je - sus brings:
3. Sin - ners in de - ris-ion crowned Him, Mock-ing thus the Sav-iour s claim;
4. Hark, those bursts of ac - cla - ma - tion! Hark, those loud tri-um-phant chords!

From the fight re - turned vic - to - rious, Ev - 'ry knee to Him shall bow:
In the seat of pow'r en-throne Him, While the vault of heav - en rings:
Saints and an - gels crowd a-round Him, Own His ti - tle, praise His name:
Je - sus takes the high - est sta - tion: O what joy the sight af - fords!

Crown Him, crown Him! Crown Him, crown Him! Crowns be-come the Vic-tor's brow.
Crown Him, crown Him! Crown Him, crown Him! Crown the Sav - iour King of kings.
Crown Him, crown Him! Crown Him, crown Him! Spread a - broad the Vic - tor's fame.
Crown Him, crown Him! Crown Him, crown Him! King of kings, and Lord of lords!

130 How Calm and Beautiful the Morn

He is not here, for He is risen.—MATT. 28: 6

THOMAS HASTINGS   HASTINGS 8. 6. 8. 6. 8. 8.   THOMAS HASTINGS, 1831

1. How calm and beau - ti - ful the morn That gilds the sa - cred tomb,
2. Ye mourn-ing saints, dry ev - 'ry tear For your de - part - ed Lord;
3. And when the shades of eve - ning fall, When life's last hour draws nigh,

How Calm and Beautiful the Morn—Concluded

Where Christ the cru - ci - fied was borne, And veiled in mid - night gloom!
Be - hold the place, He is not here, The tomb is all un - barred;
If Je - sus shine up - on the soul, How bliss - ful then to die!

O weep no more the Sav-iour slain; The Lord is ris'n—He lives a - gain.
The gates of death were closed in vain, The Lord is ris'n—He lives a - gain.
Since He has ris'n that once was slain, Ye die in Christ to live a - gain.

Christ the Lord is Risen   131

O death, where is thy sting? O grave, where is thy victory?—I Cor. 15: 55

CHARLES WESLEY, 1739   CLARION 7. 7. 7. 7.   EDWARD F. RIMBAULT, 1866

1. "Christ the Lord is ris'n to - day," Sons of men and an - gels say:
2. Vain the stone, the watch, the seal; Christ has burst the gates of hell:
3. Lives a - gain our glo - rious King: Where, O death, is now thy sting?
4. Soar we now where Christ has led, Fol-l'wing our ex - alt - ed Head:
5. Hail the Lord of earth and heav'n! Praise to Thee by both be giv'n:

Raise your joys and tri-umphs high, Sing, ye heav'ns, and earth re - ply!
Death in vain for - bids His rise; Christ has o - pened Par - a - dise.
Once He died, our souls to save: Where thy vic - to - ry, O grave?
Made like Him, like Him we rise; Ours the cross, the grave, the skies.
Thee we greet tri - um-phant now: Hail, the Res - ur - rec - tion Thou!

132

Welcome, Happy Morning

I have the keys of hell and of death.— REV. 1: 18

VENANTIUS FORTUNATUS, c. 530-609 FORTUNATUS 11s. 5 l. ARTHUR S. SULLIVAN, 1872

1. "Wel-come, hap-py morn-ing!" age to age shall say: Hell to - day is
2. Earth her joy con - fess - es, cloth-ing her for spring, All fresh gifts re-
3. Mak - er and Re-deem - er, life and health of all, Thou from heav'n be-
4. Loose the souls long pris-oned, bound with Satan's chain; All that now is

van-quished, heav'n is won to - day! Lo! the Dead is liv - ing,
turned with her re - turn - ing King; Bloom in ev - 'ry mead - ow,
hold - ing hu - man na - ture's fall, Of the Fa - ther's God - head
fall - en raise to life a - gain; Show Thy face in bright - ness,

God for - ev - er - more! Him their true Cre - a - tor, all His
leaves on ev - 'ry bough, Speak His sor - row end - ed, hail His
true and on - ly Son, Man - hood to de - liv - er, man - hood
bid the na - tions see; Bring a - gain our day - light: day re-

works a - dore! "Wel-come, hap-py morn-ing!" age to age shall say.
tri - umph now. Hell to - day is van-quished, heav'n is won to - day!
didst put on. "Wel-come, hap-py morn-ing!" age to age shall say.
turns with Thee! Hell to - day is van-quished, heav'n is won to - day!

All Glory, Laud and Honor

I am He that liveth, and was dead.—REV. 1: 18

THEODULPH, c. 800   ST. THEODULPH 7. 6. 7. 6. D.   MELCHIOR TESCHNER, c. 1613

1. All glo - ry, laud and hon - or To Thee, Re - deem - er, King!
2. The com - pa - ny of an - gels Are prais - ing Thee on high;
3. To Thee be - fore Thy pas - sion They sang their hymns of praise:

D.C.—*All glo - ry, laud and hon - - or To Thee, Re - deem - er, King!*

FINE

To whom the lips of chil - dren Made sweet ho - san - nas ring.
And mor - tal men, and all things Cre - a - ted, make re - ply.
To Thee, now high ex - alt - ed, Our mel - o - dy we raise.

To whom the lips of chil - dren Made sweet ho - san - nas ring.

Thou art the King of Is - rael, Thou Da - vid's roy - al Son,
The peo - ple of the He - brews With palms be - fore Thee went:
Thou didst ac - cept their prais - es; Ac - cept the prayers we bring,

D. C.

Who in the Lord's name com - est, The King and bless - ed One.
Our praise and prayers and an - thems Be - fore Thee we pre - sent.
Who in all good de - light - est, Thou good and gra - cious King.

134 ## Golden Harps Are Sounding

In the midst of the throne—a Lamb as it had been slain.—Rev. 5: 6

FRANCES R. HAVERGAL HERMAS 6s. 5s. 12 l. FRANCES R. HAVERGAL, 1871

1. Gold-en harps are sounding, An-gel voi-ces ring, Pearl-y gates are o-pened,
2. He who came to save us, He who bled and died, Now is crowned with glory
3. Pray-ing for His chil-dren In that bless-ed place, Call-ing them to glo-ry,

O-pened for the King: Christ, the King of glo-ry, Je-sus, King of love,
At His Fa-ther's side. Nev-er-more to suf-fer, Nev-er-more to die,
Sending them His grace; His bright home pre-par-ing, Faithful ones, for you;

REFRAIN

Is gone up in tri-umph To His throne a-bove.
Je-sus, King of glo-ry, Is gone up on high. All His work is end-ed,
Je-sus ev-er liv-eth, Ev-er lov-eth too.

Joy-ful-ly we sing; Je-sus hath as-cend-ed: Glo-ry to our King!

Hail the Day

As they beheld, He was taken up.—ACTS 1: 9

CHARLES WESLEY, 1739   ESSEX 7s. 5 l.   THOMAS CLARK

1. Hail the day that sees Him rise, Heav'nward from our wishful eyes! Christ, a-while to
2. There the glorious triumph waits: Lift your heads, e-ter-nal gates; Wide un-fold the
3. Cir-cled round with angel pow'rs, Their triumphant Lord and ours, Con-quer-or o'er
4. Him tho' highest heav'n receives, Still He loves the earth He leaves; Tho' re-turn-ing
5. Sav-iour, part-ed from our sight, High a-bove yon az-ure height, Grant our hearts may

mor-tals giv'n, Re-as-cends His na-tive heav'n, Re-as-cends His na-tive heav'n.
ra-diant scene; Take the King of glo-ry in! Take the King of glo-ry in!
death and sin, Take the King of glo-ry in! Take the King of glo-ry in!
to His throne, Still He calls mankind His own, Still He calls man-kind His own.
thith-er rise, Foll'wing Thee beyond the skies, Foll'wing Thee beyond the skies.

The Head That Once Was Crowned With Thorns   136

If so be that we suffer with Him, that we may be also glorified together.—ROM. 8: 17

THOMAS KELLY, 1820   ST. MAGNUS C. M.   J. CLARK

1. The head, that once was crowned with thorns, Is crowned with glo-ry now;
2. The high-est place that heav'n af-fords Is His, is His by right,
3. The joy of all who dwell a-bove; The joy of all be-low,
4. The cross He bore is life and health, Tho' shame and death to Him:

A roy-al di-a-dem a-dorns The might-y Vic-tor's brow.
The King of kings, and Lord of lords, And heav'n's e-ter-nal Light.
To whom He man-i-fests His love, And grants His name to know.
His peo-ple's hope, His peo-ple's wealth, Their ev-er-last-ing theme.

137 ## Rise, Glorious Conqueror

He led captivity captive.—EPH. 4: 8

MATTHEW BRIDGES, 1848. Alt.   DORT 6.6.4.6.6.6.4.   LOWELL MASON, 1832

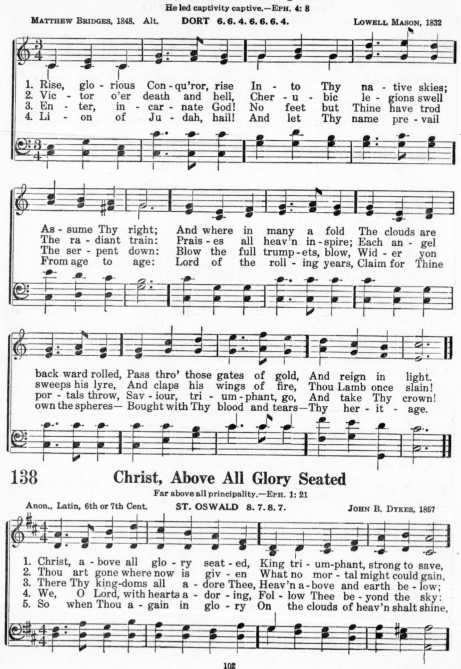

1. Rise, glo - rious Con - qu'ror, rise In - to Thy na - tive skies;
2. Vic - tor o'er death and hell, Cher - u - bic le - gions swell
3. En - ter, in - car - nate God! No feet but Thine have trod
4. Li - on of Ju - dah, hail! And let Thy name pre - vail

As - sume Thy right; And where in many a fold The clouds are
The ra - diant train: Prais - es all heav'n in - spire; Each an - gel
The ser - pent down: Blow the full trump - ets, blow, Wid - er yon
From age to age: Lord of the roll - ing years, Claim for Thine

back - ward rolled, Pass thro' those gates of gold, And reign in light.
sweeps his lyre, And claps his wings of fire, Thou Lamb once slain!
por - tals throw, Sav - iour, tri - um - phant, go, And take Thy crown!
own the spheres— Bought with Thy blood and tears—Thy her - it - age.

138 ## Christ, Above All Glory Seated

Far above all principality.—EPH. 1: 21

Anon., Latin, 6th or 7th Cent.   ST. OSWALD 8.7.8.7.   JOHN B. DYKES, 1857

1. Christ, a - bove all glo - ry seat - ed, King tri - um - phant, strong to save,
2. Thou art gone where now is giv - en What no mor - tal might could gain,
3. There Thy king - doms all a - dore Thee, Heav'n a - bove and earth be - low;
4. We, O Lord, with hearts a - dor - ing, Fol - low Thee be - yond the sky:
5. So when Thou a - gain in glo - ry On the clouds of heav'n shalt shine,

Christ, Above All Glory—Concluded

Dy - ing, Thou hast death de - feat - ed,   Bur - ied, Thou hast spoiled the grave.
On   th e - ter - nal throne of heav - en   In   Thy Fa - ther's pow'r to reign.
While the depths of hell be - fore Thee   Trembling and de - feat - ed bow.
Hear our prayers Thy grace im - plor - ing,   Lift our souls to   Thee   on high;
We Thy flock may stand be - fore Thee,   Owned for - ev - er - more as Thine.

Rejoice, the Lord is King

139

Let the children of Zion be joyful in their King.—Ps. 149: 2

ARTHUR'S SEAT   6. 6. 6. 6. 8. 8.

CHARLES WESLEY, 1746

Arr. from JOHN GOSS
by U. C. BURNAP, 1874

1. Re - joice, the Lord is   King: Your Lord and King a - dore;
2. Je - sus, the Sav - iour, reigns,   The   God of   truth and   love;
3. His   king - dom can - not   fail,   He   rules o'er earth and heav'n;
4. He   sits at God's right   hand   Till   all   His   foes   sub - mit,

Mor - tals, give thanks and sing, ...   And tri - umph ev - er - more: Lift up your
When He had purged our stains, ..   He took His seat a - bove: Lift up your
The keys of death and hell....   Are to   our Je - sus giv'n: Lift up your
And bow to   His com - mand, ..   And fall be - neath His feet: Lift up your

heart, lift   up   your voice; Re - joice, a - gain.... I   say, re - joice.
heart, lift   up   your voice; Re - joice, a - gain.... I   say, re - joice.
heart, lift   up   your voice; Re - joice, a - gain.... I   say, re - joice.
heart, lift   up   your voice; Re - joice, a - gain.... I   say, re - joice.

140 See, the Conqueror Mounts in Triumph

The King of glory shall come in.—Ps. 24: 7

ST. ASAPH 8. 7. 8. 7. D.

CHRISTOPHER WORDSWORTH, 1862

WILLIAM S. BAMBRIDGE, 1872

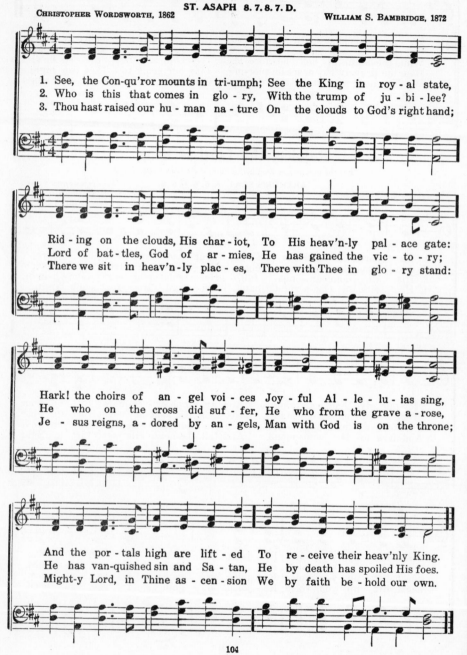

1. See, the Con-qu'ror mounts in tri-umph; See the King in roy - al state,
2. Who is this that comes in glo - ry, With the trump of ju - bi - lee?
3. Thou hast raised our hu - man na - ture On the clouds to God's right hand;

Rid - ing on the clouds, His char - iot, To His heav'n-ly pal - ace gate:
Lord of bat - tles, God of ar - mies, He has gained the vic - to - ry;
There we sit in heav'n-ly plac - es, There with Thee in glo - ry stand:

Hark! the choirs of an - gel voi - ces Joy - ful Al - le - lu - ias sing,
He who on the cross did suf - fer, He who from the grave a - rose,
Je - sus reigns, a - dored by an - gels, Man with God is on the throne;

And the por - tals high are lift - ed To re - ceive their heav'n'ly King.
He has van-quished sin and Sa - tan, He by death has spoiled His foes.
Might-y Lord, in Thine as - cen - sion We by faith be - hold our own.

Crown Him With Many Crowns

141

We see Jesus crowned with glory and honor.—Heb. 2: 9

MATTHEW BRIDGES, 1851   DIADEMATA S. M. D.   GEORGE J. ELVEY, 1868

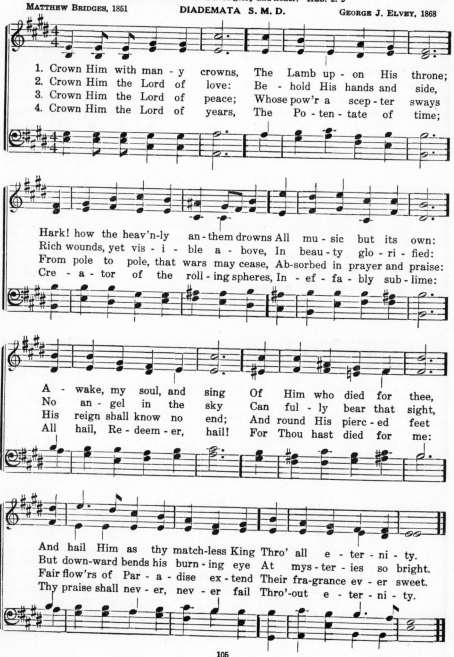

1. Crown Him with man - y crowns, The Lamb up - on His throne;
2. Crown Him the Lord of love: Be - hold His hands and side,
3. Crown Him the Lord of peace; Whose pow'r a scep - ter sways
4. Crown Him the Lord of years, The Po - ten - tate of time;

Hark! how the heav'n-ly an - them drowns All mu - sic but its own:
Rich wounds, yet vis - i - ble a - bove, In beau - ty glo - ri - fied:
From pole to pole, that wars may cease, Ab-sorbed in prayer and praise:
Cre - a - tor of the roll - ing spheres, In - ef - fa - bly sub - lime:

A - wake, my soul, and sing Of Him who died for thee,
No an - gel in the sky Can ful - ly bear that sight,
His reign shall know no end; And round His pierc - ed feet
All hail, Re - deem - er, hail! For Thou hast died for me:

And hail Him as thy match-less King Thro' all e - ter - ni - ty.
But down-ward bends his burn - ing eye At mys - ter - ies so bright.
Fair flow'rs of Par - a - dise ex - tend Their fra-grance ev - er sweet.
Thy praise shall nev - er, nev - er fail Thro'-out e - ter - ni - ty.

142 Ten Thousand Times Ten Thousand

A great multitude which no man could number.—REV. 7: 9

HENRY ALFORD, 1867   ALFORD 7.6.8.6.D.   JOHN B. DYKES, 1875

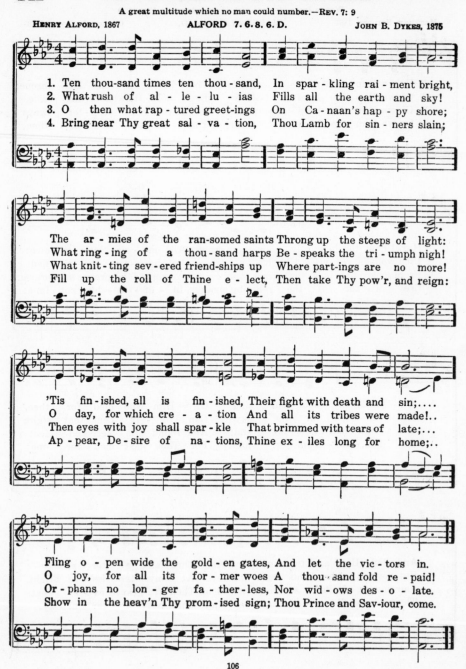

1. Ten thou-sand times ten thou-sand, In spar-kling rai-ment bright,
2. What rush of al-le-lu-ias Fills all the earth and sky!
3. O then what rap-tured greet-ings On Ca-naan's hap-py shore;
4. Bring near Thy great sal-va-tion, Thou Lamb for sin-ners slain;

The ar-mies of the ran-somed saints Throng up the steeps of light:
What ring-ing of a thou-sand harps Be-speaks the tri-umph nigh!
What knit-ting sev-ered friend-ships up Where part-ings are no more!
Fill up the roll of Thine e-lect, Then take Thy pow'r, and reign:

'Tis fin-ished, all is fin-ished, Their fight with death and sin;....
O day, for which cre-a-tion And all its tribes were made!..
Then eyes with joy shall spar-kle That brimmed with tears of late;...
Ap-pear, De-sire of na-tions, Thine ex-iles long for home;..

Fling o-pen wide the gold-en gates, And let the vic-tors in.
O joy, for all its for-mer woes A thou-sand fold re-paid!
Or-phans no lon-ger fa-ther-less, Nor wid-ows des-o-late.
Show in the heav'n Thy prom-ised sign; Thou Prince and Sav-iour, come.

Face to Face

Mrs. Frank A. Breck

Grant Colfax Tullar

Moderato

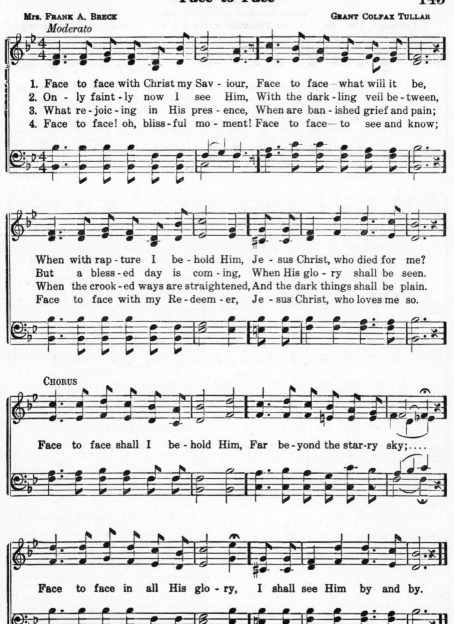

1. Face to face with Christ my Sav - iour, Face to face — what will it be,
2. On - ly faint - ly now I see Him, With the dark - ling veil be - tween,
3. What re - joic - ing in His pres - ence, When are ban - ished grief and pain;
4. Face to face! oh, bliss - ful mo - ment! Face to face — to see and know;

When with rap - ture I be - hold Him, Je - sus Christ, who died for me?
But a bless - ed day is com - ing, When His glo - ry shall be seen.
When the crook - ed ways are straightened, And the dark things shall be plain.
Face to face with my Re - deem - er, Je - sus Christ, who loves me so.

CHORUS

Face to face shall I be - hold Him, Far be - yond the star - ry sky;....

Face to face in all His glo - ry, I shall see Him by and by.

144

Lo! He Comes

Behold, He cometh with clouds.—REV. 1: 7

J. CENNICK, c. 1750. Alt.   ST. THOMAS 8. 7. 8. 7. 4. 7.   SAMUEL WEBBE, 1740-1816

1. Lo! He comes, with clouds de-scend-ing Once for fa-vored sin-ners slain;
2. Ev-'ry eye shall now be-hold Him Robed in dread-ful maj-es-ty;
3. Ev-'ry is-land, sea and moun-tain, Heav'n and earth shall flee a-way;
4. Now re-demp-tion, long ex-pect-ed, See in sol-emn pomp ap-pear;
5. Yea, A-men! let all a-dore Thee, High on Thine e-ter-nal throne;

Thou-sand thou-sand saints at-tend-ing Swell the tri-umph of His train;
Those who set at naught and sold Him, Pierced, and nailed Him to the tree,
All who hate Him, must, con-found-ed, Hear the trump pro-claim the day:
All His saints, by man re-ject-ed, Now shall meet Him in the air:
Sav-iour, take the pow'r and glo-ry, Claim the king-dom for Thine own:

Al-le-lu-ia! Al-le-lu-ia! God ap-pears on earth to reign.
Deep-ly wail-ing, Deep-ly wail-ing, Shall the true Mes-si-ah see.
Come to judg-ment! Come to judgment! Come to judg-ment! Come a-way!
Al-le-lu-ia! Al-le-lu-ia! See the day of God ap-pear.
Al-le-lu-ia! Al-le-lu-ia! Thou shalt reign, and Thou a-lone.

145

Come, Thou Long Expected Jesus

The desire of all nations.—HAGG. 2: 7

WILSON 8. 7. 8. 7.

CHARLES WESLEY, 1744   From FELIX MENDELSSOHN-BARTHOLDY

1. Come, Thou long-ex-pect-ed Je-sus! Born to set Thy peo-ple free,
2. Is-rael's strength and con-so-la-tion, Hope of all the saints Thou art;
3. Born Thy peo-ple to de-liv-er, Born a child, and yet a King,
4. By Thine own e-ter-nal Spir-it, Rule in all our hearts a-lone;

Come, Thou Long Expected Jesus—Concluded

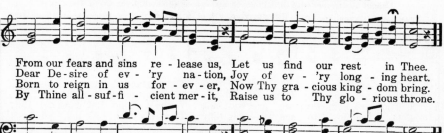

From our fears and sins re - lease us, Let us find our rest in Thee.
Dear De - sire of ev - 'ry na - tion, Joy of ev - 'ry long - ing heart.
Born to reign in us for - ev - er, Now Thy gra - cious king - dom bring.
By Thine all - suf - fi - cient mer - it, Raise us to Thy glo - rious throne.

The Bridegroom Soon Will Call Us   146

Behold, the Bridegroom cometh.—MATT. 25: 6

EVARTS 7. 6. 7. 6. D.

JOHN WALTHER, 1552

From German,
LOWELL MASON, 1841

1. The Bridegroom soon will call us, Come, all ye wedding guests! May not His voice ap-
2. There shall we see de - light - ed Our dear Redeemer's face, Who leads our souls be-
3. They will not blush to own us As broth-ers, sis-ters dear, Love ev - er will be
4. In man-sions fair and spacious Will God the feast prepare, And ev - er kind and

pall us, While slumber binds our breasts; May all our lamps be burn-ing, And oil be
night-ed To glo-ry by His grace; The pa-tri-archs shall meet us, The prophets'
shown us When we with them appear; We all shall come be-fore Him, Who for us
gracious, Bid us its rich-es share; There bliss that knows no measure From springs of

found in store, That we, with Him re - turn - ing, May o - pen find the door.
ho - ly band, A - pos - tles, martyrs, greet us In that ce - les - tial land.
Man be-came, As Lord and God a - dore Him, And ev - er bless His name.
love shall flow, And nev - er chang-ing pleas-ure His boun-ty will be - stow.

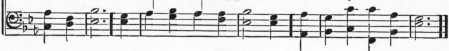

147 Thou Art Coming

Caught up together with them in the clouds, to meet the Lord in the air.—I THES. 4: 17

FRANCES R. HAVERGAL, 1873   BEVERLY 8. 7. 8. 8. 7. 7. 7. 7. 7.   WILLIAM H. MONK, 1875

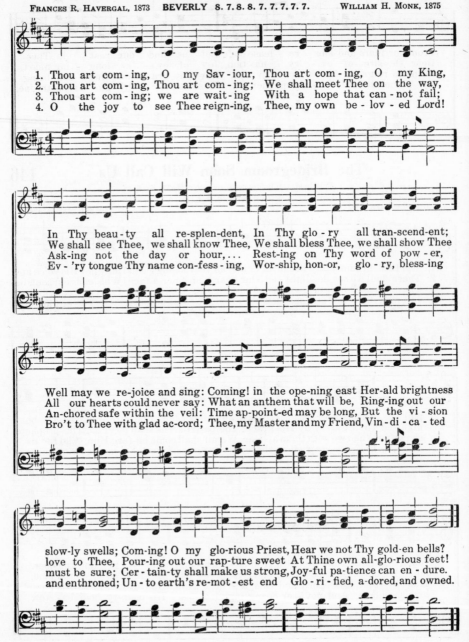

1. Thou art com-ing, O my Sav-iour, Thou art com-ing, O my King,
2. Thou art com-ing, Thou art com-ing; We shall meet Thee on the way,
3. Thou art com-ing; we are wait-ing With a hope that can-not fail;
4. O the joy to see Thee reign-ing, Thee, my own be-lov-ed Lord!

In Thy beau-ty all re-splen-dent, In Thy glo-ry all tran-scend-ent;
We shall see Thee, we shall know Thee, We shall bless Thee, we shall show Thee
Ask-ing not the day or hour,... Rest-ing on Thy word of pow-er,
Ev-'ry tongue Thy name con-fess-ing, Wor-ship, hon-or, glo-ry, bless-ing

Well may we re-joice and sing: Coming! in the ope-ning east Her-ald brightness
All our hearts could never say: What an anthem that will be, Ring-ing out our
An-chored safe within the veil: Time ap-point-ed may be long, But the vi-sion
Bro't to Thee with glad ac-cord; Thee, my Master and my Friend, Vin-di-ca-ted

slow-ly swells; Com-ing! O my glo-rious Priest, Hear we not Thy gold-en bells?
love to Thee, Pour-ing out our rap-ture sweet At Thine own all-glo-rious feet!
must be sure; Cer-tain-ty shall make us strong, Joy-ful pa-tience can en-dure.
and enthroned; Un-to earth's re-mot-est end Glo-ri-fied, a-dored, and owned.

Come, Lord, and Tarry Not

148

Even so, come, Lord Jesus.—Rev. 22: 20

HORATIUS BONAR, 1857   SIENNA S. M.   J. H. DEANE, 1869

1. Come, Lord, and tar - ry   not; Bring the long-looked-for day; O why these
2. Come, for Thy saints still   wait; Dai - ly as - cends their sigh; The Spir - it
3. Come, and make all   things new; Build up this ru - ined earth, Re-store our
4. Come, and be - gin Thy   reign Of ev - er - last - ing peace; Come take the

years of wait - ing   here,   These a - ges of   de - lay?
and the Bride say,   Come!   Dost Thou not hear   the   cry?
fad - ed Par - a -   dise,   Cre - a - tion's sec -   ond birth.
king-dom to Thy -   self,   Great King of right - eous - ness. A - MEN.

Jesus, Thy Church

149

Looking for that blessed hope.—Tit. 2: 13

WM. HILEY BATHURST, 1831   LUTON L. M.   GEORGE BURDER, 1780

1. Je - sus, Thy Church with longing eyes For Thine ex - pect - ed com - ing waits:
2. E'en now, when tempests round us fall, And win - try clouds o'ercast the sky,
3. Come, gracious Lord, our hearts renew, Our foes re - pel, our wrongs re-dress,
4. Teach us in watch-ful-ness and prayer To wait for the ap - point - ed hour;

When will the prom-ised light a - rise, And glo - ry beam from Zi - on's gates?
Thy words with pleasure we re - call, And deem that our re-demp-tion's nigh.
Man's root-ed en - mi - ty sub-due, And crown Thy gos - pel with suc - cess.
And fit us by Thy grace to share The tri - umphs of Thy con-q'ring pow'r.

150 Christ the Lord Cometh?

The coming of the Lord draweth nigh.—JAMES 5: 8

E. G. WESLEY

WILLIAM W. BENTLEY

With vigor

1. Christ the Lord com-eth? per-chance at the dawn, Where earth a-wak-eth to
2. Christ the Lord com-eth? earth's evening may bring Back to His vine-yard our
3. Christ the Lord com-eth? man know-eth not when, But when ye think not He

wel-come the morn; Hath He not told us the hour draweth near; Watching and
Sav-iour and King; Death shall be conquered and sin o-ver-thrown; When He re-
com-eth a-gain; To all found watching He bringeth no fear, Nev-er a

REFRAIN

read-y, His sum-mons to hear?
turn-eth to gath-er His own. Je-sus is com-ing! we know not how soon,
shad-ow, a part-ing, a tear.

Com-ing at mid-night, at morn-ing or noon; Eve-ning may bring Him to

rit.

bear us a-way; For Him I'm watch-ing and wait-ing each day.

Rejoice, All Ye Believers

The wise took oil in their vessels with their lamps.—MATT. 25: 4

LAURENTIUS LAURENTI, 1700 **GREENLAND 7. 6. 7. 6. D.** Arr. from J. MICHAEL HAYDN

1. Re - joice, all ye be - liev - ers! And let your lights ap - pear;
2. See that your lamps are burn - ing; Re - plen - ish them with oil;
3. Ye saints, who here in pa - tience Your cross and suf-f'rings bore,
4. Our hope and ex - pec - ta - tion, O Je - sus, now ap - pear;

The eve - ning is ad - vanc - ing, And dark - er night is near.
And wait for your sal - va - tion, The end of earth - ly toil.
Shall live and reign for - ev - er, When sor - row is no more:
A - rise, Thou Sun so longed for, O'er this be - night - ed sphere.

The Bride-groom is a - ris - ing, And soon He will draw nigh;
The watch - ers on the moun - tain Pro - claim the Bride-groom near,
A - round the throne of glo - ry The Lamb ye shall be - hold,
With hearts and hands up - lift - ed, We plead, O Lord, to see

Up! pray, and watch, and wres - tle! At mid - night comes the cry.
Go meet Him as He com - eth, With Al - le - lu - ias clear.
In tri - umph cast be - fore Him Your di - a - dems of gold.
The day of earth's re - demp - tion That brings us un - to Thee.

152 Gracious Spirit, Love Divine

The Holy Spirit of promise,—the earnest of our inheritance.—EPH. 1: 13, 14

JOHN STOCKER, 1777   BUCKLAND 7. 7. 7. 7.   L. G. HAYNE, 1863

1. Gra - cious Spir - it! Love di - vine! Let Thy light with - in me shine;
2. Speak Thy par-d'ning grace to me; Set the bur-dened sin - ner free;
3. Life and peace to me im - part; Seal sal - va - tion on my heart;
4. Let me nev - er from Thee stray; Keep me in the nar - row way;

All my guilt - y fears re - move; Fill me with Thy heav'n-ly love.
Lead me to the Lamb of God; Wash me in His pre-cious blood.
Dwell Thy-self with - in my breast, Ear - nest of im - mor - tal rest.
Fill my soul with joy di - vine; Keep me, Lord, for - ev - er Thine.

153 Come, Holy Spirit, Heavenly Dove

The love of God shed abroad in our hearts by the Holy Ghost.—ROM. 5: 5

ISAAC WATTS, 1707   MT. CALVARY C. M.   ROBERT P. STEWART

1. Come, Ho - ly Spir - it, Heav'n-ly Dove, With all Thy quick-'ning pow'rs;
2. Look how we grov - el here be - low, Fond of these earth - ly toys;
3. And shall we then for - ev - er live At this poor dy - ing rate?
4. Come, Ho - ly Spir - it, Heav'n-ly Dove, With all Thy quick-'ning powr's;

Kin - dle a flame of sa - cred love In these cold hearts of ours.
Our souls, how heav - i - ly they go, To reach e - ter - nal joys.
Our love so faint, so cold to Thee, And Thine to us so great!
Come, shed a - broad a Sav-iour's love, And that shall kin - dle ours.

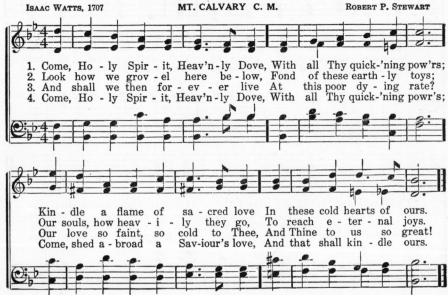

Holy Ghost, Dispel Our Sadness

He dwelleth with you, and shall be in you.—JOHN. 14: 17

LIGHT OF THE WORLD 8. 7. 8. 7. D.

PAUL GERHARDT, c. 1648. Alt.

FERDINAND H. HIMMEL

1. Ho - ly Ghost, dis - pel our sad - ness; Pierce the clouds of na-ture's night;
2. Au - thor of the new cre - a - tion, Come with unc - tion and with pow'r:

Come, Thou source of joy and glad - ness, Breathe Thy life, and spread Thy light:
Make our hearts Thy hab - i - ta - tion; On our souls Thy gra - ces show'r:

From the height which knows no meas - ure, As a gra - cious show'r descend,
Hear, O hear our sup - pli - ca - tion, Bless-ed Spir - it, God of peace!

Bring-ing down the rich - est treas-ure Man can wish, or God can send.
Rest up - on this con - gre-ga - tion, With the full - ness of Thy grace.

155 **Come, Gracious Spirit, Heavenly Dove**

He will guide you into all truth.—JN. 16: 13, 14

S. BROWNE, 1680-1732   BACA L. M.   WILLIAM B. BRADBURY

1. Come, gra-cious Spir - it, heav'n-ly Dove, With light and com - fort from a - bove; Be Thou our guard-ian, Thou our guide, O'er ev - 'ry thought and step pre - side, O'er ev - 'ry thought and step pre - side.
2. The light of truth to us dis - play, And make us know and choose Thy way; Plant ho - ly fear in ev - 'ry heart, That we from God may ne'er de - part, That we from God may ne'er de - part.
3. Lead us to ho - li - ness—the road Which we must take to dwell with God; Lead us to Christ, the liv - ing way, Nor let us from His pas-tures stray, Nor let us from His pas - tures stray.
4. Lead us to God, our fi - nal rest, To be with Him for-ev - er blest; Lead us to heav'n, its bliss to share—Full - ness of joy for - ev - er there, Full-ness of joy for - ev - er there.

156 **Come, Holy Spirit, Come**

He will reprove the world of sin, and of righteousness, and of judgment.—JN. 16: 8

MORNINGTON S. M.

JOSEPH HART, 1759   G. C. WELLESLEY,
          EARL OF MORNINGTON, 1760

1. Come, Ho - ly Spir - it, come! Let Thy bright beams a - rise;
2. Re - vive our droop - ing faith, Our doubts and fears re - move;
3. Con - vince us of our sin; Then lead to Je - sus' blood;
4. Dwell, there-fore, in our hearts; Our minds from bond - age free;

Come, Holy Spirit, Come—Concluded

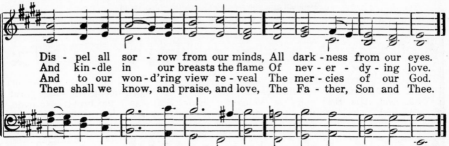

Dis - pel all sor - row from our minds, All dark - ness from our eyes.
And kin - dle in our breasts the flame Of nev - er - dy - ing love.
And to our won - d'ring view re - veal The mer - cies of our God.
Then shall we know, and praise, and love, The Fa - ther, Son and Thee.

Holy Spirit, Faithful Guide   157

I will guide thee with mine eye.—Ps. 32: 8

M. M. WELLS, 1853   GUIDE 7. 7. 7. 7. D.   MARCUS MORRIS WELLS

1. Ho - ly Spir - it, faith - ful Guide, Ev - er near the Chris-tian's side,
2. Ev - er pres - ent, tru - est Friend, Ev - er near, Thine aid to lend,
3. When our days of toil shall cease, Wait-ing still for sweet re - lease,

Gen - tly lead us by the hand, Pil - grims in a des - ert land.
Leave us not to doubt and fear, Grop - ing on in dark - ness drear.
Noth - ing left but heav'n and prayer, Won-d'ring if our names are there,

D. S.—Whisper soft - ly, "Wan-d'rer, come! Fol - low Me, I'll guide thee home."

Wea - ry souls for - e'er re - joice, While they hear the sweet-est voice,
When the storms are rag - ing sore, Hearts grow faint, and hopes give o'er,
Wad - ing deep the dis - mal flood, Plead - ing naught but Je - sus' blood,

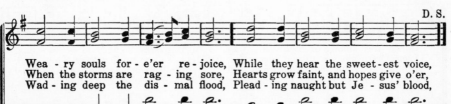

158 Our Blest Redeemer

He shall give you another Comforter.—JN. 14: 16

HARRIET AUBER, 1829   ST. CUTHBERT 8. 6. 8. 4.   JOHN B. DYKES, 1861

1. Our blest Re-deem-er, ere He breathed His ten-der last fare-well,
2. He came sweet in-fluence to im-part, A gra-cious, will-ing guest,
3. And His that gen-tle voice we hear, Soft as the breath of even,
4. And ev-'ry vir-tue we pos-sess, And ev-'ry vic-t'ry won,
5. Spir-it of pu-ri-ty and grace, Our weak-ness, pity-ing, see:

A Guide, a Com-fort-er, be-queathed With us to dwell.
While He can find one hum-ble heart Where-in to rest.
That checks each tho't, that calms each fear, And speaks of heav'n.
And ev-'ry thought of ho-li-ness, Are His a-lone.
O make our hearts Thy dwell-ing-place, And wor-thier Thee.

159 Holy Ghost, With Light Divine

Lead me in Thy truth and teach me.—Ps. 25: 5

LAST HOPE 7. 7. 7. 7.

ANDREW REED, 1787-1862   L. M. GOTTSCHALK, Arr. by H. P. M.

1. Ho-ly Ghost, with light di-vine, Shine up-on this heart of mine;
2. Ho-ly Ghost, with pow'r di-vine, Cleanse this guilt-y heart of mine;
3. Ho-ly Ghost, with joy di-vine, Cheer this sad-dened heart of mine;
4. Ho-ly Spir-it, all di-vine, Dwell with-in this heart of mine;

Chase the shades of night a-way, Turn my dark-ness in-to day.
Long hath sin, with-out con-trol, Held do-min-ion o'er my soul.
Bid my man-y woes de-part; Heal my wound-ed, bleed-ing heart.
Cast down ev-'ry i-dol throne; Reign su-preme, and reign a-lone.

Ancient of Days

The Ancient of Days did sit, whose garment was white as snow.—DAN. 7: 9–22

WILLIAM C. DOANE, 1886 HYMN TO JOY 11. 10. 11. 10. J. ALBERT JEFFERY, 1886

1. An - cient of Days, who sit - test throned in glo - ry,
2. O Ho - ly Fa - ther, who hast led Thy chil - dren
3. O Ho - ly Je - sus, Prince of Peace and Sav - iour,
4. O Ho - ly Ghost, the Lord and the Life - giv - er,
5. O Tri - une God, with heart and voice a - dor - ing,

To Thee all knees are bent, all voi - ces pray;
In all the a - - ges, with the fire and cloud,
To Thee we owe the peace that still pre - vails,
Thine is the quick - 'ning pow'r that gives in - crease;
Praise we the good - - ness that doth crown our days;

Thy love has blessed the wide world's won - drous sto - ry
Through seas dry - shod, through wea - ry wastes be - wil - d'ring;
Still - ing the rude wills of men's wild be - hav - ior,
From Thee have flowed, as from a pleas - ant riv - er,
Pray we that Thou wilt hear us, still im - plor - ing

With light and life since E - den's dawn - ing day.
To Thee, in rev - 'rent love, our hearts are bowed.
And calm - ing pas - sion's fierce and storm - y gales.
Our plen - ty, wealth, pros - per - i - ty and peace.
Thy love and fa - vor kept to us al - ways.

161 Holy, Holy, Holy, Lord God

Holy, holy, holy, Lord God Almighty, which was, and is, and is to come.—REV. 4: 8

ST. ATHANASIUS 7s. 6 l.

CHRISTOPHER WORDSWORTH, 1862

EDWARD J. HOPKINS, 1872

1. Ho - ly, Ho - ly, Ho - ly, Lord God of hosts, E - ter - nal King,
2. Thou-sands, tens of thou-sands, stand, Spir - its blest, be - fore Thy throne,
3. Thee a - pos - tles, proph - ets Thee, Thee the no - ble mar - tyr band,
4. Al - le - lu - ia, Lord, to Thee, Fa - ther, Son, and Ho - ly Ghost;

By the heav'ns and earth a - dored! An - gels and arch - an - gels sing,
Speed-ing thence at Thy com-mand; And, when Thy be - hests are done,
Praise with sol - emn ju - bi - lee; Thee the Church in ev - 'ry land;
God - head One, and Per - sons Three! Join us with the heav'n - ly host,

Chant-ing ev - er - last - ing - ly To the bless - ed Trin - i - ty.
Sing - ing ev - er - last - ing - ly To the bless - ed Trin - i - ty.
Sing - ing ev - er - last - ing - ly To the bless - ed Trin - i - ty.
Sing - ing ev - er - last - ing - ly To the bless - ed Trin - i - ty. A - MEN.

162 We Give Immortal Praise

Now unto the King eternal, immortal, invisible, the only wise God, be honor and glory forever and ever, Amen.—I TIM. 1: 17

ISAAC WATTS, 1709

WATTS 6. 6. 6. 6. 8. 8.

J. S. B. HODGES

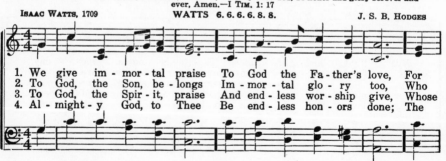

1. We give im - mor - tal praise To God the Fa - ther's love, For
2. To God, the Son, be - longs Im - mor - tal glo - ry too, Who
3. To God, the Spir - it, praise And end - less wor - ship give, Whose
4. Al - might - y God, to Thee Be end - less hon - ors done; The

We Give Immortal Praise—Concluded

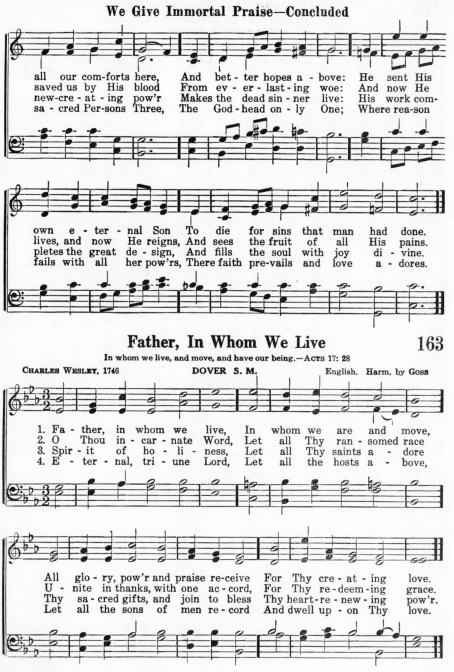

all our com-forts here, And bet - ter hopes a - bove: He sent His
saved us by His blood From ev - er - last - ing woe: And now He
new-cre - at - ing pow'r Makes the dead sin - ner live: His work com-
sa - cred Per-sons Three, The God - head on - ly One; Where rea-son

own e - ter - nal Son To die for sins that man had done.
lives, and now He reigns, And sees the fruit of all His pains.
pletes the great de - sign, And fills the soul with joy di - vine.
fails with all her pow'rs, There faith pre-vails and love a - dores.

Father, In Whom We Live   163

In whom we live, and move, and have our being.—ACTS 17: 28

CHARLES WESLEY, 1746   DOVER S. M.   English. Harm. by GOSS

1. Fa - ther, in whom we live, In whom we are and move,
2. O Thou in - car - nate Word, Let all Thy ran - somed race
3. Spir - it of ho - li - ness, Let all Thy saints a - dore
4. E - ter - nal, tri - une Lord, Let all the hosts a - bove,

All glo - ry, pow'r and praise re-ceive For Thy cre - at - ing love.
U - nite in thanks, with one ac-cord, For Thy re - deem - ing grace.
Thy sa - cred gifts, and join to bless Thy heart-re - new - ing pow'r.
Let all the sons of men re - cord And dwell up - on Thy love.

5

164
Pleasant Are Thy Courts
How amiable are Thy tabernacles.—Ps. 84: 1

HENRY F. LYTE, 1834   MAIDSTONE 7. 7. 7. 7. D.   WALTER B. GILBERT, 1862

1. Pleas-ant are Thy courts a - bove, In the land of light and love;
2. Hap - py birds that sing and fly Round Thy al - tars, O Most High!
3. Hap - py souls! their prais - es flow E - ven in this vale of woe;
4. Lord, be mine this prize to win; Guide me thro' a world of sin;

Pleas-ant are Thy courts be - low, In this land of sin and woe.
Hap - pier souls that find a rest In a heav'n-ly Fa - ther's breast!
Wa - ters in the des - ert rise, Man - na feeds them from the skies:
Keep me by Thy sav - ing grace; Give me at Thy side a place.

O my spir - it longs and faints For the con - verse of Thy saints,
Like the wan-d'ring dove, that found No re - pose on earth a - round,
On they go from strength to strength Till they reach Thy throne at length,
Sun and shield a - like Thou art; Guide and guard my err - ing heart.

For the bright-ness of Thy face, For Thy full - ness, God of grace!
They can to their ark re - pair And en - joy it ev - er there.
At Thy feet a - dor - ing fall, Who hast led them safe thro' all.
Grace and glo - ry flow from Thee; Show'r, O show'r them, Lord, on me!

To Thy Temple I Repair

165

I will come into Thy house in the multitude of Thy mercies.—Ps. 5: 7

JAMES MONTGOMERY, 1812   GUISBOROUGH 7. 7. 7. 7.   C. T. BOWEN

1. To Thy tem-ple I re-pair; Lord, I love to wor-ship there,
2. While Thy glo-rious praise is sung, Touch my lips, un-loose my tongue,
3. While the prayers of saints as-cend, God of love, to mine at-tend;
4. While Thy min-is-ters pro-claim Peace and par-don in Thy name,
5. From Thy house when I re-turn, May my heart with-in me burn,

When with-in the veil I meet Christ be-fore the mer-cy-seat.
That my joy-ful soul may bless Thee, the Lord my right-eous-ness.
Hear me, for Thy Spir-it pleads; Hear, for Je-sus in-ter-cedes.
Thro' their voice, by faith, may I Hear Thee speaking from the sky.
And at eve-ning let me say, "I have walked with God to-day." A-MEN.

Thy Presence, Gracious God, Afford

166

I will hear what the Lord will speak.—Ps. 85: 8

JOHN FAWCETT   QUEBEC L. M.   HENRY BAKER, 1862

1. Thy pres-ence, gra-cious God, af-ford; Pre-pare us to re-ceive Thy Word;
2. Dis-tract-ing tho'ts and cares re-move, And fix our hearts and hopes a-bove;
3. To us Thy sa-cred Word ap-ply, With sov'reign pow'r and en-er-gy;
4. Fa-ther, in us Thy Son re-veal; Teach us to know and do Thy will;

Now let Thy voice en-gage our ear, And faith be mixed with what we hear.
With food di-vine may we be fed, And sat-is-fied with liv-ing bread.
And may we in Thy faith and fear Re-duce to prac-tice what we hear.
Thy sav-ing pow'r and love dis-play, And guide us to the realms of day.

167 In Thy Holy Place

To behold the beauty of the Lord, and to inquire in His temple.—Ps. 27: 4

S. F. COFFMAN, 1901

7. 7. 7. 7. 8. 7. 8. 7.

J. D. BRUNK, 1911

1. In Thy ho - ly place we bow, Per-fumes sweet to heav - en rise,
2. Ho - ly light doth fill this place,—Spir - it light our way to guide;
3. On Thy ho - ly bread we feed, Hun - ger nev - er more to know:

cres. *dim.*

While our gold - en cen - sers glow With the fire of sac - ri - fice.
In the pres - ence of Thy face Sin and dark-ness ne'er can hide.
Thou sup - pli - est all our need; Fa - ther, whith-er shall we go?

p *cres.*

Saints low bend - ing, prayers as-cend-ing, Ho - ly lips and hands im-plore;—
Heav - en's gleam-ing, full - ness streaming, Life and truth for man is found;
Ne'er for - sak - ing, here par - tak - ing Bread our souls to sat - is - fy;

m cres. *dim.*

Faith be - liev - ing and re - ceiv - ing Grace from Him whom we a - dore.
Light per-vad - ing, nev - er fad - ing, Light-ing all the world a - round.
Here a - bid - ing and con - fid - ing, We shall nev - er want nor die.

Once More We Come Before Our God

168

Blessed are they that hear the word of God, and keep it.—Lk. 11: 28

JOSEPH HART, 1712-1768　　　　　　SOHO C. M.　　　　　　JOSEPH BARNBY, 1881

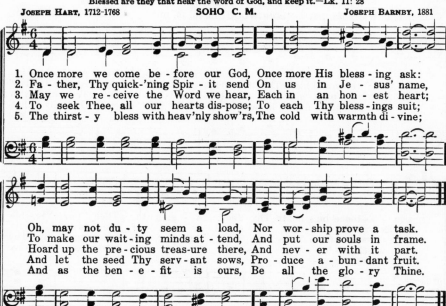

1. Once more we come be - fore our God, Once more His bless - ing ask:
2. Fa - ther, Thy quick-'ning Spir - it send On us in Je - sus' name,
3. May we re - ceive the Word we hear, Each in an hon - est heart;
4. To seek Thee, all our hearts dis-pose; To each Thy bless - ings suit;
5. The thirst - y bless with heav'nly show'rs, The cold with warmth di - vine;

Oh, may not du - ty seem a load, Nor wor - ship prove a task.
To make our wait - ing minds at - tend, And put our souls in frame.
Hoard up the pre - cious treas-ure there, And nev - er with it part.
And let the seed Thy serv - ant sows, Pro - duce a - bun - dant fruit.
And as the ben - e - fit is ours, Be all the glo - ry Thine.

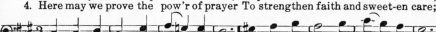

Jesus, Where'er Thy People Meet

169

Worship Him in spirit and in truth.—Jn. 4: 21-24

WILLIAM COWPER, 1769　　　　　WESTCOTT L. M.　　　　　JOSEPH BARNBY

1. Je - sus, wher-e'er Thy peo - ple meet, There they behold Thy mer - cy seat;
2. For Thou, with-in no walls con-fined, Dost dwell with those of hum-ble mind;
3. Great Shepherd of Thy cho - sen few, Thy for-mer mer-cies here re - new;
4. Here may we prove the pow'r of prayer To strengthen faith and sweet-en care;

Wher-e'er they seek Thee, Thou art found, And ev - 'ry place is hal-lowed ground.
Such ev - er bring Thee where they come, And, go - ing, take Thee to their home.
Here, to our wait - ing hearts, proclaim The sweet-ness of Thy sav - ing name.
To teach our faint de - sires to rise, And bring all heav'n be - fore our eyes.

170 Father, Again in Jesus' Name We Meet

Where two or three are gathered together in My name.—MATT. 18: 20

LUCY E. G. WHITMORE, 1824   LONGWOOD 10. 10. 10. 10.   JOSEPH BARNBY, 1872

1. Fa - ther, a - gain in Je - sus' name we meet, And bow in
2. O we would bless Thee for Thy cease - less care, And all Thy
3. A - las, un - wor - thy of Thy bound - less love, Too oft with
4. O by that name in which all full - ness dwells, O by that

pen - i - tence be - neath Thy feet: A - gain to Thee our fee - ble
works from day to day de - clare: Is not our life with hour - ly
care - less feet from Thee we rove; But now, en - cour - aged by Thy
love which ev - 'ry love ex - cels, O by that blood so free - ly

voi - ces raise, To sue for mer - cy, and to sing Thy praise.
mercies crowned? Does not Thine arm en - cir - cle us a - round?
voice, we come, Re - turn - ing sin - ners to a Fa - ther's home.
shed for sin, O - pen blest mer - cy's gate, and take us in. A - MEN.

171 We Love the Place, O God

I was glad when they said unto me, Let us go unto the house of the Lord.—PS. 122: 1

WILLIAM BULLOCK, 1854. Alt.   QUAM DILECTA 6. 6. 6. 6.   HENRY L. JENNER, 1861

1. We love the place, O God, Where - in Thine hon - or dwells;
2. We love the house of prayer, Where - in Thy serv - ants meet;
3. We love the Word of life, The Word that tells of peace,
4. We love to sing be - low For mer - cies free - ly giv'n;
5. Lord Je - sus, give us grace On earth to love Thee more,

We Love the Place, O God—Concluded

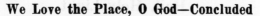

The joy of Thine a - bode　All oth - er joy ex - cels.
For Thou, O Lord, art there　Thy cho - sen ones to greet.
Of com - fort in the strife,　And joys that nev - er cease.
But O we long to know　The tri - umph song of heav'n.
In heav'n to see Thy face,　And with Thy saints a - dore.

When Morning Gilds the Skies　172

Sing forth the honor of His name.—Ps. 66: 2

Anon. (German, c. 1800)　　LAUDES DOMINI 6s. 6 l.　　JOSEPH BARNBY, 1868

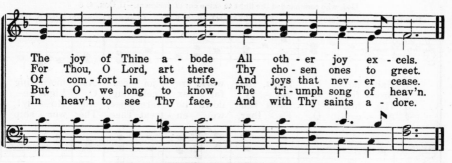

1. When morn - ing gilds the skies,　My heart a - wak - ing cries,
2. When sleep her balm de - nies,　My si - lent spir - it sighs,
3. Does sad - ness fill my mind?　A sol - ace here I find,
4. Let earth's wide cir - cle round　In joy - ful notes re - sound,

May Je - sus Christ be praised: A - like at work and prayer
May Je - sus Christ be praised: When e - vil thoughts mo - lest,
May Je - sus Christ be praised: Or fades my earth - ly bliss?
May Je - sus Christ be praised: Let air and sea and sky,

To Je - sus I re - pair;....　May Je - sus Christ be praised.
With this I shield my breast,..　May Je - sus Christ be praised.
My com - fort still is this,....　May Je - sus Christ be praised.
From depth to height, re - ply,.....　May Je - sus Christ be praised.

173

Hail, Holy Light

God, who commanded the light to shine out of darkness.—II Cor. 4: 6

EDWIN P. PARKER, 1890   ST. CLEMENT 9. 8. 9. 8.   CLEMENT C. SCHOLEFIELD, 1874

1. Hail, ho - ly Light, the world re - joi - ces As morn - ing
2. Break forth, in glo - ry far ex - cel - ling, O Light e -
3. The heav'n - ly hosts fall down be - fore Thee, And, Ho - ly!
4. Ac - cept, O Fa - ther, we en - treat Thee, The wor - ship

breaks and shad - ows fly; All na - ture blends her myr - iad
ter - nal, Love di - vine! Let Thy bright beams, all shades dis -
cry, nor ev - er rest; The saints on earth, with them a -
which Thy chil - dren bring; O grant us grace in heav'n to

voi - ces To greet the Day - spring from on high.
pel - ling, A - round us and with - in us shine.
dore Thee, Cre - a - tor, Sav - iour, Spir - it blest.
greet Thee, And with all saints Thy love to sing.

174

This is the Day of Light

Upon the first day of the week, very early in the morning.—Lk. 24: 1

JOHN ELLERTON, 1867   DAYSPRING S. M.   C. BRYAN

1. This is the day of light; Let there be light to - day;
2. This is the day of rest; Our fail - ing strength re - new;
3. This is the day of peace; With peace our spir - its fill;
4. This is the day of prayer; Let earth to heav'n draw near;

123

This is the Day of Light—Concluded

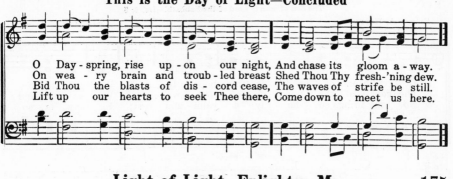

O Day-spring, rise up-on our night, And chase its gloom a-way.
On wea-ry brain and troub-led breast Shed Thou Thy fresh-'ning dew.
Bid Thou the blasts of dis-cord cease, The waves of strife be still.
Lift up our hearts to seek Thee there, Come down to meet us here.

Light of Light, Enlighten Me 175

I am the light of the world.—JN. 8: 12

BENJAMIN SCHMOLCK, 1714   HINCHMAN 7. 8. 7. 8. 7. 7.   UZZIAH C. BURNAP, 1869

1. Light of light, en-light-en me, Now a-new the day is dawn-ing;
2. Fount of all our joy and peace, To Thy liv-ing wa-ters lead me;
3. Let me with my heart to-day, Ho-ly, Ho-ly, Ho-ly, sing-ing,
4. Hence all care, all van-i-ty, For the day to God is ho-ly;

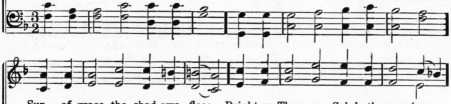

Sun of grace, the shad-ows flee; Bright-en Thou my Sab-bath morn-ing;
Thou from earth my soul re-lease, And with grace and mer-cy feed me;
Rapt a-while from earth a-way, All my soul to Thee up-spring-ing,
Come, Thou glo-rious Maj-es-ty, Deign to fill this tem-ple low-ly;

With Thy joy and sun-shine blest, Hap-py is my day of rest.
Bless Thy Word, that it may prove Rich in fruits that Thou dost love.
Have a fore-taste in-ly giv'n How they wor-ship Thee in heav'n.
Naught to-day my soul shall move, Sim-ply rest-ing in Thy love.

176 O Holy Day

The Son of man is Lord of the Sabbath.—Lk. 6: 5

ELISHA A. HOFFMAN

CHAS. EDW. POLLOCK

Rather slow

1. How calm and how bright is this ho - ly day! We haste to the
2. The courts of the tem - ple of God we love; We en - ter and
3. No day brings so ho - ly a calm and rest; No day is so

courts of the Lord a - way; We wor - ship and pray and ex -
here our de - vo - tion prove; We lay our ob - la - tions down
rich - ly with com - fort blest; Our faith is in - creased and our

ult in His praise, And we hal - low and hon - or this best of all days.
low at His feet, And in songs of re - joic - ing our thanks we re - peat.
love is re - newed, And our hearts are with pow - er from heav - en en - dued.

REFRAIN

O ho - ly day! O hap - py day! O day of days the best!

We wor - ship at God's glo - rious throne, And there find peace and rest.

O Day of Rest and Gladness

The Sabbath of rest, holy to the Lord.—Ex. 31: 15

MENDEBRAS 7. 6. 7. 6. D.

CHRISTOPHER WORDSWORTH, 1862

Arr. from German Melody
by LOWELL MASON, 1830

1. O day of rest and glad-ness, O day of joy and light,
2. On thee, at the cre - a - tion, The light first had its birth;
3. To - day on wea-ry na - tions The heav'n-ly man - na falls:
4. New grac - es ev - er gain - ing From this our day of rest,

O balm of care and sad - ness, Most beau - ti - ful, most bright;
On thee, for our sal - va - tion, Christ rose from depths of earth;
To ho - ly con - vo - ca - tions The heav'n-ly trump-et calls,
We reach the rest re - main - ing To spir - its of the blest.

On thee the high and low - ly, Be - fore th' e - ter - nal throne,
On thee our Lord, vic - to - rious, The Spir - it sent from heav'n;
Where Gos - pel light is glow - ing With pure and ra - diant beams,
To Ho - ly Ghost be prais - es, To Fa - ther, and to Son;

Sing Ho - ly, Ho - ly, Ho - ly, To the great Three in One.
And thus on thee, most glo - rious, A trip - le light was giv'n.
And liv - ing wa - ter flow - ing, With soul - re - fresh-ing streams.
The Church her voice up - rais - es To Thee, blest Three in One.

178 Safely Through Another Week

Ye shall keep My sabbaths, and reverence My sanctuary.—Lev. 19: 30

JOHN NEWTON, 1779   SABBATH 7. 7. 7. 7. D.   LOWELL MASON

1. Safe - ly thro' an - oth - er week God has brought us on our way;
2. While we seek sup-plies of grace, Thro' the blest Re-deem-er's name,
3. Here we come, Thy name to praise: Let us feel Thy pres-ence near;
4. May the Gos-pel's joy-ful sound Con - quer sin - ners, com-fort saints,

Let us each a bless-ing seek, Wait - ing in His courts to - day—
Show Thy rec - on - cil-ing face, Take a - way our sin and shame;
May Thy glo - ry meet our gaze, While we in Thy house ap - pear;
Make the fruits of grace a - bound, Bring re - lief to all com-plaints;

Day of all the week the best, Em - blem of e - ter - nal rest,
From our world-ly care set free, May we rest this day in Thee,
Here af - ford us, Lord, a taste Of our ev - er - last - ing rest,
Thus let all our wor-ship prove, Till we join Thy courts a - bove,

Day of all the week the best, Em - blem of e - ter - nal rest.
From our world-ly care set free, May we rest this day in Thee.
Here af - ford us, Lord, a taste Of our ev - er - last - ing rest.
Thus let all our wor-ship prove, Till we join Thy courts a - bove.

Welcome, Sweet Day of Rest

179

A day in Thy courts is better than a thousand.—Ps. 84: 10

SWEET DAY S. M.

Isaac Watts, 1709

B. C. Unseld

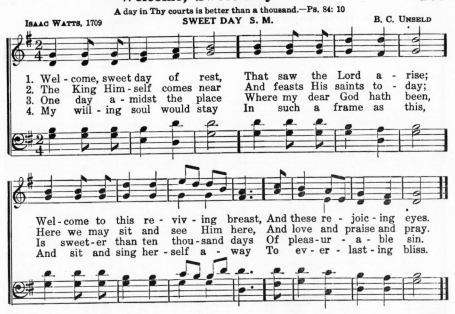

1. Wel - come, sweet day of rest, That saw the Lord a - rise;
2. The King Him - self comes near And feasts His saints to - day;
3. One day a - midst the place Where my dear God hath been,
4. My will - ing soul would stay In such a frame as this,

Wel - come to this re - viv - ing breast, And these re - joic - ing eyes.
Here we may sit and see Him here, And love and praise and pray.
Is sweet - er than ten thou - sand days Of pleas - ur - a - ble sin.
And sit and sing her - self a - way To ev - er - last - ing bliss.

This is the Day the Lord Hath Made

180

This is the day which the Lord hath made.—Ps. 118: 24

ARLINGTON C. M.

Isaac Watts, 1719

T. A. Arne

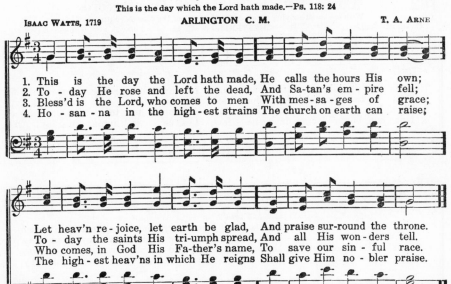

1. This is the day the Lord hath made, He calls the hours His own;
2. To - day He rose and left the dead, And Sa - tan's em - pire fell;
3. Bless'd is the Lord, who comes to men With mes - sa - ges of grace;
4. Ho - san - na in the high - est strains The church on earth can raise;

Let heav'n re - joice, let earth be glad, And praise sur-round the throne.
To - day the saints His tri - umph spread, And all His won - ders tell.
Who comes, in God His Fa - ther's name, To save our sin - ful race.
The high - est heav'ns in which He reigns Shall give Him no - bler praise.

181 Hail to the Sabbath Day

The sabbath of the Lord thy God.—Ex. 20: 10, 11

STEPHEN G. BULLFINCH, 1809-1870   THATCHER S. M.   Arr. from GEORGE F. HANDEL

1. Hail to the Sab - bath day! The day di - vine - ly giv'n,
2. Lord, in this sa - cred hour, With - in Thy courts we bend,
3. But Thou art not a - lone In courts by mor - tals trod;
4. Thy tem - ple is the arch Of yon un - meas - ured sky;
5. Lord, may that ho - lier day Dawn on Thy serv - ant's sight;

When men to God their hom - age pay, And earth draws near to heav'n.
And bless Thy love, and own Thy pow'r, Our Fa - ther and our Friend.
Nor on - ly is the day Thine own When man draws near to God.
Thy Sab - bath, the stu - pen - dous march Of vast e - ter - ni - ty.
And pur - er wor - ship may we pay In heav'n's un-cloud - ed light.

182 Come, Let Us Join With One Accord

With one mind striving together for the faith of the Gospel.—PHIL. 1: 27

CHARLES WESLEY   CHESTERFIELD C. M.   THOMAS HAWEIS

1. Come, let us join with one ac - cord In hymns a - round the throne! This
2. This is the day which God hath blest, The bright-est of the sev'n, Type
3. Then let us in His name sing on, And has - ten to that day When
4. Not one, but all our days be - low, Let us in hymns em - ploy; And

is the day our ris - ing Lord Hath made and called His own.
of that ev - er - last - ing rest The saints en - joy in heav'n.
our Re - deem - er shall come down, And shad - ows pass a - way.
in our Lord re - joic - ing, go To His e - ter - nal joy.

Be Still, Be Still

GEN. 28: 17; EX. 3: 5

Be still, and know that I am God.—PS. 46: 10

8s. 5 l.

J. B. HERBERT

Be still! be still! for all a-round On ei-ther hand is ho - - - ly
ho - ly ground, is

ground; Here in His house, the Lord to-day Will lis-ten while His peo-ple pray;
ho - ly ground;

Here in His house, the Lord to - day Will lis - ten while His peo - ple pray:

Our Father who art in heaven, Hallowed be Thy name;
Give us this day our dai - ly bread,
And lead us not into temptation, but de - - - liver us from evil:

Thy kingdom come; Thy will be done in earth, as it is in heav'n.
And forgive us our debts, as we for-give our debtors.
For Thine is the kingdom, and the power, and the glory, for-ever and ever. A-MEN.

184 Lord, We Come Before Thee Now

O come, let us worship and bow down.—Ps. 95: 6

WILLIAM HAMMOND, 1745   ST. BEES 7. 7. 7. 7.   JOHN B. DYKES, 1862

1. Lord, we come be-fore Thee now; At Thy feet we hum-bly bow;
2. Lord, on Thee our souls de-pend; In com-pas-sion now de-scend;
3. Send some mes-sage from Thy Word, That may joy and peace af-ford;
4. Com-fort those who weep and mourn, Let the time of joy re-turn;

O do not our suit dis-dain: Shall we seek Thee, Lord, in vain?
Fill our hearts with Thy rich grace, Tune our lips to sing Thy praise.
Let Thy Spir-it now im-part Full sal-va-tion to each heart.
Heal the sick, the cap-tive free, Let us all re-joice in Thee. A-MEN.

185 Tread Softly

FANNY J. CROSBY   (SOLO AND QUARTET)   W. H. DOANE

Gently   *p*

1. Be si-lent, be si-lent, A whis-per is heard, Be si-lent, and
2. Be si-lent, be si-lent, For ho-ly this place, This al-tar that
3. Be si-lent, be si-lent, Breathe humbly our prayer, A fore-taste of
4. Be si-lent, be si-lent, His mer-cy re-cord; Be si-lent, be

REFRAIN

lis-ten, Oh, treas-ure each word.
ech-oes The mes-sage of grace. Tread soft-ly, tread soft-ly, The
E-den This mo-ment we share.
si-lent, And wait on the Lord. Tread soft-ly here, tread softly here,

Tread Softly—Concluded

Mas - ter is here; Tread soft - ly, tread soft - ly, He bids us draw near.
Tread softly here, tread softly here,

Praise Ye the Lord, Ye Saints 186

Ps. 150, Metrical

SOTO L. M.   LOWELL MASON

1. Praise ye the Lord, ye saints be - low, And in His courts His
2. Praise ye the Lord; all crea - tures, sing The prais - es of your

good - ness show; Praise ye the Lord, ye hosts a - bove, In heav'n a-
God and King; Let all that breathe, His praise pro-claim And glo - ri-

dore His bound-less love, In heav'n a - dore His bound - less love.
fy His ho - ly name, And glo - ri - fy His ho - ly name.

187 Holy is the Lord

Holy, holy, holy, is the Lord of hosts.—Isa. 6: 3

FANNY J. CROSBY

WILLIAM B. BRADBURY

1. Ho - ly, ho - ly, ho - ly is the Lord! Sing, O ye peo - ple,
2. Praise Him, praise Him, shout a - loud for joy! Watch-man of Zi - on,
3. King E - ter - nal, bless-ed be His name! So may His chil - dren

glad - ly a - dore Him; Let the moun-tains trem - ble at His Word,
her - ald the sto - ry; Sin and death His king - dom shall de-stroy,
glad - ly a - dore Him; When in heav'n we join the hap - py strain,

Let the hills be joy - ful be - fore Him; Might - y in wis - dom,
All the earth shall sing of His glo - ry; Praise Him, ye an - gels,
When we cast our bright crowns be - fore Him; There in His like - ness,

bound - less in mer - cy, Great is Je - ho - vah, King o - ver all.
ye who be - hold Him Robed in His splen - dor, match - less, di - vine.
joy - ful a - wak - ing, There we shall see Him, there we shall sing.

Holy is the Lord—Concluded

CHORUS

Ho-ly, ho-ly, ho-ly is the Lord, Let the hills be joy-ful be-fore Him.

We Now Have Met to Worship Thee 188

For the edifying of the body of Christ.—EPH. 4: 12

J. S. S. STEPHENSON L. M. D. J. S. SHOEMAKER, 1889

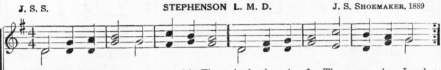

1. { We now have met to wor-ship Thee, And glo-ri-fy Thy name, dear Lord;
{ Help ev-'ry one at-ten-tive be, And heed the teach-ing of Thy Word.
2. { As-sist Thy serv-ant to pro-claim The Gos-pel mes-sage plain and pure,
{ That all who hear ac-cept the same, And make in Thee sal-va-tion sure.

Fill ev-'ry heart with love di-vine, Teach ev-'ry tongue Thy praise to sing;
In Thee a-lone help us to trust, And in Thy love and laws a-bide,

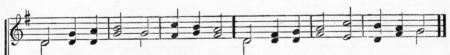

Help each to say, Lord, we are Thine, And all we have to Thee we bring.
That when our bod-ies turn to dust, Our souls in heav'n be glo-ri-fied.

189 Once More Before We Part

Let us come before His presence with thanksgiving.—Ps. 95: 2

JOSEPH HART, 1762   SWEET DAY. S. M.   B. C. UNSELD

1. Once more be - fore we part, Oh, bless the Sav - iour's name!
2. Lord, in Thy grace we came, That bless - ing still im - part,
3. Still on Thy ho - ly Word We'll live, and feed, and grow!
4. Now, Lord, be - fore we part, Help us to bless Thy name;

Let ev - 'ry tongue and ev - 'ry heart A - dore and praise the same.
We met in Je - sus' sa - cred name, In Je - sus' name we part.
And still go on to know the Lord, And prac-tice what we know.
Let ev - 'ry tongue and ev - 'ry heart A - dore and praise the same.

190 Lord, Dismiss Us

The Lord bless thee and keep thee.—NUM. 6: 24-26

SICILIAN MARINERS 8. 7. 8. 7. 4. 7.

Ascribed to JOHN FAWCETT, c. 1774. Alt.   Sicilian Melody

1. { Lord, dis - miss us with Thy bless-ing; Fill our hearts with joy and peace; }
   { Let us each, Thy love pos - sess - ing, Tri - umph in re - deem-ing grace: }
2. { Thanks we give and ad - o - ra - tion For Thy Gos - pel's joy - ful sound: }
   { May the fruits of Thy sal - va - tion In our hearts and lives a - bound: }
3. { So that when Thy love shall call us, Sav - iour, from the world a - way, }
   { Let no fear of death ap - pall us, Glad Thy sum - mons to o - bey: }

O re - fresh us, O re - fresh us, Trav - 'ling thro' this wil-der-ness.
Ev - er faith-ful, Ev - er faith-ful To the truth may we be found;
May we ev - er, May we ev - er Reign with Thee in end-less day.

O Gentle Saviour

Now the God of peace be with you all.—Rom. 15: 33

191

Thomas R. Birks

10. 10.

Arthur Sullivan

1. O gen - tle Sav - iour, from Thy throne on high
2. Go where we go, a - bide where we a - bide,
3. O lead us dai - ly with Thine eye of love,

Look down in love and hear our hum - ble cry.
In life, in death, our com - fort, strength and guide.
And bring us safe - ly to our home a - bove. A - MEN.

Bless Me, O My Father

I will not let Thee go, except Thou bless me.—Gen. 32: 26

192

B. W. R. Taylor

EVENING INVOCATION 8. 7. 8. 7.

H. B. Whitney

1. Bless me, O my Fa - ther, bless me, Kneel-ing at Thy throne of grace;
2. Bless - ed Sav-iour, Thou who gav-est Full re-demp-tion by Thy blood,
3. Breathe up-on me, gra-cious Spir-it, Ben - e - dic-tion full and strong;
4. Sa - cred Trin-i - ty of pow - er, Mys-tic U - ni - ty a - bove,

Here I sought Thee, here I find Thee, In Thine ark and rest - ing-place.
Wash me from my foul of-fens - es, Cleanse me, O Thou Son of God!
Keep my feet in safe-ty's path-way, Keep my soul from sin and wrong.
Sanc - ti - fy this eve-ning hour.... With Thine end-less, bound-less love.

193 Saviour, Again to Thy Dear Name

The Lord will bless His people with peace.—Ps. 29: 11

JOHN ELLERTON, 1866. Alt.   ELLERS 10. 10. 10. 10.   EDWARD J. HOPKINS, 1369

1. Sav - iour, a - gain to Thy dear name we raise With one ac - cord our
2. Grant us Thy peace up - on our home-ward way; With Thee be - gan, with
3. Grant us Thy peace, Lord, thro' the com - ing night; Turn Thou for us its
4. Grant us Thy peace thro'-out our earth - ly life, Our balm in sor - row,

part - ing hymn of praise; We come to bless Thee ere our wor - ship
Thee shall end the day; Guard Thou the lips from sin, the hearts from
dark - ness in - to light; From harm and dan - ger keep Thy chil - dren
and our stay in strife; Then, when Thy voice shall bid our con - flict

cease; Then, low - ly bow - ing, wait Thy word of peace.
shame, That in this house have called up - on Thy name.
free, For dark and light are both a - like to Thee.
cease, Call us, O Lord, to Thine e - ter - nal peace. A - MEN.

194 Our Day of Praise is Done

They shall still be praising Thee.—Ps. 84: 4

JOHN ELLERTON, 1867   SCHUMANN S. M.   Arr. from SCHUMANN

1. Our day of praise is done, The eve - ning shad - ows fall;
2. A - round the throne on high, Where night can nev - er be,
3. Too faint our an - thems here, Too soon of praise we tire;
4. Yet, Lord, to Thy dear will If Thou at - tune the heart,
5. 'Tis Thine each soul to calm, Each way - ward tho't re - claim,

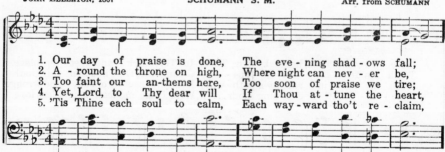

142

Our Day of Praise is Done—Concluded

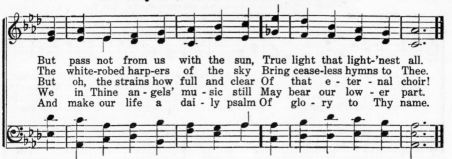

But pass not from us with the sun, True light that light-'nest all.
The white-robed harp-ers of the sky Bring cease-less hymns to Thee.
But oh, the strains how full and clear Of that e - ter - nal choir!
We in Thine an-gels' mu - sic still May bear our low - er part.
And make our life a dai - ly psalm Of glo - ry to Thy name.

Father of Love and Power

195

The Lord shall bless thee out of Zion.—Ps. 128: 5

GEORGE L. RAWSON, 1857   KIRBY BEDON 6. 6. 4. 6. 6. 6. 4.   EDWARD BUNNETT, 1887

1. Fa - ther of love and pow'r, Guard Thou our eve - ning hour,
2. Je - sus, Em-man - u - el, Come in Thy love to dwell,
3. Spir - it of Ho - li - ness, Gen - tle, trans-form-ing grace,

Shield with Thy might. For all Thy care this day Our grate-ful thanks we
In hearts con-trite. For all our sins we grieve, But we Thy grace re-
In - dwell-ing light, Soothe Thou each weary breast, Now let Thy peace pos-

pay, And to our Fa - ther pray,— Bless us to - night.
ceive, And in Thy Word be - lieve; Bless us to - night.
sessed Calm us to per - fect rest; Bless us to - night. A - MEN.

196 ## Lord, In the Morning

To show forth Thy lovingkindness in the morning.—Ps. 92: 1, 2

ISAAC WATTS, 1719   WARWICK C. M.   S. STANLEY, 1800

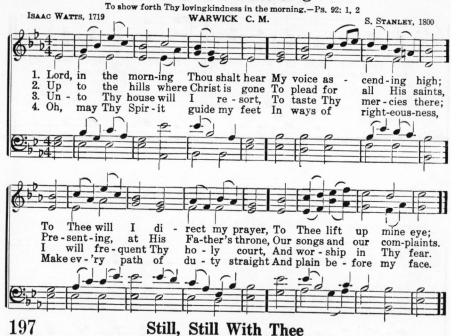

1. Lord, in the morn-ing Thou shalt hear My voice as-cend-ing high;
2. Up to the hills where Christ is gone To plead for all His saints,
3. Un-to Thy house will I re-sort, To taste Thy mer-cies there;
4. Oh, may Thy Spir-it guide my feet In ways of right-eous-ness,

To Thee will I di-rect my prayer, To Thee lift up mine eye;
Pre-sent-ing, at His Fa-ther's throne, Our songs and our com-plaints.
I will fre-quent Thy ho-ly court, And wor-ship in Thy fear.
Make ev-'ry path of du-ty straight And plain be-fore my face.

197 ## Still, Still With Thee

When I awake, I am still with Thee.—Ps. 139: 18

CONSOLATION 11. 10. 11. 10.

HARRIET B. STOWE, 1811-1896   Arr. from FELIX MENDELSSOHN-BARTHOLDY

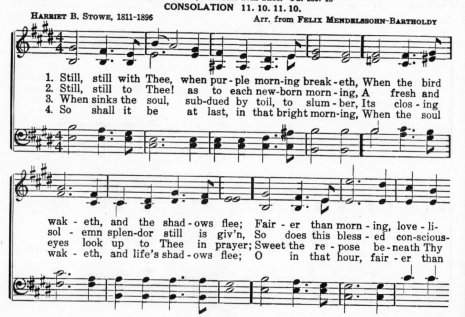

1. Still, still with Thee, when pur-ple morn-ing break-eth, When the bird
2. Still, still to Thee! as to each new-born morn-ing, A fresh and
3. When sinks the soul, sub-dued by toil, to slum-ber, Its clos-ing
4. So shall it be at last, in that bright morn-ing, When the soul

wak-eth, and the shad-ows flee; Fair-er than morn-ing, love-li-
sol-emn splen-dor still is giv'n, So does this bless-ed con-scious-
eyes look up to Thee in prayer; Sweet the re-pose be-neath Thy
wak-eth, and life's shad-ows flee; O in that hour, fair-er than

Still, Still With Thee—Concluded

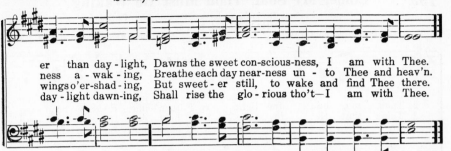

er than day-light, Dawns the sweet con-scious-ness, I am with Thee.
ness a - wak - ing, Breathe each day near-ness un - to Thee and heav'n.
wings o'er-shad-ing, But sweet-er still, to wake and find Thee there.
day - light dawn-ing, Shall rise the glo - rious tho't—I am with Thee.

O God, I Thank Thee For Each Sight   198

I will sing of the mercies of the Lord forever.—Ps. 89: 1, 2

CAROLINE ATHERTON MASON, 1823-1890   HOPE L. M.   HERBERT S. IRONS, 1834-1905

1. O God, I thank Thee for each sight Of beau - ty
2. That life I con - se - crate to Thee, And ev - er,
3. An - oth - er day in which to cast Some si - lent

that Thy hand doth give; For sun - ny skies and air and
as the day is born, On wings of joy my soul would
deed of love a - broad, That, great'ning as it jour - neys

light; O God, I thank Thee that I live.
flee, And thank Thee for an - oth - er morn;
past, May do some ear - nest work for God. A - MEN.

199 Come, My Soul, Thou Must Be Waking

Cause me to hear Thy lovingkindness in the morning.—Ps. 143: 8

HAYDN 8. 4. 7. 8. 4. 7.

F. R. L. VON CANITZ, publ. 1700

Arr. from FRANZ JOSEPH HAYDN. 1791

1. Come, my soul, thou must be wak-ing; Now is break-ing
2. Thou, too, hail the light re - turn-ing; Read-y burn-ing
3. Think that He thy ways be - hold-eth; He un-fold-eth
4. On - ly God's free gifts a - buse not, Light re-fuse not,

O'er the earth an - oth - er day: Come to Him who made this
Be the in - cense of thy pow'rs; For the night is safe - ly
Ev - 'ry fault that lurks with - in; Ev - 'ry stain of shame glossed
But His Spir - it's voice o - bey; Thou with Him shalt dwell, be-

splen - dor; See thou ren - der All thy fee - ble pow'rs can pay.
end - ed, God hath tend - ed With His care thy help - less hours.
o - ver Can dis - cov - er, And dis - cern each deed of sin.
hold - ing Light en - fold - ing All things in un - cloud - ed day.

200 I Owe the Lord a Morning Song

But I will sing of Thy power; yea, I will sing also of Thy mercy in the morning.—Ps. 59: 16

AMOS HERR

GRATITUDE C. M.

AMOS HERR, 1890

1. I owe the Lord a morn-ing song Of grat - i-tude and praise,
2. He kept me safe an - oth - er night; I see an - oth - er day;
3. Keep me from dan - ger and from sin; Help me Thy will to do,
4. Keep me till Thou wilt call me hence, Where nev - er night can be;

I Owe the Lord a Morning Song—Concluded

For the kind mer - cy He has shown In length-'ning out my days.
Now may His Spir - it, as the light, Di - rect me in His way.
So that my heart be pure with - in; And I Thy good-ness know.
And save me, Lord, for Je - sus' sake,—He shed His blood for me.

Every Morning Mercies New 201

They are new every morning: great is Thy faithfulness.—LAM. 3: 22, 23

G. PHILIMORE, 1821-1884   KELSO 7s. 6 l.   EDWARD J. HOPKINS

1. Ev - 'ry morn-ing mer - cies new Fall as fresh as morn - ing dew;
2. Still the great-ness of Thy love Dai - ly doth our sins re - move;
3. Let our prayers each morn pre-vail, That these gifts may nev - er fail;
4. As the morn-ing light re-turns, As the sun with splen-dor burns,

Ev - 'ry morn-ing let us pay Trib - ute with the ear - ly day;
Dai - ly, far as east from west, Lifts the bur - den from the breast;
And, as we con - fess the sin And the tempt-er's pow'r with - in,
Teach us still to turn to Thee, Ev - er bless - ed Trin - i - ty,

For Thy mer - cies, Lord, are sure; Thy com - pas - sion doth en - dure.
Gives un-bought, to those who pray, Strength to stand in e - vil day.
Feed us with the Bread of Life; Fit us for our dai - ly strife.
With our hands our hearts to raise, In un - fail - ing prayer and praise.

202 My Opening Eyes With Rapture See

In the morning will I direct my prayer unto Thee, and will look up.—Ps. 5: 3

JAMES HUTTON,-d. 1795 ERNAN L. M. LOWELL MASON, 1850

1. My ope-ning eyes with rap-ture see The dawn of this re - turn-ing day;
2. I yield my heart to Thee a - lone, Nor would receive an - oth - er guest;
3. O bid this tri-fling world re - tire, And drive each carnal tho't a - way,
4. Thus, to Thy courts when I re - pair, My soul shall rise on joy - ful wing,

My tho'ts, O God, re - turn to Thee, While thus my ear-ly vows I pay.
E - ter-nal King, e - rect Thy throne And reign sole mon-arch in my breast.
Nor let me feel one vain de - sire, One sin-ful tho't thro' all the day.
The won-ders of Thy love de - clare, And join the strains which an-gels sing.

203 New Every Morning is Thy Love

Every day will I bless thee.—Ps. 145: 2

JOHN KEBLE, 1822 MELCOMBE. L. M. SAMUEL WEBBE, 1782

1. New ev - 'ry morn-ing is Thy love Our wak-'ning and up - ris - ing prove;
2. New mer-cies, each re - turn-ing day, Hov - er a - round us while we pray;
3. If, on our dai - ly course, our mind Be set to hal - low all we find,
4. The triv - ial round, the com-mon task Will fur - nish all we ought to ask;—
5. On - ly, O Lord, in Thy dear love, Fit us for per - fect rest a - bove,

Thro' sleep and dark-ness safe-ly bro't, Re-stored to life and pow'r and tho't.
New per - ils past, new sins for-giv'n, New tho'ts of God, new hopes of heav'n.
New treas-ures still, of count-less price, God will pro - vide for sac - ri - fice.
Room to de - ny our-selves, a road To bring us dai - ly near - er God.
And help us, this and ev - 'ry day, To live more near-ly as we pray.

148

Softly Now the Light of Day

204

Thou shalt lie down, and thy sleep shall be sweet.—PROV. 3: 24

GEORGE W. DOANE, 1824   MERCY 7. 7. 7. 7.   LOUIS M. GOTTSCHALK. Arr.

1. Soft - ly now the light of day Fades up - on our sight a - way;
2. Thou, whose all - per - vad - ing eye Naught es - capes, with-out, with - in,
3. Soon from us the light of day Shall for - ev - er pass a - way;

Free from care, from la - bor free, Lord, we would commune with Thee.
Par - don each in - firm - i - ty, O - pen fault, and se - cret sin.
Then, from sin and sor - row free, Take us, Lord, to dwell with Thee.

Holy Father, Cheer Our Way

205

At evening time it shall be light.—ZECH. 14: 7

R. H. ROBINSON, 1842-1892   VESPERI LUX 7. 7. 7. 5.   JOHN B. DYKES

1. Ho - ly Fa - ther, cheer our way With Thy love's per - pet - ual ray:
2. Ho - ly Sav - iour, calm our fears When earth's brightness dis-ap - pears:
3. Ho - ly Spir - it, be Thou nigh When in mor - tal pains we lie;
4. Ho - ly, bless - ed Trin - i - ty, Dark - ness is not dark to Thee:

rall.

Grant us ev - 'ry clos - ing day Light at eve - ning - time.
Grant us in our la - ter years Light at eve - ning - time.
Grant us, as we come to die, Light at eve - ning - time.
Those Thou keep-est al - ways see Light at eve - ning - time. A - MEN.

206 The Day is Gently Sinking to a Close

He that followeth Me shall not walk in darkness.—Jn. 8: 12

CHRISTOPHER WORDSWORTH, 1863   NACHTLIED 10s. 6 l.   HENRY SMART, 1872

1. The day is gen-tly sink-ing to a close,.... Faint-er and yet more
2. Thou, who in dark-ness walking didst ap - pear..... Up - on the waves, and
3. Our changeful lives are ebb - ing to an end;..... On - ward to dark-ness
4. The wea - ry world is mould'ring to de - cay,.... Its glo - ries wane, its

faint the sun-light glows: O bright-ness of Thy Fa-ther's glo-ry, Thou
Thy dis - ci - ples cheer, Come, Lord, in lone - some days, when storms assail,
and to death we tend: O Con-qu'ror of the grave, be Thou our guide,
pag-eants fade a - way: In that last sun - set, when the stars shall fall,

E - ter - nal Light of light, be with us now: Where Thou art pres - ent,
And earth-ly hopes and hu - man suc - cors fail; When all is dark, may
Be Thou our light in death's dark e - ven - tide; Then in our mor - tal
May we a - rise, a - wak-ened by Thy call, With Thee, O Lord, for-

dark-ness can-not be; Mid-night is glo-rious noon, O Lord, with Thee.
we be-hold Thee nigh, And hear Thy voice, "Fear not, for it is I."
hour will be no gloom, No sting in death, no ter - ror in the tomb.
ev - er to a - bide In that blest day which has no e - ven - tide.

150

Day is Dying in the West

To show . . . Thy faithfulness every night.—Ps. 92: 1, 2

CHAUTAUQUA 7. 7. 7. 7. 4. Ref.

MARY A. LATHBURY, 1841

W. F. SHERWIN, 1877

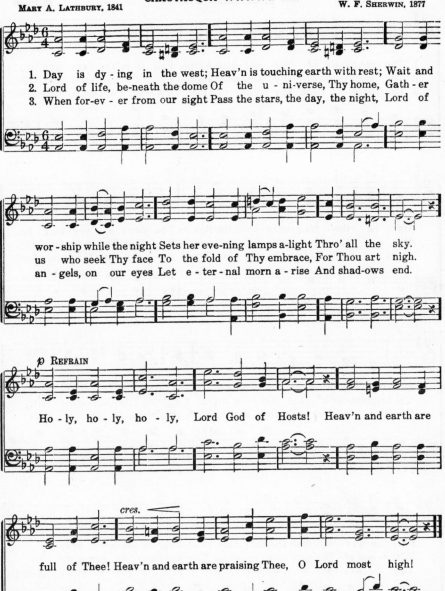

1. Day is dy-ing in the west; Heav'n is touching earth with rest; Wait and
2. Lord of life, be-neath the dome Of the u-ni-verse, Thy home, Gath-er
3. When for-ev-er from our sight Pass the stars, the day, the night, Lord of

wor-ship while the night Sets her eve-ning lamps a-light Thro' all the sky.
us who seek Thy face To the fold of Thy embrace, For Thou art nigh.
an-gels, on our eyes Let e-ter-nal morn a-rise And shad-ows end.

REFRAIN

Ho-ly, ho-ly, ho-ly, Lord God of Hosts! Heav'n and earth are

cres.

full of Thee! Heav'n and earth are praising Thee, O Lord most high!

208 The Shadows of the Evening Hours

Until the day break and the shadows flee away.—S. S. 4: 6

A. A. PROCTER, 1862   ST. LEONARD C. M. D.   H. HILES

1. The shad-ows of the eve-ning hours Fall from the dark-'ning sky;
2. The sor-rows of Thy serv-ants, Lord, O do not Thou de-spise,
3. Let peace, O Lord, Thy peace, O God, Up-on our souls de-scend;

Up-on the fra-grance of the flow'rs The dews of eve-ning lie.
But let the in-cense of our prayers Be-fore Thy mer-cy rise.
From mid-night fears, and per-ils, Thou Our trem-bling hearts de-fend:

Be-fore Thy throne, O Lord of heav'n, We kneel at close of day;
The bright-ness of the com-ing night Up-on the dark-ness rolls;
Give us a res-pite from our toil; Calm and sub-due our woes;

Look on Thy chil-dren from on high, And hear us while we pray.
With hopes of fu-ture glo-ry chase The shad-ows on our souls.
Thro' the long day we la-bor, Lord, O give us now re-pose. A-MEN.

Saviour, Breathe An Evening Blessing

I will both lay me down in peace and sleep.—Ps. 4: 8

EVENING SONG 8. 7. 8. 7. D.

JAMES EDMESTON, 1820

J. H. HALL

Not too fast.

1. Sav-iour, breathe an eve-ning bless - ing, Ere re - pose our spir - its seal;
2. Tho' the night be dark and drear - y, Dark-ness can-not hide from Thee;

Sin and want we come con - fess - ing; Thou canst save and Thou canst heal.
Thou art He who dost not wea - ry, Watch-est where Thy peo - ple be.

Tho' de-struc-tion walk a-round us, Tho' the ar - rows past us fly,
Should swift death this night o'ertake us, And com-mand us to the tomb,

m   *f*

An - gel guards from Thee surround us; We are safe, if Thou art nigh.
May the morn in heav'n a - wake us, Clad in bright e - ter - nal bloom.

153

6

210 Abide With Me

Abide with us: for it is toward evening.—Lk. 24: 29

HENRY F. LYTE, 1847   EVENTIDE 10s. 4 l.   WILLIAM H. MONK, 1861

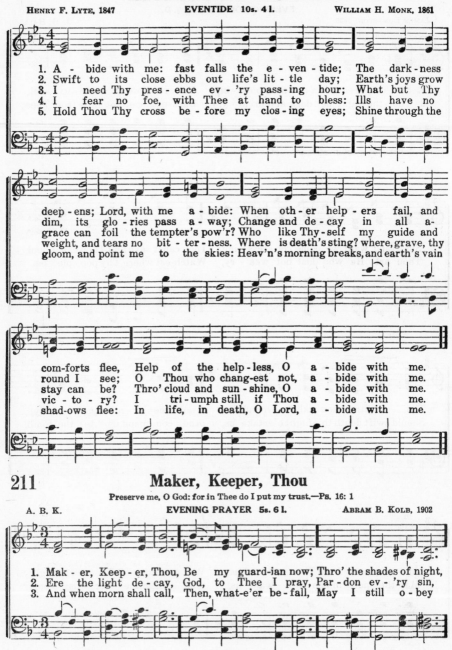

1. A - bide with me: fast falls the e - ven - tide; The dark - ness
2. Swift to its close ebbs out life's lit - tle day; Earth's joys grow
3. I need Thy pres - ence ev - 'ry pass - ing hour; What but Thy
4. I fear no foe, with Thee at hand to bless: Ills have no
5. Hold Thou Thy cross be - fore my clos - ing eyes; Shine through the

deep - ens; Lord, with me a - bide: When oth - er help - ers fail, and
dim, its glo - ries pass a - way; Change and de - cay in all a -
grace can foil the tempter's pow'r? Who like Thy - self my guide and
weight, and tears no bit - ter - ness. Where is death's sting? where, grave, thy
gloom, and point me to the skies: Heav'n's morning breaks, and earth's vain

com - forts flee, Help of the help - less, O a - bide with me.
round I see; O Thou who chang - est not, a - bide with me.
stay can be? Thro' cloud and sun - shine, O a - bide with me.
vic - to - ry? I tri - umph still, if Thou a - bide with me.
shad - ows flee: In life, in death, O Lord, a - bide with me.

211 Maker, Keeper, Thou

Preserve me, O God: for in Thee do I put my trust.—Ps. 16: 1

A. B. K.   EVENING PRAYER 5s. 6 l.   ABRAM B. KOLB, 1902

1. Mak - er, Keep - er, Thou, Be my guard - ian now; Thro' the shades of night,
2. Ere the light de - cay, God, to Thee I pray, Par - don ev - 'ry sin,
3. And when morn shall call, Then, what - e'er be - fall, May I still o - bey

Maker, Keeper, Thou—Concluded

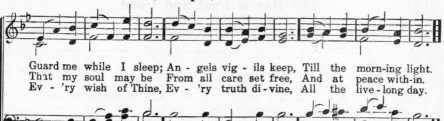

Guard me while I sleep; An - gels vig - ils keep, Till the morn-ing light.
That my soul may be From all care set free, And at peace with-in.
Ev - 'ry wish of Thine, Ev - 'ry truth di - vine, All the live - long day.

Softly the Silent Night

212

When Thou sleepest, it shall keep thee.—Prov. 6: 22

BLATCHFORD 6. 4. 6. 4. 6. 6. 6. 4.

AMBROSE M. BLATCHFORD, 1875

Anon. Alt.

1. Soft - ly the si - lent night Fall - eth from God, On wea - ry
2. Slow - ly on fail - ing wing Day - light has passed; Sleep, like an
3. And when the gleam of morn Touch - es our eyes, And the re-

wan - der - ers O - ver life's road; And as the stars on high
an - gel kind, Folds us at last. Peace be our lot this night,
turn - ing day Bids us a - rise,— Hap - py be - neath Thy will,

Light up the dark'ning sky, Lord, un - to Thee we cry,— Fa - ther a - bove!
Safe be our slum-ber light, Watched by Thy angels bright, Fa - ther a - bove!
Stead-fast in joy or ill, Lord, may we serve Thee still, Fa - ther a - bove!

213

The Day is Past and Gone

In the night His song shall be with me.—Ps. 42: 8

JOHN LELAND, 1840

VESPERS S. M.

J. D. BRUNK

1. The day is past and gone; The eve-ning shades ap-pear:....
2. Lord, keep me safe this night, Se-cure from all our fears;....
3. And when our days are past, And we from time re-move,....

Oh, may we all re-mem-ber well, The night of death draws near.
May an-gels guard us while we sleep, Till morn-ing light ap-pears.
Oh, may we in Thy bos-om rest, The bos-om of Thy love.

214

Sun of My Soul

The darkness and the light are both alike to Thee.— Ps. 139: 12

HURSLEY L. M.

JOHN KEBLE, 1827

PETER RITTER, 1792
Arr. by WILLIAM H. MONK, 1861

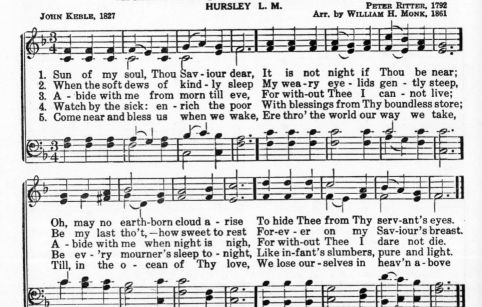

1. Sun of my soul, Thou Sav-iour dear, It is not night if Thou be near;
2. When the soft dews of kind-ly sleep My wea-ry eye-lids gen-tly steep,
3. A-bide with me from morn till eve, For with-out Thee I can-not live;
4. Watch by the sick: en-rich the poor With blessings from Thy boundless store;
5. Come near and bless us when we wake, Ere thro' the world our way we take,

Oh, may no earth-born cloud a-rise To hide Thee from Thy serv-ant's eyes.
Be my last tho't,—how sweet to rest For-ev-er on my Sav-iour's breast.
A-bide with me when night is nigh, For with-out Thee I dare not die.
Be ev-'ry mourner's sleep to-night, Like in-fant's slumbers, pure and light.
Till, in the o-cean of Thy love, We lose our-selves in heav'n a-bove

This Night, O Lord, We Bless Thee

There shall no evil befall thee.—Ps. 91: 9, 10

215

JAMES D. BURNS, 1856   BENTLEY 7. 6. 7. 6. D.   JOHN P. HULLAH, 1866

1. This night, O Lord, we bless Thee For Thy pro-tect-ing care,
2. On Thee our whole re-li-ance From day to day we cast;
3. What may be on the mor-row Our fore-sight can-not see;

And, ere we rest, ad-dress Thee In low-ly, fer-vent prayer:
To Thee, with firm af-fi-ance, Would cleave from first to last;
But, be it joy or sor-row, We know it comes from Thee.

From e-vil and temp-ta-tion De-fend us thro' the night,
To Thee, thro' Je-sus' mer-it, For need-ful grace we come;
And noth-ing can take from us, Wher-e'er our steps may move,

And round our hab-i-ta-tion Be Thou a wall of light.
And trust that Thy good Spir-it Will guide us safe-ly home.
The staff of Thy sure prom-ise, The shield of Thy true love.

216

Now the Day is Over

He giveth His beloved sleep.—Ps. 127: 2

SABINE BARING-GOULD, 1865   MERRIAL 6. 5. 6. 5.   JOSEPH BARNBY

1. Now the day is o - ver, Night is draw-ing nigh;
2. Je - sus, grant the wea - ry Calm and sweet re - pose;
3. Grant to lit - tle chil - dren Vi - sions bright of Thee;
4. Thro' the long night watch - es May Thine an - gels spread
5. When the morn - ing wak - ens, Then may I a - rise

Shad - ows of the eve - ning Steal a - cross the sky.
With Thy ten - d'rest bless - ing May our eye - lids close.
Guard the sail - ors toss - ing On the deep, blue sea.
Their white wings a - bove me, Watch-ing round my bed.
Pure, and fresh, and sin - less In Thy ho - ly eyes. A - MEN.

217

Now From the Altar of My Heart

Let my prayer be set forth before Thee as incense.—Ps. 141: 2

JOHN MASON, 1863   BEATITUDO C. M.   JOHN B. DYKES, 1875

1. Now from the al - tar of my heart Let sweet-est in - cense rise:
2. A - wake, my love! a - wake, my joy! A - wake, my heart and tongue!
3. This day God was my sun and shield, My keep - er and my guide;
4. Lord of my time, whose hand hath set New time up - on my score,

As - sist me, Lord, to of - fer up Mine eve - ning sac - ri - fice.
Sleep not, when mer - cies loud - ly call; Break forth in - to a song.
His care was on my frail-ty shown, His mer - cies mul - ti - plied.
Then shall I praise for all my time, When time shall be no more. A - MEN.

158

Awake, My Soul

218

In the morning shall my prayer come before Thee.—Ps. 84: 13. R. V.

THOMAS KEN, c. 1692   MORNING HYMN L. M.   FRANCOIS H. BARTHOLEMON, 1791

1. A-wake, my soul, and with the sun Thy dai - ly stage of du - ty run:
2. By in-fluence of the light di - vine Let thy own light to oth - ers shine;
3. Wake and lift up thy - self, my heart, And with the an - gels bear thy part,
4. Di - rect, con - trol, sug-gest, this day, All I de - sign, or do, or say;

Shake off dull sloth, and joy - ful rise To pay thy morn-ing sac - ri - fice.
Re - flect all heav'n's pro-pi - tious rays In ar - dent love and cheerful praise.
Who all night long, un - wear-ied, sing High praise to the e - ter - nal King.
That all my pow'rs, with all their might, In Thy sole glo - ry may u - nite.

Father, We Thank Thee

219

Giving thanks always for all things.—EPH. 5: 20

HURSLEY L. M.   PETER RITTER, 1792
Arr. by WILLIAM H. MONK, 1861

1. Fa-ther, we thank Thee for the night, And for the pleas-ant morn-ing light,
2. Help us to do the things we should, To be to oth - ers kind and good;

For rest and food, and lov - ing care, And all that makes the day so fair.
In all our work, and all our play, To love Thee bet - ter ev - 'ry day.

220 Love At Home

Now Jesus loved Martha, and her sister Mary, and Lazarus.—Jn. 11: 5

7. 5. 7. 5. 7. 7. 7. 5. Ref.

JOHN H. McNAUGHTON, 1829-1896

JOHN H McNAUGHTON
Arr. by J. D. BRUNK, 1904

1. There is beau-ty all a-round, When there's love at home; There is joy in
2. In the cot-tage there is joy, When there's love at home; Hate and en-vy
3. Kind-ly heav-en smiles a-bove, When there's love at home; All the earth is
4. Je-sus, show Thy mer-cy mine, *Then* there's love at home; Sweetly whis-per

ev - 'ry sound, When there's love at home; Peace and plen-ty here a-bide,
ne'er an-noy, When there's love at home; Ros - es blos-som 'neath our feet,
filled with love, When there's love at home; Sweet-er sings the brook-let by,
"I am thine," *Then* there's love at home; Source of love, Thy cheer-ing light

Smil-ing sweet on ev - 'ry side, Time doth soft-ly, sweetly glide, When there's
All the earth's a gar-den sweet, Mak-ing life a bliss complete, When there's
Brighter beams the az - ure sky; Oh, there's One who smiles on high When there's
Far ex-ceeds the sun so bright—Can dis-pel the gloom of night, *Then* there's

love at home, Love at home, love at
love at home, Love at home, love at
love at home, Love at home, love at
love at home, Love at home, love at
Love at home, yes, love at home, Love at home, oh,

Love At Home—Concluded

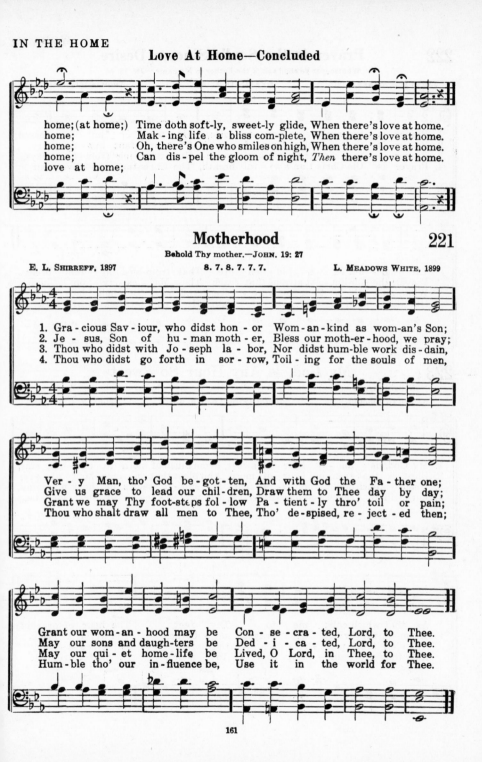

home; (at home;) Time doth soft-ly, sweet-ly glide, When there's love at home.
home; Mak - ing life a bliss com-plete, When there's love at home.
home; Oh, there's One who smiles on high, When there's love at home.
home; Can dis-pel the gloom of night, *Then* there's love at home.
love at home;

Motherhood 221

Behold Thy mother.—JOHN. 19: 27

E. L. SHIRREFF, 1897   8. 7. 8. 7. 7. 7.   L. MEADOWS WHITE, 1899

1. Gra - cious Sav - iour, who didst hon - or Wom-an-kind as wom-an's Son;
2. Je - sus, Son of hu - man moth - er, Bless our moth-er-hood, we pray;
3. Thou who didst with Jo - seph la - bor, Nor didst hum-ble work dis-dain,
4. Thou who didst go forth in sor - row, Toil - ing for the souls of men,

Ver - y Man, tho' God be-got-ten, And with God the Fa - ther one;
Give us grace to lead our chil-dren, Draw them to Thee day by day;
Grant we may Thy foot-steps fol - low Pa - tient-ly thro' toil or pain;
Thou who shalt draw all men to Thee, Tho' de-spised, re - ject-ed then;

Grant our wom-an - hood may be Con - se - cra - ted, Lord, to Thee.
May our sons and daugh-ters be Ded - i - ca - ted, Lord, to Thee.
May our qui - et home - life be Lived, O Lord, in Thee, to Thee.
Hum - ble tho' our in-fluence be, Use it in the world for Thee.

222

Prayer is the Soul's Sincere Desire

Whatsoever ye shall ask of the Father in My name.—Jn. 15: 16

JAMES MONTGOMERY, 1818 BYEFIELD C. M. THOMAS HASTINGS, 1840

1. Prayer is the soul's sin-cere de-sire, Ut-tered or un-ex-pressed;
2. Prayer is the sim-plest form of speech That in-fant lips can try;
3. Prayer is the con-trite sin-ner's voice Re-turn-ing from his ways,
4. Prayer is the Chris-tian's vi-tal breath, The Chris-tian's na-tive air,

The mo-tion of a hid-den fire That trem-bles in the breast.
Prayer, the sub-lim-est strains that reach The Maj-es-ty on high.
While an-gels in their songs re-joice, And say, "Be-hold, he prays!"
His watch-word at the gate of death—He en-ters heav'n with prayer.

223

My God, is Any Hour So Sweet

Delight thyself also in the Lord; and He shall give thee the desires of thine heart.—Ps. 37: 4

CHARLOTTE ELLIOTT, 1835 ALMSGIVING 8. 8. 8. 4. JOHN B. DYKES, 1875

1. My God, is an-y hour so sweet, From blush of morn to eve-ning star,
2. Blest is that tran-quil hour of morn, And blest that sol-emn hour of eve,
3. Hushed is each doubt, gone ev-'ry fear; My spir-it seems in heav'n to stay;
4. Lord, till I reach yon bliss-ful shore, No priv-i-lege so dear shall be

As that which calls me to Thy feet, The hour of prayer?
When, on the wings of prayer up-borne, The world I leave.
And e'en the pen-i-ten-tial tear Is wiped a-way.
As thus my in-most soul to pour In prayer to Thee.

Sweet Hour of Prayer

My heart said unto Thee, Thy face, Lord, will I seek.—Ps. 27: 8

WILLIAM W. WALFORD, c. 1842   8. 8. 8. 8. D.   WILLIAM B. BRADBURY, 1859

1. Sweet hour of prayer, sweet hour of prayer, That calls me from a world of care,
2. Sweet hour of prayer, sweet hour of prayer, Thy wings shall my pe - ti - tion bear
3. Sweet hour of prayer, sweet hour of prayer, May I thy con - so - la - tion share,

And bids me, at my Father's throne, Make all my wants and wish-es known!
To Him, whose truth and faith-ful-ness En - gage the wait - ing soul to bless:
Till, from Mount Pisgah's loft-y height, I view my home, and take my flight:

In sea - sons of dis - tress and grief, My soul has oft - en found re - lief,
And since He bids me seek His face, Be - lieve His Word, and trust His grace,
This robe of flesh I'll drop, and rise, To seize the ev - er - last - ing prize;

And oft es-caped the tempter's snare, By thy re - turn, sweet hour of prayer.
I'll cast on Him my ev - 'ry care, And wait for thee, sweet hour of prayer.
And shout, while passing thro' the air, Farewell, farewell, sweet hour of prayer.

225 'Tis the Blessed Hour of Prayer

It is good for me to draw near to God.—Ps. 73: 28

FANNY J. CROSBY

W. H. DOANE

1. 'Tis the bless-ed hour of prayer, when our hearts low-ly bend, And we
2. 'Tis the bless-ed hour of prayer, when the Sav-iour draws near, With a
3. 'Tis the bless-ed hour of prayer, when the tempt-ed and tried To the
4. At the bless-ed hour of prayer, trust-ing Him we be-lieve That the

gath-er to Je-sus, our Sav-iour and Friend: If we come to Him in
ten-der com-pas-sion His chil-dren to hear; When He tells us we may
Sav-iour who loves them their sor-row con-fide; With a sym-pa-thiz-ing
bless-ings we're need-ing we'll sure-ly re-ceive, In the full-ness of this

faith, His pro-tec-tion to share;
cast at His feet ev-'ry care; What a balm for the wea-ry! O how
heart He re-moves ev-'ry care;
trust we shall lose ev-'ry care;

D. S.—*What a balm for the wea-ry! O how*

FINE. REFRAIN

D. S.

sweet to be there! Bless-ed hour of prayer, Bless-ed hour of prayer!

sweet to be there!

Copyright, 1880, by W. H. Doane

What a Friend We Have in Jesus

There is a friend that sticketh closer than a brother.—Prov. 18: 24

JOSEPH SCRIVEN, 1855 ERIE 8. 7. 8. 7. D. CHARLES C. CONVERSE, 1868

1. What a friend we have in Je - sus, All our sins and griefs to bear;
2. Have we tri - als and temp - ta - tions? Is there troub-le an - y - where?
3. Are we weak and heav - y la - den, Cum-bered with a load of care?

What a priv - i - lege to car - ry Ev - 'ry-thing to God in prayer!
We should nev - er be dis - cour - aged: Take it to the Lord in prayer!
Pre - cious Sav-iour, still our ref - uge; Take it to the Lord in prayer!

O what peace we oft - en for - feit, O what need-less pain we bear,
Can we find a friend so faith - ful, Who will all our sor-rows share?
Do thy friends de-spise, for-sake thee? Take it to the Lord in prayer!

All be - cause we do not car - ry Ev - 'ry-thing to God in prayer.
Je - sus knows our ev - 'ry weak-ness; Take it to the Lord in prayer!
In His arms He'll take and shield thee, Thou wilt find a sol - ace there.

227

The Prayer Upon the Mountain

He went up into a mountain apart to pray.—MATT. 14: 23

J. W. WAYLAND

C. M.

J. D. BRUNK

Andante

1. A - lone up - on the moun-tain drear, A - bove the troub - led sea,
2. The mul - ti - tude in won - der lay,—No king - ly crown would He;
3. The wind and waves were loud and high Up - on the troub - led sea;

Where God a - lone could come and hear, Prayed Christ of Gal - i - lee.
But watch-ing tow'rd the gates of day, Prayed Christ of Gal - i - lee.
Un - seen a - bove, yet ev - er nigh, Prayed Christ of Gal - i - lee.

REFRAIN

How oft - en when on wea - ry ways, How oft on moun-tains bare,

How oft - en aft - er toil-some days, We need a night of prayer!

Copyright, 1927, by Mrs. John D. Brunk. Used by permission

228

From Every Stormy Wind

A hiding place from the wind, and a covert from the tempest.—ISA. 32: 2

HUGH STOWELL, 1831

RETREAT L. M.

THOMAS HASTINGS

1. From ev - 'ry storm - y wind that blows, From ev - 'ry swell-ing tide of woes,
2. There is a place where Je-sus sheds The oil of glad-ness on our heads,
3. There is a scene where spirits blend, Where friend holds fellowship with friend,
4. Ah! whith-er could we flee for aid, When tempted, des - o - late, dis-mayed?
5. There, there on ea - gle wings we soar, And sin and sense mo-lest no more;

From Every Stormy Wind—Concluded

There is a calm, a sure re-treat; 'Tis found be - neath the mer - cy seat.
A place than all be-sides more sweet; It is the blood-bo't mer - cy seat.
Tho' sun-dered far, by faith they meet A - round one com - mon mer - cy seat.
Or how the hosts of hell de - feat, Had suf-f'ring saints no mer - cy seat?
And heav'n comes down our souls to greet, While glo - ry crowns the mer - cy seat.

At Jesus' Feet

229

E. E. HEWITT

EMMA ACKLEY MILLER

DUET. Tenor and Alto

1. A - mid life's ev - er-changeful scenes, My trust-ful soul on Je - sus leans;
2. Lo, there is cleans - ing for my sin, His pre-cious blood makes peace within;
3. Be - set by sor - row, toil or care, I al - ways find blest com-fort there;
4. Faith, hope and love are quickened there, New life I gain, in con-stant prayer;

The sun may shine, the storm may beat, I'll hum-bly bow at Je - sus' feet.
And strength is there, and cour-age true, That I His ho - ly will may do.
He gives me o - ver-com - ing grace, And guid-ing light, His steps to trace.
Some day, in bright-er realms we'll meet, Till then, I'll tar - ry at His feet.

CHORUS

There is no place on earth so sweet As kneel-ing down at Je - sus' feet;

In close com-mun - ion, there we meet My lov - ing Sav - iour and my King.

230

How Firm a Foundation

Jesus Christ the same yesterday, and to-day, and forever.— HEB. 13: 8

ADESTE FIDELES 11. 11. 11. 11.

GEORGE KEITH, 1787

J. READING
WADE'S Cantus Diversi, 1751

1. How firm a foun-da-tion, ye saints of the Lord, Is laid for your faith in His
2. "Fear not, I am with thee, O be not dis-mayed; For I am thy God, and will
3. "When thro' the deep waters I call thee to go, The riv-ers of sor - row shall
4. "The soul that on Je-sus hath leaned for re-pose, I will not, I will not de-

ex-cel-lent Word! What more can He say than to you He hath said—Who un - to the
still give thee aid; I'll strengthen thee, help thee, and cause thee to stand, Up - held by My
not o-ver-flow; For I will be with thee thy troubles to bless, And sanc-ti - fy
sert to his foes; That soul, tho' all hell should endeavor to shake, I'll nev-er, no,

Sav-iour for ref-uge have fled? Who un - to the Sav-iour for ref-uge have fled?
righteous, om-nip-o-tent hand, Up - held by My righteous, om-nip-o - tent hand.
to thee thy deepest dis - tress, And sanc - ti- fy to thee thy deep-est dis-tress.
nev - er, no, nev-er for - sake, I'll nev - er, no, nev-er, no, nev-er, for-sake."

231

Book Divine

The law of Thy mouth is better unto me than thousands of gold and silver.—Ps. 119: 72

HORTON 7. 7. 7. 7.

JOHN BURTON, JR., 1803–1877

XAVIER SCHNEIDER VON WARTENSEE, 1786

1. Ho - ly Bi - ble, book di - vine! Pre - cious treas - ure, thou art mine!
2. Mine to chide me when I rove; Mine to show a Sav-iour's love;
3. Mine to com - fort in dis - tress, If the Ho - ly Spir - it bless;
4. Mine to tell of joys to come, In the saint's e - ter - nal home:

168

Book Divine—Concluded

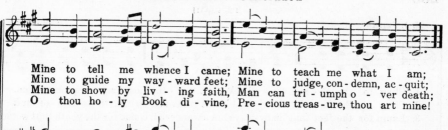

Mine to tell me whence I came; Mine to teach me what I am;
Mine to guide my way-ward feet; Mine to judge, con-demn, ac-quit;
Mine to show by liv-ing faith, Man can tri-umph o-ver death;
O thou ho-ly Book di-vine, Pre-cious treas-ure, thou art mine!

Break Thou the Bread of Life
232

If any man eat of this bread, he shall live forever.—Jn. 6: 51

MARY A LATHBURY, 1880   6. 4. 6. 4. D.   W. F SHERWIN. 1877

1. Break Thou the bread of life, Dear Lord, to me, As Thou didst
2. Bless Thou the truth, re-vealed This day to me, As Thou didst
3. Spir-it and life are they, Words Thou dost speak; I has-ten

break the loaves Be-side the sea; Be-yond the sa-cred page
bless the bread By Gal-i-lee; Then shall all bond-age cease,
to o-bey, But I am weak; Thou art my on-ly help,

I seek Thee, Lord; My spir-it pants for Thee, O liv-ing Word!
All fet-ters fall; And I shall find in Thee My All-in-All!
Thou art my life; Heed-ing Thy ho-ly Word I win the strife

233 **Cling to the Bible**

Ps. 119: 111

M. J. Smith   J. R. Murray

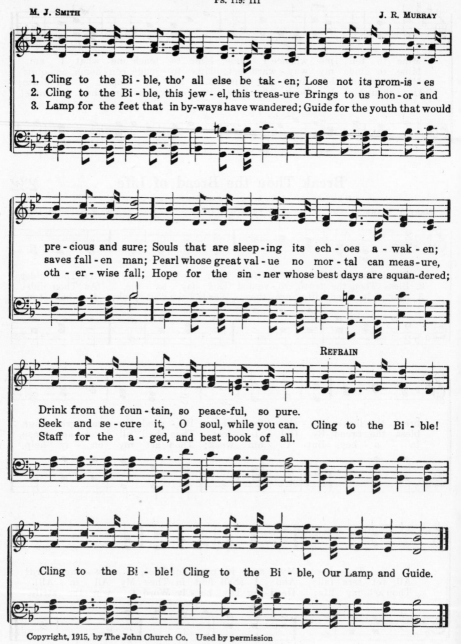

1. Cling to the Bi - ble, tho' all else be tak - en; Lose not its prom-is - es
2. Cling to the Bi - ble, this jew - el, this treas-ure Brings to us hon - or and
3. Lamp for the feet that in by-ways have wandered; Guide for the youth that would

pre - cious and sure; Souls that are sleep-ing its ech - oes a - wak - en;
saves fall - en man; Pearl whose great val - ue no mor - tal can meas-ure,
oth - er - wise fall; Hope for the sin - ner whose best days are squan-dered;

REFRAIN

Drink from the foun - tain, so peace-ful, so pure.
Seek and se - cure it, O soul, while you can. Cling to the Bi - ble!
Staff for the a - ged, and best book of all.

Cling to the Bi - ble! Cling to the Bi - ble, Our Lamp and Guide.

Forever Settled in the Heavens

Ps. 119: 89-96 Metrical

Psalter   ROCKINGHAM New L. M.   LOWELL MASON, 1830

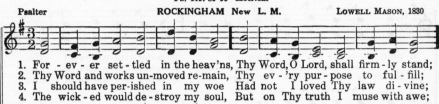

1. For - ev - er set-tled in the heav'ns, Thy Word, O Lord, shall firm-ly stand;
2. Thy Word and works un-moved re-main, Thy ev - 'ry pur-pose to ful - fill;
3. I should have per-ished in my woe Had not I loved Thy law di-vine;
4. The wick - ed would de-stroy my soul, But on Thy truth I muse with awe;

Thy faith-ful-ness shall nev - er fail; The earth a - bides at Thy com-mand.
All things are Thine and Thee o - bey, And all as serv-ants wait Thy will.
That law I nev - er can for-get; O save me, Lord, for I am Thine.
Im - per-fect I have found all else, But bound-less is Thy won-drous law.

Words Copyright, 1911, by the United Presbyterian Board of Publication. Used by permission

In Vain Would Boasting Reason Find

For the preaching of the cross is to them that perish foolishness.—I COR. 1: 18

MENDON L. M.

ANNE STEELE, 1760   German Melody
Arr. by SAMUEL DYER, 1828

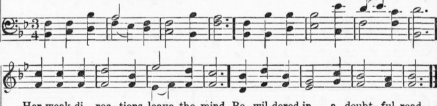

1. In vain would boast-ing rea - son find The path to hap - pi - ness and God:
2. Je - sus, Thy words a - lone im - part E - ter - nal life; on these I live;
3. Here let my con-stant feet a - bide; Thou art the true, the liv - ing way;
4. The va-rious forms that men de - vise To shake my faith with treach'rous art,

Her weak di - rec-tions leave the mind Be - wil-dered in a doubt-ful road.
Di - vin-er com-forts cheer my heart Than all the pow'rs of na - ture give.
Let Thy good Spir - it be my guide To the bright realms of end - less day.
I scorn as van - i - ty and lies, And bind Thy Gos - pel to my heart.

236 Wonderful Words of Life

P. P. B.

P. P. BLISS

1. Sing them o - ver a - gain to me, Won-der-ful words of Life;
2. Christ, the bless-ed One, gives to all Won-der-ful words of Life;
3. Sweet-ly ech - o the gos - pel call, Won-der-ful words of Life;

Let me more of their beau - ty see, Won-der-ful words of Life;
Sin - ner, list to the lov - ing call, Won-der-ful words of Life;
Of - fer par - don and peace to all, Won-der-ful words of Life;

Words of life and beau - ty, Teach me faith and du - ty;
All so free - ly giv - en, Woo - ing us to heav - en;
Je - sus, on - ly Sav - iour, Sanc - ti - fy for - ev - er.

CHORUS

Beau - ti - ful words, won-der-ful words, Won-der-ful words of Life;....

Beau - ti - ful words, won-der-ful words, Won-der-ful words of Life...

O Word of God Incarnate

237

The Word was made flesh, and dwelt among us.—JN. 1: 14

MUNICH 7. 6. 7. 6. D.

W. WALSHAM HOWE, 1867

MEININGEN, 1693
Har. by FELIX MENDELSSOHN-BARTHOLDY

1. O Word of God in - car - nate, O Wis - dom from on high,
2. The Church from her dear Mas - ter Re - ceived the gift di - vine,
3. It float - eth like a ban - ner Be - fore God's host un - furled;
4. O make Thy Church, dear Sav - iour, A lamp of pu - rest gold,

O Truth, un-changed, un - chang - ing, O Light of our dark sky;
And still that light she lift - eth O'er all the earth to shine.
It shin - eth like a bea - con A - bove the dark - ling world;
To bear be - fore the na - tions Thy true light as of old;

We praise Thee for the ra - diance That from the hal - lowed page,
It is the gold - en cas - ket Where gems of truth are stored,
It is the chart and com - pass That o'er life's surg - ing sea,
O teach Thy wan-d'ring pil - grims By this their path to trace,

A lan - tern to our foot - steps Shines on from age to age.
It is the heav'n-drawn pic - ture Of Christ, the liv - ing Word.
'Mid mists and rocks and quick - sands, Still guides, O Christ, to Thee.
Till, clouds and dark - ness end - ed, They see Thee face to face.

238

How Precious is the Book

I have esteemed the words of His mouth more than my necessary food.—JOB. 23: 12

JOHN FAWCETT, c. 1782   **SAWLEY C. M.**   JAMES WALCH, 1860

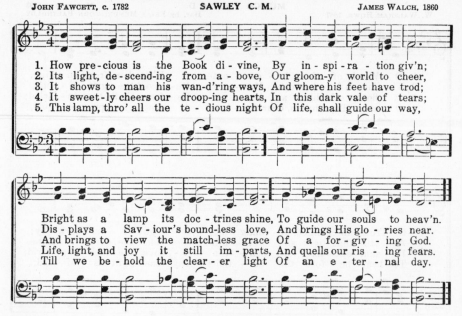

1. How pre-cious is the Book di-vine, By in-spi-ra-tion giv'n;
2. Its light, de-scend-ing from a-bove, Our gloom-y world to cheer,
3. It shows to man his wan-d'ring ways, And where his feet have trod,
4. It sweet-ly cheers our droop-ing hearts, In this dark vale of tears;
5. This lamp, thro' all the te-dious night Of life, shall guide our way,

Bright as a lamp its doc-trines shine, To guide our souls to heav'n.
Dis-plays a Sav-iour's bound-less love, And brings His glo-ries near.
And brings to view the match-less grace Of a for-giv-ing God.
Life, light, and joy it still im-parts, And quells our ris-ing fears.
Till we be-hold the clear-er light Of an e-ter-nal day.

239

Lamp of Our Feet

Thy word is a lamp unto my feet, and a light unto my path.—PS. 119: 105

BERNARD BARTON, 1826   **LAMBETH C. M.**   S. WEBBE, 1740-1816
                                                   WILHELM F. A. SCHULTES, 1871

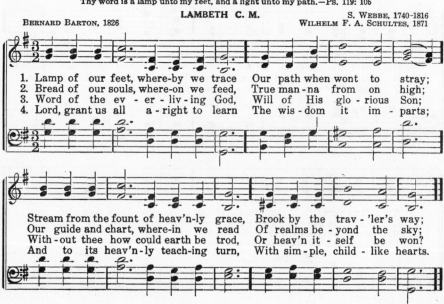

1. Lamp of our feet, where-by we trace Our path when wont to stray;
2. Bread of our souls, where-on we feed, True man-na from on high;
3. Word of the ev-er-liv-ing God, Will of His glo-rious Son;
4. Lord, grant us all a-right to learn The wis-dom it im-parts;

Stream from the fount of heav'n-ly grace, Brook by the trav-'ler's way;
Our guide and chart, where-in we read Of realms be-yond the sky;
With-out thee how could earth be trod, Or heav'n it-self be won?
And to its heav'n-ly teach-ing turn, With sim-ple, child-like hearts.

Thy Word Have I Hid in My Heart

Adapted by E. O. S.

E. O. SELLERS

1. Thy Word is a lamp to my feet, A light to my path al - way;
2. For - ev - er, O Lord, is Thy Word Es - tab-lished and fixed on high;
3. At morn-ing, at noon, and at night, I ev - er will give Thee praise;
4. Thro' Him Whom Thy Word hath foretold, The Sav-iour and Morn-ing Star,

To guide and to save me from sin, And show me the heav'n-ly way.
Thy faith-ful-ness un - to all men A - bid - eth for - ev - er nigh.
For Thou art my por - tion, O Lord, And shall be thro' all my days!
Sal - va - tion and peace have been bro't To those who have strayed a-far.

CHORUS—Ps. 119: 11.

Thy Word have I hid in my heart,.......... That I might not
in my heart,

sin a - gainst Thee,............. That I might not sin, That
a - gainst Thee,

ad lib.

I might not sin, Thy Word have I hid in my heart.

175

241

The Heavens Declare Thy Glory

Ps. 119: 1-9. Metrical

CRAWFORD L. M.

Isaac Watts, 1719

Arr. from Haydn
W. H. Doane

1. The heav'ns declare Thy glo-ry, Lord; In ev-'ry star Thy wis-dom shines; But when our eyes be-
2. Sun, moon, and stars convey Thy praise Round the whole earth, and never stand; So when Thy truth be-
3. Nor shall Thy spreading Gospel rest, Till thro' the world Thy truth has run; Till Christ has all the
4. Great Sun of Righteousness, a-rise, Bless the dark world with heav'nly light; Thy Gospel makes the

hold Thy Word, We read Thy name in fair-er lines, We read Thy name in fair-er lines.
gan its race, It touched and glanced on ev-'ry land, It touched and glanced on ev-'ry land.
na-tions blest That see the light, or feel the sun, That see the light, or feel the sun.
sim-ple wise, Thy laws are pure, Thy judgments right, Thy laws are pure, Thy judg-ments right.

242

Not By Thy Mighty Hand

Behold a sower went forth to sow.—Matt. 13: 3

J. R. Woodford, 1863

SCHUMANN S. M.

Arr. from Schumann

1. Not by Thy might-y hand, Thy won-drous works a-lone,
2. Forth from th' e-ter-nal gates, Thine ev-er-last-ing home,
3. And Thou wilt come a-gain, And heav'n be-neath Thee bow,
4. That, when in Thy great day The tares shall sev-ered be,

But by the mar-vels of Thy Word, Thy glo-ry, Lord, is known.
To sow the seed of truth be-low, Thou didst vouch-safe to come.
To reap the har-vest Thou hast sown, Sow-er and Reap-er Thou.
We may be sure-ly gath-ered in With all Thy saints to Thee.

I Know That My Redeemer Liveth

JESSIE H. BROWN

J. H. FILLMORE

1. I know that my Re-deem-er liv - eth, And on the earth...... a-gain shall stand;
2. I know His promise nev-er fail - eth, The word He speaks,.... it can-not die;
3. I know my mansion He pre-par - eth, That where He is........ there I may be;

I know e - ter - nal life He giv - eth, That grace and pow'r........ are in His hand.
That cru - el death my flesh as - sail - eth, Yet I shall see .... Him by and by.
O won-drous tho't, for me He car - eth, And He at last........ will come for me.

CHORUS

I know, I know........ that Je - sus liv - eth, And on the earth............ a-gain shall stand; I know, I know...... that life He giv-eth, That grace and pow'r ..... are in His hand.

I know, I know,
And on the earth
I know, I know
That grace and pow'r

244 Teach Me, O Lord

PSALM 119: 33-40

Psalter   BISHOP L. M.   JOSEPH P. HOLBROOK

1. Teach me, O Lord, Thy way of truth, And from it
2. In Thy com-mand-ments make me walk, For in Thy
3. Turn Thou my eyes from van-i-ty, And cause me
4. Turn Thou a-way re-proach and fear, Thy right-eous

I will not de-part; That I may stead-fast-
law my joy shall be; Give me a heart that
in Thy ways to tread; O let Thy serv-ant
judg-ments I con-fess; To know Thy pre-cepts

ly o-bey, Give me an un-der-stand-ing heart.
loves Thy will, From dis-con-tent and en-vy free.
prove Thy Word, And thus to god-ly fear be led.
I de-sire, Re-vive me in Thy right-eous-ness.

Words Copyright, 1911, by the United Presbyterian Board of Publication. Used by permission

245 We Walk By Faith

For we walk by faith, not by sight.—II COR. 5: 7

HENRY ALFORD, 1844   HERMANN C. M.   NICHOLAS HERMANN, 1485-1561

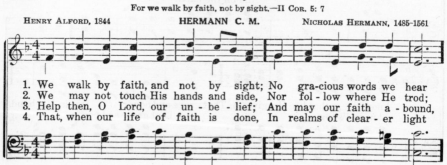

1. We walk by faith, and not by sight; No gra-cious words we hear
2. We may not touch His hands and side, Nor fol-low where He trod;
3. Help then, O Lord, our un-be-lief; And may our faith a-bound,
4. That, when our life of faith is done, In realms of clear-er light

We Walk By Faith—Concluded

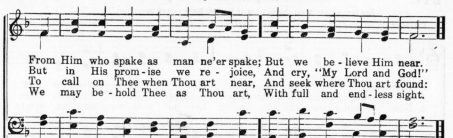

From Him who spake as man ne'er spake; But we be-lieve Him near.
But in His prom-ise we re - joice, And cry, "My Lord and God!"
To call on Thee when Thou art near, And seek where Thou art found:
We may be-hold Thee as Thou art, With full and end-less sight.

Faith is a Living Power From Heaven 246

We are . . . of them that believe to the saving of the soul.—HEB. 10: 39

P. HERBERT, 1566   SESSIONS L. M.   L. O. EMERSON, 1847

1. Faith is a liv - ing pow'r from heav'n Which grasps the
2. Faith finds in Christ what - e'er we need To save and
3. Faith to the con - science whis - pers peace; And bids the
4. Such faith in us, O God, im - plant, And to our

prom - ise God has giv'n; Se - cure - ly fixed on
strength - en, guide and feed; Strong in His grace it
mourn - er's sigh - ing cease; By faith the chil - dren's
prayers Thy fa - vor grant, In Je - sus Christ, Thy

Christ a - lone, A trust that can - - not be o'er-thrown.
joys to share His cross, in hope...... His crown to wear.
right we claim, And call up - on........ our Fa - ther's name.
sav - ing Son, Who is our fount..... of health a - lone.

179

247

Depth of Mercy

Let him return unto the Lord, and He will have mercy upon him.—ISA. 55: 7

CHARLES WESLEY, 1740   SEYMOUR 7. 7. 7 7.   CARL M. VON WEBER

1. Depth of mer - cy! can there be Mer - cy still re - served for me?
2. I have long with-stood His grace, Long pro-voked Him to His face;
3. Now in - cline me to re - pent; Let me now my sins la - ment;

Can my God His wrath for - bear,—Me, the chief of sin - ners, spare?
Would not heark-en to His calls, Grieved Him by a thou - sand falls.
Now my foul re - volt de - plore, Weep, be - lieve, and sin no more.

248

Come, My Soul, Thy Suit Prepare

Ask, and it shall be given you.—MATT. 7: 7

HORTON 7. 7. 7. 7.

JOHN NEWTON, 1779   ZAVIER SCHNYDER VON WARTENSEE, 1786-1868

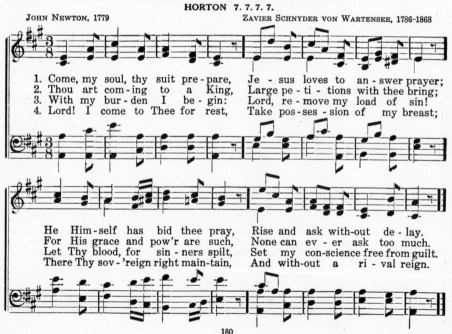

1. Come, my soul, thy suit pre - pare, Je - sus loves to an - swer prayer;
2. Thou art com-ing to a King, Large pe - ti - tions with thee bring;
3. With my bur - den I be - gin: Lord, re - move my load of sin!
4. Lord! I come to Thee for rest, Take pos - ses - sion of my breast;

He Him-self has bid thee pray, Rise and ask with-out de - lay.
For His grace and pow'r are such, None can ev - er ask too much.
Let Thy blood, for sin - ners spilt, Set my con-science free from guilt;
There Thy sov - 'reign right main-tain, And with-out a ri - val reign.

My Sins, My Sins, My Saviour

I acknowledged my sins unto Thee, and my iniquity have I not hid.—Ps. 32: 5

JOHN S. B. MONSELL, 1863   MONSELL 7. 6. 7. 6. D.

1. My sins, my sins, my Sav-iour! They take such hold on me,
2. My sins, my sins, my Sav-iour! How sad on Thee they fall;
3. My sins, my sins, my Sav-iour! Their guilt I nev-er knew
4. There-fore my songs, my Sav-iour! E'en in this time of woe,

I am not a-ble to look up, Save on-ly, Christ, to Thee;
Seen thro' Thy gen-tle pa-tience, I ten-fold feel them all;
Till with Thee in the des-ert I near Thy pas-sion drew;
Shall tell of all Thy good-ness To suf-f'ring man be-low;

In Thee is all for-give-ness, In Thee a-bun-dant grace;
I know they are for-giv-en, But still, their pain to me
Till with Thee in the gar-den I heard Thy plead-ing prayer,
Thy good-ness and Thy fa-vor, Whose pres-ence from a-bove

My shad-ow and my sun-shine The bright-ness of Thy face.
Is all the grief and an-guish They laid, my Lord, on Thee.
And saw the sweat-drops, blood-y, That told Thy sor-row there.
Re-joice those hearts, my Sav-iour, That live in Thee and love.

250 O God, According to Thy Grace

PSALM 51

Psalter   VOX DILECTI C. M. D.   JOHN B. DYKES

1. O God, ac-cord-ing to Thy grace Be mer-ci-ful to me,
2. A-gainst Thee on-ly have I sinned, Done e-vil in Thy sight;
3. From all pol-lu-tion make me clean, Yea, whit-er than the snow;
4. From out Thy pres-ence cast me not, Thy face no more to see;

In Thy a-bound-ing love blot out All my in-iq-ui-ty;
Lord, in Thy judg-ment Thou art just, And in Thy sen-tence right.
O let my bro-ken heart re-joice And glad-ness make me know;
Thy Ho-ly Spir-it and His grace Take not a-way from me.

O wash me whol-ly from my guilt And make me clean with-in,
Be-hold, in e-vil I was formed, And I was born in sin,
Blot out all my in-iq-ui-ties, And hide my sins from view;
Re-store me Thy sal-va-tion's joy, My will-ing heart up-hold;

For my trans-gres-sions I con-fess, I ev-er see my sin.
But Thou wilt make me wise in heart, Thou seek-est truth with-in.
Cre-ate in me a spir-it right, O God, my heart re-new.
Then sin-ners shall be turned to Thee When I Thy ways un-fold.

The Solid Rock

251

The Lord is my defense, and rock of my refuge.—Ps. 94: 22

EDWARD MOTE, 1834   **L. M.**   WILLIAM B. BRADBURY

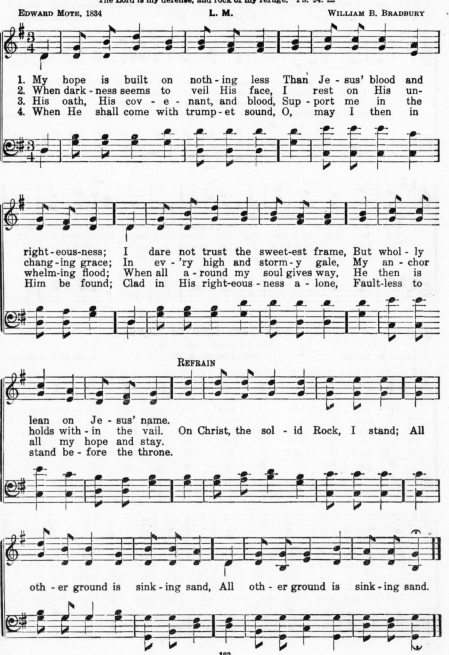

1. My hope is built on noth-ing less Than Je - sus' blood and right-eous-ness; I dare not trust the sweet-est frame, But whol-ly lean on Je - sus' name.
2. When dark-ness seems to veil His face, I rest on His un-chang-ing grace; In ev - 'ry high and storm-y gale, My an - chor holds with-in the vail.
3. His oath, His cov - e - nant, and blood, Sup - port me in the whelm-ing flood; When all a - round my soul gives way, He then is all my hope and stay.
4. When He shall come with trump-et sound, O, may I then in Him be found; Clad in His right-eous - ness a - lone, Fault-less to stand be - fore the throne.

REFRAIN

On Christ, the sol - id Rock, I stand; All oth - er ground is sink-ing sand, All oth - er ground is sink-ing sand.

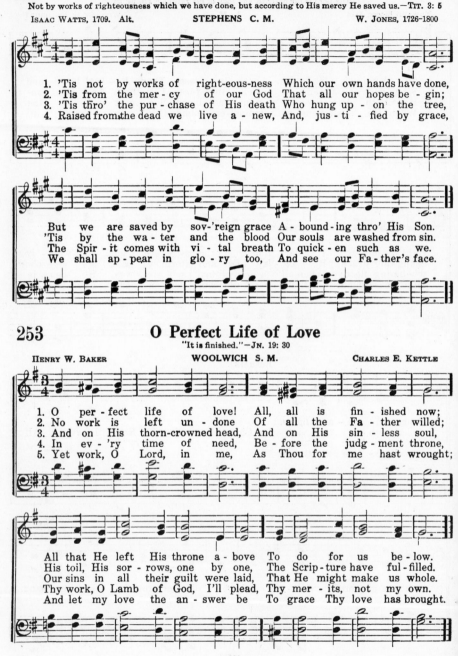

252 'Tis Not By Works of Righteousness

Not by works of righteousness which we have done, but according to His mercy He saved us.—Tit. 3: 5

ISAAC WATTS, 1709. Alt. STEPHENS C. M. W. JONES, 1726-1800

1. 'Tis not by works of right-eous-ness Which our own hands have done,
2. 'Tis from the mer-cy of our God That all our hopes be-gin;
3. 'Tis thro' the pur-chase of His death Who hung up-on the tree,
4. Raised from the dead we live a-new, And, jus-ti-fied by grace,

But we are saved by sov-'reign grace A-bound-ing thro' His Son.
'Tis by the wa-ter and the blood Our souls are washed from sin.
The Spir-it comes with vi-tal breath To quick-en such as we.
We shall ap-pear in glo-ry too, And see our Fa-ther's face.

253 O Perfect Life of Love

"It is finished."—JN. 19: 30

HENRY W. BAKER WOOLWICH S. M. CHARLES E. KETTLE

1. O per-fect life of love! All, all is fin-ished now;
2. No work is left un-done Of all the Fa-ther willed;
3. And on His thorn-crowned head, And on His sin-less soul,
4. In ev-'ry time of need, Be-fore the judg-ment throne,
5. Yet work, O Lord, in me, As Thou for me hast wrought;

All that He left His throne a-bove To do for us be-low.
His toil, His sor-rows, one by one, The Scrip-ture have ful-filled.
Our sins in all their guilt were laid, That He might make us whole.
Thy work, O Lamb of God, I'll plead, Thy mer-its, not my own.
And let my love the an-swer be To grace Thy love has brought.

I Lay My Sins On Jesus

254

The Lord hath laid on Him the iniquity of us all.—ISA. 53: 6

ST. HILDA 7. 6. 7. 6. D.

HORATIUS BONAR, 1847

JUSTIN H. KNECHT, 1799
EDWARD HUSBAND, 1871

1. I lay my sins on Je - sus, The spot - less Lamb of God;
2. I lay my wants on Je - sus; All full - ness dwells in Him;
3. I long to be like Je - sus, Meek, lov - ing, low - ly, mild;

He bears them all and frees us From the ac - curs - ed load:
He heal - eth my dis - eas - es, He doth my soul re - deem:
I long to be like Je - sus, The Fa - ther's ho - ly child:

I bring my guilt to Je - sus, To wash my crim - son stains
I lay my griefs on Je - sus, My bur - dens and my cares;
I long to be with Je - sus A - mid the heav'n - ly throng;

White in His blood most pre - cious, Till not a stain re - mains.
He from them all re - leas - es, He all my sor - rows shares.
To sing with saints His prais - es, And learn the an - gels' song.

255 Once For All

Justified by His grace, through the redemption that is in Christ Jesus.—Rom. 3: 24

P. P. Bliss

P. P. Bliss

1. Free from the law, oh, hap-py con-di-tion, Je-sus hath bled, and
2. Now are we free—there's no con-dem-na-tion, Je-sus pro-vides a
3. "Chil-dren of God," oh, glo-ri-ous call-ing, Sure-ly His grace will

there is re-mis-sion, Cursed by the law and bruised by the fall,
per-fect sal-va-tion; "Come un-to Me," oh, hear His sweet call,
keep us from fall-ing; Pass-ing from death to life at His call,

CHORUS

Grace hath re-deemed us once for all.
Come, and He saves us once for all. Once for all, oh, sin-ner, re-
Bless-ed sal-va-tion once for all.

ceive it; Once for all, oh, broth-er, be-lieve it; Cling to the

Cross, the bur-den will fall, Christ hath re-deemed us once for all.

Cross of Jesus

And I, if I be lifted up from the earth, will draw all men unto Me. —Jn. 12: 32

MESSIAH 7. 7. 7. 7. D.

J. Wellington Frizelle

Arr. from Louis.J. F. Herold

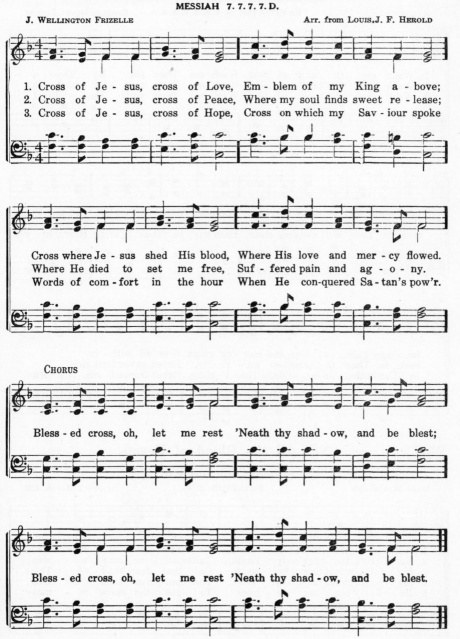

1. Cross of Je - sus, cross of Love, Em - blem of my King a - bove;
2. Cross of Je - sus, cross of Peace, Where my soul finds sweet re - lease;
3. Cross of Je - sus, cross of Hope, Cross on which my Sav - iour spoke

Cross where Je - sus shed His blood, Where His love and mer - cy flowed.
Where He died to set me free, Suf - fered pain and ag - o - ny.
Words of com - fort in the hour When He con-quered Sa - tan's pow'r.

CHORUS

Bless - ed cross, oh, let me rest 'Neath thy shad - ow, and be blest;

Bless - ed cross, oh, let me rest 'Neath thy shad - ow, and be blest.

257

Wash Me, O Lamb of God

Wash me throughly from mine iniquity.—Ps. 51: 2

H. B. BEEGLE   **BAYSWATER 6. 4. 6. 4. 6. 6. 6. 4.**   CHARLES HENRY PURDAY

1. Wash me, O Lamb of God, Wash me from sin; By Thy a-
2. Wash me, O Lamb of God, Wash me from sin; By faith Thy
3. Wash me, O Lamb of God, Wash me from sin; Thou, while I

ton - ing blood, Oh, make me clean; Purge me from ev - 'ry stain, Let me Thine
cleansing blood Now makes me clean: So near Thou art to me, So sweet my
trust in Thee, Wilt keep me clean; Each day to Thee I bring Heart, life, yea,

im - age gain; In love and mer - cy reign O'er all with - in.
rest in Thee; O bless - ed pu - ri - ty, — Saved, saved from sin.
ev - 'ry - thing; Saved, while to Thee I cling, Saved from all sin. A - MEN.

258

Not All the Blood of Beasts

By His own blood He entered in once into the holy place, having obtained eternal redemption for us.—HEB. 9: 12

ISAAC WATTS, 1709   **BOYLSTON S. M.**   LOWELL MASON, 1832

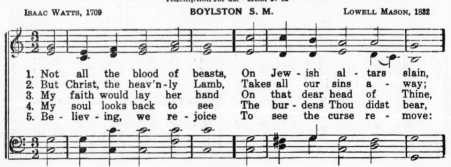

1. Not all the blood of beasts, On Jew - ish al - tars slain,
2. But Christ, the heav'n - ly Lamb, Takes all our sins a - way;
3. My faith would lay her hand On that dear head of Thine,
4. My soul looks back to see The bur - dens Thou didst bear,
5. Be - liev - ing, we re - joice To see the curse re - move:

Not All the Blood of Beasts—Concluded

Could give the guilt - y con-science peace, Or wash a - way the stain.
A sac - ri - fice of no - bler name And rich - er blood than they.
While, like a pen - i - tent, I stand, And there con-fess my sin.
When hang-ing on the curs - ed tree, And hopes her guilt was there.
We bless the Lamb with cheer - ful voice, And sing His bleed - ing love.

Glory to His Name   259

God forbid that I should glory save in the cross of our Lord Jesus Christ.—GAL. 6: 14

E. A. HOFFMAN   9. 9. 9. 5. Ref.   J. H. STOCKTON

1. Down at the cross where my Sav - iour died, Down where for cleansing from
2. I   am so won-drous-ly saved from sin, Je - sus so sweet-ly a-
3. O pre-cious foun-tain, that saves from sin! I   am so glad I have
4. Come to this foun-tain so rich and sweet; Cast thy poor soul at the

sin I cried, There to my heart was the blood ap-plied: Glo - ry to His name.
bides with-in; There at the cross where He took me in: Glo - ry to His name.
en - tered in; There Je-sus saves me and keeps me clean: Glo - ry to His name.
Saviour's feet; Step in to - day, and be made complete: Glo - ry to His name.

D. S.—There to my heart was the blood ap-plied: Glo - ry to His name.

REFRAIN   D. S.

Glo - ry to His name,.... Glo - ry to His name; ...

260 Wonderful Saviour

For when we were yet without strength, in due time Christ died for the ungodly.—Rom. 5: 6

W. K. JACOBS, 1902   P. M.   W. K. JACOBS

In majestic style

1. Won - der - ful Sav - iour, Re - deem - er, Thou in ten - d'rest love
2. Thou hast in great - est com - pas - sion Died our souls to save:
3. O - pen my heart e'er to hear Thee, Quick to hear Thy voice;

Watch-est o'er ev - 'ry be - liev - er, From Thy throne a - bove.
Pur - chased for us our re - demp - tion, Hope be - yond the grave.
Fill Thou my soul with Thy prais - es, Let my heart re - joice.

REFRAIN

Won - der - ful Sav - iour! Mer - ci - ful Sav - iour!
Je - sus, won-der-ful Sav-iour! Je - sus, mer-ci - ful Sav-iour!

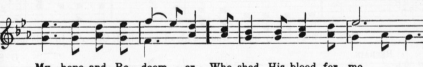

My hope and Re - deem - er, Who shed His blood for me.
Who shed His blood for me. (for me.)

Copyright by W. K. Jacobs. Used by permission

Nothing But the Blood

The blood of Jesus Christ cleanseth us from all sin.—I JN. 1: 7

R. Lowry   Robert Lowry

1. What can wash a - way my sin? Noth-ing but the blood of Je - sus;
2. For my cleans-ing this I see, Noth-ing but the blood of Je - sus;
3. Noth-ing can for sin a - tone—Noth-ing but the blood of Je - sus;
4. This is all my hope and peace—Noth-ing but the blood of Je - sus;
5. Glo - ry! glo - ry! thus I sing—Noth-ing but the blood of Je - sus;

What can make me pure with - in? Noth-ing but the blood of Je - sus.
For my par - don this my plea— Noth-ing but the blood of Je - sus.
Naught of good that I have done— Noth-ing but the blood of Je - sus.
This is all my right-eous - ness— Noth-ing but the blood of Je - sus.
All my praise for this I bring— Noth-ing but the blood of Je - sus.

REFRAIN

Oh, pre - cious is the flow That makes me white as snow;

No oth - er fount I know, Noth-ing but the blood of Je - sus.

Copyright, 1904, by Mary Runyon Lowry. Renewal. Used by permission

262 Cross of Christ, O Sacred Tree

DANIEL T. TAYLOR

ALBERT H. GROVE

1. Cross of Christ, O sa-cred tree, Hide my sins and shel-ter me;
2. Cross of Christ, O sa-cred tree, Let me to Thy shad-ow flee;
3. Cross of Christ, O sa-cred tree, Type of love's deep mys-ter - y;
4. Cross of Christ, O sa-cred tree, This my boast shall ev - er be,

Claim or mer - it have I none, I am vile and all un - done;
Here they mocked the Cru - ci - fied, Here the roy - al suf-f'rer died;
'Twas my sins pro-voked this love, I this match-less pas - sion moved;
That Thy blood for me was shed, That for me He groaned and bled.

I to Thee for suc - cor fly— Give me ref - uge or I die.
Here was shed th' a-ton - ing blood, Here ex - pired the Son of God;
For my soul this love was stored, On my head the bless-ing poured.
Now I catch that gra - cious eye, Now I know I shall not die.

Cross of Christ, O sa - cred tree, All my hopes are set on Thee.
Cross of Christ, O sa - cred tree, Can the guilt - y trust in Thee?
Cross of Christ, O sa - cred tree, Now I solve love's mys-ter - y.
Cross of Christ, O sa - cred tree, All my guilt is lost in Thee.

Hail to the Lord's Anointed

He shall judge thy people with righteousness, and thy poor with judgment.—Ps. 72: 2

JAMES MONTGOMERY, 1821   **SALVE DOMINE**   7. 6. 7. 6. D.   LAWRENCE W. WATSON, 1909

1. Hail to the Lord's A - noint - ed,   Great Da - vid's great - er Son!
2. He comes with suc - cor speed - y   To those who suf - fer wrong;
3. He shall come down like show - ers   Up - on the fruit - ful earth;
4. For Him shall prayer un - ceas - ing   And dai - ly vows as - cend;
5. O'er ev - 'ry foe vic - to - rious,   He on His throne shall rest,

Hail to the time ap - point - ed,   His reign on earth be - gun!
To help the poor and need - y,   And bid the weak be strong;
And love, joy, hope like flow - ers,   Spring in His path to birth.
His king - dom still in - creas - ing,   A king - dom with - out end.
From age to age more glo - rious,   All bless - ing and all blest.

He comes to break op - pres - sion,   To set the cap - tive free,
To give them songs for sigh - ing,   Their dark - ness turn to light,
Be - fore Him, on the moun - tains   Shall peace, the her - ald, go;
The moun - tain dews shall nour - ish   A seed in weak - ness sown,
The tide of time shall nev - er   His cov - e - nant re - move;

To take a - way trans - gres - sion,   And rule in eq - ui - ty.
Whose souls, con - demned and dy - ing,   Were pre - cious in His sight.
And right - eous - ness, in foun - tains,   From hill to val - ley flow.
Whose fruit shall spread and flour - ish,   And shake like Leb - a - non.
His name shall stand for - ev - er;   That name to us is Love.

264

Saviour, I Follow On

Kept by the power of God through faith unto salvation.—I Pet. 1: 5

C. S. Robinson

ST. EDMUND 6. 4. 6. 4. 6. 6. 6. 4.

Arthur Sullivan, 1872

1. Sav-iour! I fol-low on, Guid-ed by Thee, See-ing not yet the hand That lead-eth me; Hushed be my heart and still, Fear I no fur-ther ill; On-ly to meet Thy will My will shall be.

2. Riv-en the rock for me Thirst to re-lieve, Man-na from heav-en falls Fresh ev-'ry eve; Nev-er a want se-vere Caus-eth my eye a tear, But Thou dost whis-per near, "On-ly be-lieve!"

3. Oft-en to Ma-rah's brink Have I been brought: Shrink-ing the cup to drink, Help I have sought; And with the prayer's ascent, Je-sus the branch hath rent—Quick-ly re-lief hath sent, Sweet'ning the draught.

4. Sav-iour! I long to walk Clos-er with Thee; Led by Thy guiding hand, Ev-er to be Con-stant-ly near Thy side, Quickened and pu-ri-fied, Liv-ing for Him who died Free-ly for me!

265

He Lives! the Great Redeemer Lives!

He ever liveth to make intercession for us.—Heb. 7: 25

Anne Steele, 1760

BROOKFIELD L. M.

Thomas B. Southgate, 1855

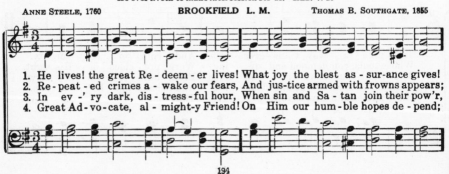

1. He lives! the great Re-deem-er lives! What joy the blest as-sur-ance gives!

2. Re-peat-ed crimes a-wake our fears, And jus-tice armed with frowns appears;

3. In ev-'ry dark, dis-tress-ful hour, When sin and Sa-tan join their pow'r,

4. Great Ad-vo-cate, al-might-y Friend! On Him our hum-ble hopes de-pend;

He Lives! the Great Redeemer Lives!—Concluded

And now, be - fore His Fa - ther, God, Pleads the full mer - its of His blood.
But in the Sav-iour's love-ly face Sweet mer - cy smiles, and all is peace.
Let this dear hope re - pel the dart, That Je - sus bears us on His heart.
Our cause can nev - er, nev - er fail, For Je - sus pleads, and must pre-vail.

Jesus Came, the Heavens Adoring 266

For even the Son of Man came . . . to give His life a ransom for many.—Mk. 10: 45

GODFREY THRING, 1864　　BENEDIC ANIMA 8. 7. 8. 7. 8. 7.　　JOHN GOSS, 1867

1. Je - sus came, the heav'ns a - dor - ing, Came with peace from realms on high;
2. Je - sus comes a - gain in mer - cy, When our hearts are bowed with care;
3. Je - sus comes to hearts re - joic - ing, Bring-ing news of sins for - giv'n;
4. Je - sus comes in joy and sor - row, Shares a - like our hopes and fears;
5. Je - sus comes on clouds tri - um - phant, When the heav'ns shall pass a - way;

Je - sus came for man's re - demp-tion, Low - ly came on earth to die;
Je - sus comes a - gain in an - swer To an ear-nest, heart-felt prayer;
Je - sus comes in sounds of glad-ness, Lead-ing souls re-deemed to heav'n;
Je - sus comes, what-e'er be - falls us, Glads our hearts, and dries our tears;
Je - sus comes a - gain in glo - ry; Let us then our hom-age pay,

Al - le - lu - ia! Al - le - lu - ia! Came in deep hu - mil - i - ty.
Al - le - lu - ia! Al - le - lu - ia! Comes to save us from de - spair.
Al - le - lu - ia! Al - le - lu - ia! Now the gate of death is riv'n.
Al - le - lu - ia! Al - le - lu - ia! Cheer-ing e'en our fail - ing years.
Al - le - lu - ia! ev - er sing - ing Till the dawn of end - less day.

267

O Everlasting Light

I am the way, the truth, and the life.—JN. 14: 6

HORATIUS BONAR   S. M.   ELI S. HALLMAN

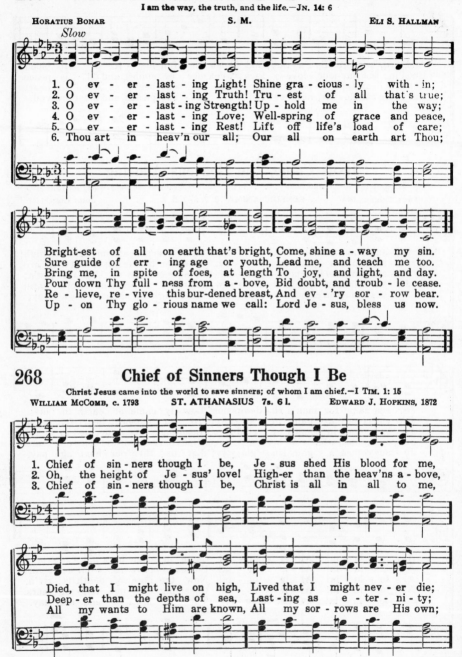

1. O ev - er - last - ing Light! Shine gra - cious - ly with - in;
2. O ev - er - last - ing Truth! Tru - est of all that's true;
3. O ev - er - last - ing Strength! Up - hold me in the way;
4. O ev - er - last - ing Love; Well-spring of grace and peace,
5. O ev - er - last - ing Rest! Lift off life's load of care;
6. Thou art in heav'n our all; Our all on earth art Thou;

Bright-est of all on earth that's bright, Come, shine a - way my sin.
Sure guide of err - ing age or youth, Lead me, and teach me too.
Bring me, in spite of foes, at length To joy, and light, and day.
Pour down Thy full - ness from a - bove, Bid doubt, and troub - le cease.
Re - lieve, re - vive this bur-dened breast, And ev - 'ry sor - row bear.
Up - on Thy glo - rious name we call: Lord Je - sus, bless us now.

268

Chief of Sinners Though I Be

Christ Jesus came into the world to save sinners; of whom I am chief.—I TIM. 1: 15

WILLIAM McCOMB, c. 1793   ST. ATHANASIUS 7s. 6 l.   EDWARD J. HOPKINS, 1872

1. Chief of sin - ners though I be, Je - sus shed His blood for me,
2. Oh, the height of Je - sus' love! High - er than the heav'ns a - bove,
3. Chief of sin - ners though I be, Christ is all in all to me,

Died, that I might live on high, Lived that I might nev - er die;
Deep - er than the depths of sea, Last - ing as e - ter - ni - ty;
All my wants to Him are known, All my sor - rows are His own;

196

Chief of Sinners Though I Be—Concluded

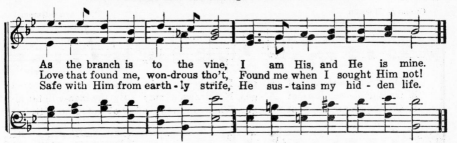

As the branch is to the vine, I am His, and He is mine.
Love that found me, won-drous tho't, Found me when I sought Him not!
Safe with Him from earth-ly strife, He sus-tains my hid-den life.

O Saviour, Where Shall Guilty Man 269

He was wounded for our transgressions.—ISA. 53: 5

Mrs. CAROLINE E. MAY, 1858   NEWCASTLE 8. 6. 8. 8. 6.   HENRY L. MORLEY, 1875

1. O Sav-iour, where shall guilt-y man Find rest ex-cept in
2. How came the ev-er-last-ing Son, The Lord of Life, to
3. To save us by Thy pre-cious blood, To make us one in
4. O make us wor-thy, gra-cious Lord, Of all Thy love to

Thee? Thine was the war-fare with his foe, The cross of
die? Why didst Thou meet the tempt-er's pow'r, Why, Je-sus,
Thee, That ours might be Thy per-fect life, Thy thorn-y
be; To Thy blest will our wills in-cline, That un-to

pain, the cup of woe, And Thine the vic-to-ry.
in Thy dy-ing hour, En-dure such ag-o-ny.
crown, Thy cross, Thy strife, And ours the vic-to-ry.
death we may be Thine, And ev-er live in Thee.

270 The Blessed Rock of Ages

GRACE L. HOSMER

ADAM GEIBEL

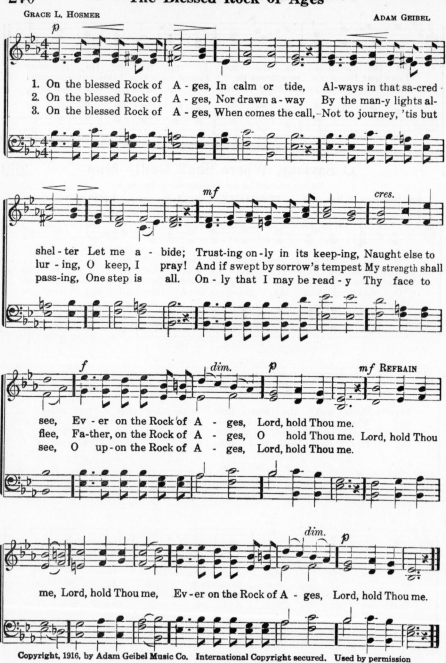

1. On the blessed Rock of A - ges, In calm or tide, Al-ways in that sa-cred
2. On the blessed Rock of A - ges, Nor drawn a - way By the man-y lights al-
3. On the blessed Rock of A - ges, When comes the call, Not to journey, 'tis but

shel - ter Let me a - bide; Trust-ing on-ly in its keep-ing, Naught else to
lur - ing, O keep, I pray! And if swept by sorrow's tempest My strength shall
pass-ing, One step is all. On - ly that I may be read - y Thy face to

see, Ev - er on the Rock of A - ges, Lord, hold Thou me.
flee, Fa-ther, on the Rock of A - ges, O hold Thou me. Lord, hold Thou
see, O up - on the Rock of A - ges, Lord, hold Thou me.

me, Lord, hold Thou me, Ev - er on the Rock of A - ges, Lord, hold Thou me.

O Lord, Within My Soul

Ye are complete in Him.—COL. 2: 10

E. A. HOFFMAN   E. A. HOFFMAN

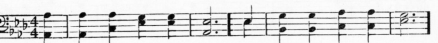

1. O   Lord, with - in   my   soul   I   long   for   pu - ri - ty,
2. I   bend be - fore Thy cross, And know my heart can be
3. I   pray   at   Thy dear feet, Sal - va - tion full en - treat,
4. My faith Thy Word be - lieves, The prom - ise made to me,

REFRAIN

To   be com - plete and   whole   A - lone through Thee.
Cleansed from its sin and   dross   A - lone through Thee. There is   no
And want to   feel my love   In Thee com - plete.
And per - fect peace re - ceives   A - lone through Thee.

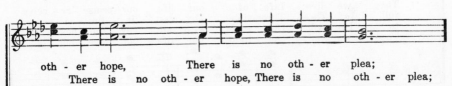

oth - er hope,   There   is   no oth - er   plea;
There is   no oth - er   hope, There is   no   oth - er plea;

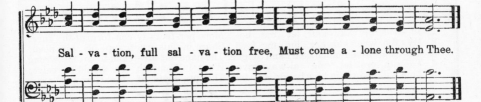

Sal - va - tion, full sal - va - tion free, Must come a - lone through Thee.

272 Lord of Our Life

In Him was life, and the life was the light of men.—JN. 1: 4

SAMUEL F. SMITH

LOUVAN L. M.

VIRGIL C. TAYLOR

1. Lord of our life, God whom we fear, Un - known, yet
2. Thine eye de - tects the spar - row's fall; Thy heart of
3. Shine in our dark - ness, Light of light, Our minds il -
4. We love Thy name, we heed Thy rod, Thy Word, our

known; un - seen, yet near; Breath of our breath, in
love ex - pands for all; Our throb - bing life is
lume, dis - perse our night; Make us re - spon - sive
law; O gra - cious God! We wait Thy will; on

Thee we live; Life of our life, our praise re - ceive.
full of Thee, Throned in Thy vast in - fin - i - ty.
to Thy will, Our souls with all Thy full - ness fill.
Thee we call; Our light, our life, our love, our all.

273 Jesus, My Saviour

Be renewed in the spirit of your mind.—EPH. 4: 23

WAYLAND L. M.

GEORGE B. HOLSINGER

1. Je - sus, my Sav - iour, let me be More per - fect - ly con - formed to Thee;
2. My foe, when hun - gry, let me feed, Share in his grief, sup - ply his need;
3. Let the en - ven-omed heart and tongue, The hand out-stretched to do me wrong,
4. To oth - ers let me al-ways give What I from oth - ers would re - ceive;
5. This will pro-claim how bright and fair The pre-cepts of the Gos - pel are;

200

Jesus, My Saviour—Concluded

Im-plant each grace, each sin de-throne, And form my tem-per like Thine own.
The haugh-ty frown may I not fear, But with a low-ly meek-ness bear.
Ex-cite no feel-ings in my breast But such as Je-sus once ex-pressed.
Good deeds for e-vil ones re-turn, Nor, when provoked, with an-ger burn.
And God Him-self, the God of love, His own re-sem-blance will ap-prove.

Draw Thou My Soul, O Christ   274

Let Him deny himself, . . . and follow me.—MATT. 16: 24

ST. EDMUND 6. 4. 6. 4. 6. 6. 4.

LUCY LARCOM, 1892   ARTHUR S. SULLIVAN, 1872

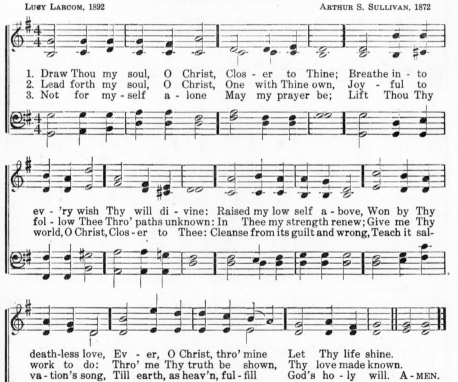

1. Draw Thou my soul, O Christ, Clos-er to Thine; Breathe in-to
2. Lead forth my soul, O Christ, One with Thine own, Joy-ful to
3. Not for my-self a-lone May my prayer be; Lift Thou Thy

ev-'ry wish Thy will di-vine: Raised my low self a-bove, Won by Thy
fol-low Thee Thro' paths unknown: In Thee my strength renew; Give me Thy
world, O Christ, Clos-er to Thee: Cleanse from its guilt and wrong, Teach it sal-

death-less love, Ev-er, O Christ, thro' mine Let Thy life shine.
work to do: Thro' me Thy truth be shown, Thy love made known.
va-tion's song, Till earth, as heav'n, ful-fill God's ho-ly will. A-MEN.

275 O Life in Whom Is Life Indeed

JESSIE BROWN POUNDS

From BAPTISTE

1. O Life in whom is life in-deed, Through whom our best de-sires are freed, Stir Thou that life in us, we plead; We come to Thee, we come to Thee!
2. O Light be-yond men's high-est thought, Be-yond all wis-dom seers have wrought, Ne'er yet that light in vain was sought; We come to Thee, we come to Thee!
3. O Good be-yond the dreams of men, Who mak-est stained lives white a-gain, Thou Christ, be-stow Thy pure-ness when We come to Thee, we come to Thee!

rit. *a tempo*

REFRAIN
Come to Thee, Come to Thee, Come to Thee, We come to Thee.

We come to Thee, We come to Thee, We come to Thee, We come to Thee.

Come to Thee, Come to Thee, Come to Thee, We come to Thee.

Is Not This the Land of Beulah?

276

Call thy land Beulah, for the Lord delighteth in thee.—ISA. 62: 4

Anon.
Mrs. HARRIET WARNER, *Re Qua*

8. 7. 8. 7. D.

J. W. DADMAN

1. I am dwell-ing on the moun-tain, Where the gold-en sun-light gleams
2. I can see far down the moun-tain, Where I wan-dered wea-ry years,
3. I am drink-ing at the foun-tain, Where I ev-er would a-bide;
4. Tell me not of heav-y cross-es, Nor the bur-dens hard to bear,
5. Oh, the Cross has won-drous glo-ry! Oft I've proved this to be true;

O'er a land whose won-drous beau-ty Far ex-ceeds my fond-est dreams;
Oft-en hin-dered in my jour-ney By the ghosts of doubts and fears,
For I've tast-ed life's pure riv-er, And my soul is sat-is-fied:
For I've found this great sal-va-tion Makes each bur-den light ap-pear:
When I'm in the way so nar-row, I can see a path-way through;

Where the air is pure, ce-les-tial, La-den with the breath of flow'rs,
Bro-ken vows and dis-ap-point-ments Thick-ly sprin-kled all the way,
There's no thirst-ing for life's pleas-ures, Nor a-dorn-ing, rich and gay,
And I love to fol-low Je-sus, Glad-ly count-ing all but dross,
And how sweet-ly Je-sus whis-pers: "Take the Cross, Thou need'st not fear,

REF.—*Is not this the land of Beu-lah, Bless-ed, bless-ed land of light,*

D. S.

They are bloom-ing by the foun-tain, 'Neath the nev-er-fad-ing bow'rs.
But the Spir-it led, un-er-ring, To the land I hold to-day.
For I've found a rich-er treas-ure, One that fad-eth not a-way.
World-ly hon-ors all for-sak-ing For the glo-ry of the Cross.
For I've tried the way be-fore thee, And the glo-ry lin-gers near."

Where the flow-ers bloom for-ev-er, And the sun is al-ways bright?

277 What Tender Mercy

God, who is rich in mercy; for His great love wherewith He loved us.—EPH. 2: 4

WM. HENRY GARDINER   10. 7. 10. 7. Ref.   W. A. OGDEN

1. When I see the way my Sav-iour leads me, Car-ing for me
2. When I see the way my Sav-iour leads me, Bear-ing pa - tient-
3. When I see the way my Sav-iour leads me, How He crowned and

day by day, Then I sad-ly bow my head and won-der
ly with me, Then I know how weak and un - de - serv - ing
blessed my days, In my grate-ful heart is deep thanks-giv-ing,

CHORUS

How I could have gone a - stray.
With-out Him I'd count-ed be.   Oh, what ten - der, ten - der mer - cy!
To my lips spring songs of praise.

Oh, what kind and lov - ing care, (lov - ing care,) Shown us

by the dear and lov - ing Shep-herd, From His dwell-ing place so fair.

O Jesus, Thou Art Standing

278

Behold, I stand at the door and knock.—Rev. 3: 20

ST. HILDA 7. 6. 7. 6. D.

W. Walsham How, 1867

Justin H. Knecht 1799
Edward Husband, 1871

1. O Je - sus, Thou art stand-ing Out - side the fast-closed door,
2. O Je - sus, Thou art knock-ing; And lo! that hand is scarred,
3. O Je - sus, Thou art plead-ing In ac - cents meek and low,—

In low - ly pa - tience wait - ing To pass the thresh - old o'er:
And thorns Thy brow en - cir - cle, And tears Thy face have marred:
"I died for you, My chil - dren, And will ye treat Me so?"

We bear the name of Chris - tians, His name and sign we bear;
O love that pass - eth knowl - edge, So pa - tient - ly to wait!
O Lord, with shame and sor - row We o - pen now the door;

O shame, thrice shame up - on us, To keep Him stand-ing there!
O sin that hath no e - qual, So fast to bar the gate!
Dear Sav - iour, en - ter, en - ter, And leave us nev - er - more.

205

279 Weeping One of Bethany

JN. 11: 35

J. R. MacDuff, 1859
Arr. J. C. B.

*Respectfully inscribed to
"The Hall Quartet"*

J. Calvin Bushey

1. Je - sus wept! those tears are o - ver, But His love is
2. Je - sus wept! and still in glo - ry He must mark the
3. Je - sus wept! that tear of sor - row If a leg - a-

still the same;... Kins - man, Friend, and Eld - er Broth - er,
mourn-er's tear;... Lov - ing still to trace the sto - ry
cy of love,.... Yes - ter - day, to - day, to - mor - row,

REFRAIN

Is His ev - er - last - ing name. Weep - ing One,
Of the hearts He strength-ened here. Weep-ing One,
He the same doth ev - er prove.

weep - ing One, Sav - iour, who can love like Thee? Weep - ing
weep-ing One,

One, weep - ing One, Weep - ing One of Beth - an - y.
Weep-ing One, weep-ing One,

Jesus, Thy Boundless Love to Me

280

To know the love of Christ which passeth knowledge.—EPH. 3: 19

ST. PETERSBURG 8s. 6l.

PAUL GERHARDT, 1666. Alt.

DIMITRI S. BORTNIANSKY, 1751-1825

1. Je - sus, Thy bound-less love to me No tho't can reach, no
2. Thy love, how cheer-ing is its ray! All pain be - fore its
3. O draw me, Sav - iour, aft - er Thee! So shall I run and
4. Still let Thy love point out my way; How won - drous things Thy
5. In suf - f'ring be Thy love my peace, In weak - ness be Thy

tongue de - clare; U - nite my thank - ful heart to Thee, And
pres - ence flies; Care, an - guish, sor - row, melt a - way, Wher-
nev - er tire. With gra - cious words still com - fort me; Be
love hath wrought! Still lead me, lest I go a - stray; Di-
love my pow'r; And when the storms of life shall cease, Je-

reign with - out a ri - - val there. Thine whol - ly, Thine a-
e'er its heal - ing beams a - rise: O Je - sus, noth - ing
Thou my hope, my sole de - sire. Free me from ev - 'ry
rect my work, in - spire my thought; And if I fall, soon
sus, in that im - por - tant hour, In death as life be

lone I am; My soul with con - stant love a - flame.
may I see, Noth - ing de - sire or seek but Thee.
weight: nor fear Nor sin can come, if Thou art here.
may I hear Thy voice, and know that love is near.
Thou my guide, And save me, who for me hast died!

281

Never a Friend Like Thee

GRACE GORDON

F. CAMPANA
Arr. ALFRED JUDSON

1. Lov-ing me ere I knew Him, Call-ing with voice so sweet, Bur-dens of
2. Sunlight of glad-ness giv - ing, Fill-ing my heart with cheer, E'er in His
3. Giv-ing me gifts im - mor - tal, Life that en-dures for aye, Opening the

life I brought Him, Knelt at His wounded feet; Naught from that love can sever,
light I'm liv - ing, Ev - er I know Him near; Mas-ter, in Thee a - bid - ing,
heav'n-ly por - tal, Leading in roy - al way; Crowning with joy ex-cel - ling,

Won-der - ful, changeless, free, Mas-ter, I'll serve Thee ev - er, Nev-er a
Shad-ows of earth must flee, Ev - er Thy chil - dren guid - ing, Nev-er a
Heir of His grace I'll be, Mas-ter, Thy praise I'm tell - ing, Nev-er a

CHORUS

Friend like Thee! Sing of a Friend so loy - al, Sing of a Friend so true,
Light like Thee! King of the heav'nly glo - ry, Low-ly of earth was He;
King like Thee!

Giv-ing His gifts so roy - al, Blessings that aye are new.
Mas-ter, we sing Thy sto - ry, Nev - er was One like (Omit) Thee.

O Saviour, I Have Naught to Plead 282

Justified freely by His grace, through the redemption that is in Christ Jesus.—ROM. 3: 24

JANE CREWDSON, 1809–1863   **AGNUS DEI 8. 8. 8. 6.**   WILLIAM BLOW, 1881

1. O Sav-iour, I have naught to plead, In earth be-neath or heav'n a-bove,
2. The need will soon be past and gone, Exceeding great, but quick-ly o'er;

But just my own ex - ceed - ing need And Thy ex - ceed - ing love
The love un-bought is all Thine own, And lasts for - ev - er-more.

One There Is Above All Others 283

I have called you friends.—JN. 15: 15

JOHN NEWTON, 1779   **OVIO 8. 7. 8. 7.**   LOWELL MASON

1. One there is a - bove all oth - ers, Well de-serves the name of Friend;
2. Which of all our friends, to save us, Could or would have shed his blood?
3. When He lived on earth a - bas - ed, Friend of sin - ners was His name;
4. Oh, for grace our hearts to soft - en! Teach us, Lord, at length to love;

His is love be - yond a broth - er's, Cost - ly, free, and knows no end.
But this Sav - iour died to have us Rec - on - ciled in Him to God.
Now a - bove all glo - ry rais - ed, He re - joi - ces in the same.
We, a - las! for - get too oft - en, What a Friend we have a - bove.

284

Grace, 'Tis a Charming Sound

The grace of God that bringeth salvation hath appeared to all men.—TIT. 2: 11

PHILIP DODDRIDGE, 1740   **SILVER STREET S. M.**   ISAAC SMITH, c. 1770

1. Grace, 'tis a charm-ing sound, Har-mo-nious to mine ear;
2. Grace first con-trived the way To save re-bel-lious man;
3. Grace first in-scribed my name In God's e-ter-nal book;
4. Grace led my rov-ing feet To tread the heav'nly road;
5. Grace all the work shall crown, Thro' ev-er-last-ing days;

Heav'n with the ech-o shall re-sound, And all the earth shall hear.
And all the steps that grace dis-play Which drew the won-drous plan.
'Twas grace that gave me to the Lamb, Who all my sor-rows took.
And new sup-plies each hour I meet, While press-ing on to God.
It lays in heav'n the top-most stone, And well de-serves the praise.

285

Sing, My Soul, His Wondrous Love

I will sing aloud of Thy mercy in the morning.—Ps. 59: 16

Anon.   **NUREMBURG 7. 7. 7. 7.**   J. R. AHLE, 1625-1673

1. Sing, my soul, His won-drous love, Who from yon bright throne a-bove,
2. Heav'n and earth by Him were made, All is by His scep-ter swayed;
3. God, the mer-ci-ful and good, Bought us with the Sav-iour's blood;
4. Sing, my soul, a-dore His name; Let His glo-ry be thy theme;

Ev-er watch-ful o'er our race, Still to man ex-tends His grace.
What are we that He should show So much love to us be-low!
And, to make our safe-ty sure, Guides us by His Spir-it pure.
Praise Him till He calls thee home, Trust His love for all to come.

Does Jesus Care?

286

Frank E. Graeff

J. Lincoln Hall

1. Does Je - sus care when my heart is pained Too deep - ly for
2. Does Je - sus care when my way is dark With a name - less
3. Does Je - sus care when I've tried and failed To re - sist some temp-
4. Does Je - sus care when I've said "good-bye" To the dear - est on

mirth and song; As the bur - dens press, and the cares dis - tress,
dread and fear? As the day - light fades in - to deep night shades,
ta - tion strong; When for my deep grief I find no re - lief,
earth to me, And my sad heart aches till it near - ly breaks—

CHORUS

And the way grows wea - ry and long?
Does He care e - nough to be near? Oh, yes, He cares, I
Tho' my tears flow all the night long?
Is it aught to Him? Does He see?

know He cares! His heart is touched with my grief; When the days are

ad lib.

rit.

wea - ry, the long nights drear - y, I know my Sav - iour cares. (He cares.)

287 Where High the Heavenly Temple Stands

Christ entered . . . into heaven itself, now to appear in the presence of God for us.—HEB. 9: 24

MICHAEL BRUCE, 1764. Alt.   BROOKFIELD L. M.   THOMAS B. SOUTHGATE, 1855

1. Where high the heav'n-ly tem - ple stands, The house of God not made with hands,
2. He who for men their Sure - ty stood, And poured on earth His pre-cious blood,
3. In ev - 'ry pang that rends the heart The Man of Sor-rows had a part;
4. With bold-ness, therefore, at the throne Let us make all our sor-rows known,

A Great High Priest our na-ture wears, The Guard-ian of man-kind ap-pears.
Pur-sues in heav'n His might-y plan, The Sav - iour and the Friend of man.
He sym-pa-thiz - es with our grief, And to the suf - f'rer sends re - lief.
And ask the aid of heav'n-ly pow'r To help us in the e - vil hour.

288 I Know That My Redeemer Lives

JOB. 19: 25

CHARLES WESLEY   BRADFORD C. M.   From GEORGE F. HANDEL

1. I know that my Re - deem - er lives, And ev - er prays for me;
2. I find Him lift - ing up my head; He brings sal - va - tion near;
3. He wills that I should ho - ly be; What can with-stand His will?
4. When God is mine, and I am His, Of Par - a - dise pos-sessed,

A to - ken of His love He gives, A pledge of lib - er - ty.
His pres - ence makes me free in - deed, And He will soon ap-pear.
The coun - sel of His grace in me He sure - ly shall ful - fill.
I taste un - ut - ter - a - ble bliss, And ev - er - last - ing rest.

Be Still, and Know That I Am God

JOHNSON OATMAN, JR.   L. M. Ref.   B. B. BEALL

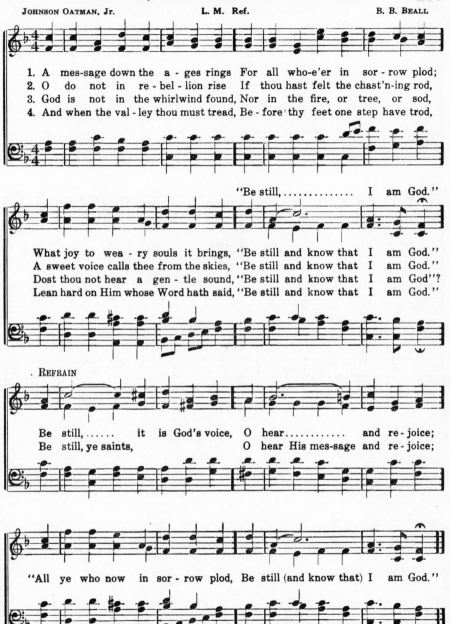

1. A mes-sage down the a - ges rings For all who-e'er in sor - row plod;
2. O do not in re - bel - lion rise If thou hast felt the chast'n-ing rod,
3. God is not in the whirlwind found, Nor in the fire, or tree, or sod,
4. And when the val - ley thou must tread, Be - fore thy feet one step have trod,

"Be still,.............. I am God."

What joy to wea - ry souls it brings, "Be still and know that I am God."
A sweet voice calls thee from the skies, "Be still and know that I am God."
Dost thou not hear a gen - tle sound, "Be still and know that I am God"?
Lean hard on Him whose Word hath said, "Be still and know that I am God."

REFRAIN

Be still,...... it is God's voice, O hear............ and re - joice;
Be still, ye saints, O hear His mes-sage and re - joice;

"All ye who now in sor - row plod, Be still (and know that) I am God."

Owned by B. B. Beall, Douglas, Ga., 1921. Used by permission

290 **Sweet Peace, the Gift of God's Love**

P. P. B.

PETER P. BILHORN

1. There comes to my heart one sweet strain, (sweet strain,) A
2. Thro' Christ on the cross peace was made, (was made,) My
3. When Jesus as Lord I had crowned, (had crowned,) My
4. In Jesus for peace I abide, (abide,) And

glad and a joyous refrain, (refrain,) I sing it a-
debt by His death was all paid, (all paid,) No other foun-
heart with this peace did abound, (abound,) In Him the rich
as I keep close to His side, (His side,) There's nothing but

gain and again, Sweet peace, the gift of God's love....
dation is laid, For peace, the gift of God's love....
blessing I found, Sweet peace, the gift of God's love....
peace doth betide, Sweet peace, the gift of God's love....

CHORUS

Peace, peace, sweet peace, Wonderful gift from above,........ Oh,
a-bove,

Sweet Peace—Concluded

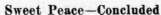

won-der-ful, won-der-ful peace, Sweet peace, the gift of God's love.

Dear Lord and Father of Mankind

291

The peace of God which passeth all understanding.—PHIL. 4: 7

JOHN G. WHITTIER, 1872   REST 8. 6. 8. 8. 6.   FREDERICK C. MAKER

1. Dear Lord and Fa-ther of man-kind, For-give our fool-ish
2. In sim-ple trust like theirs who heard, Be-side the Syr-ian
3. O Sab-bath rest by Gal-i-lee! O calm of hills a-
4. Drop Thy still dews of qui-et-ness, Till all our striv-ings
5. Breathe thro' the heats of our de-sire Thy cool-ness and Thy

ways; Re-clothe us in our right-ful mind, In pur-er
sea, The gra-cious call-ing of the Lord, Let us, like
bove, Where Je-sus knelt to share with Thee The si-lence
cease; Take from our souls the strain and stress, And let our
balm; Let sense be dumb, let flesh re-tire; Speak thro' the

lives Thy serv-ice find, In deep-er rev-'rence, praise.
them, with-out a word Rise up and fol-low Thee.
of e-ter-ni-ty In-ter-pret-ed by love!
or-dered lives con-fess The beau-ty of Thy peace.
earth-quake, wind, and fire, O still, small voice of calm. A-MEN.

215

292 Like a River, Glorious

Behold, I will extend peace to her like a river.— Isa. 66: 12

FRANCES R. HAVERGAL   6. 5. 6. 5. D.   J. MOUNTAIN

1. Like a riv - er, glo - rious Is God's per - fect peace, O - ver
2. Hid - den in the hol - low Of His bless - ed hand, Nev - er
3. Ev - 'ry joy or tri - al Fall - eth from a - bove, Traced up-

all vic - to - rious In its bright in - crease; Per - fect, yet it
foe can fol - low, Nev - er trai - tor stand; Not a surge of
on our di - al By the Sun of Love. We may trust Him

flow - eth Full - er ev - 'ry day; Per - fect, yet it grow - eth
wor - ry, Not a shade of care, Not a blast of hur - ry,
ful - ly, All for us to do; They who trust Him whol - ly

CHORUS

Deep - er all the way.
Touch the spir - it there. Stayed up - on Je - ho - vah, Hearts are
Find Him whol - ly true.

ful - ly blest; Find - ing, as He prom - ised, Per - fect peace and rest.

I Will Extol Thee, O My God

PSALM 145

Psalter   **GERARD C. M.**   Arr. ARTHUR S. SULLIVAN

1. I will ex-tol Thee, O my God, And praise Thee, O my King;
2. Each gen-er-a-tion to the next Shall tes-ti-mo-ny bear,
3. Thy might-y acts and ter-ri-ble Shall men with awe con-fess;

Yea, ev-'ry day and ev-er-more Thy prais-es I will sing.
And to Thy praise, from age to age, Thy wondrous acts de-clare.
Of Thy great good-ness they shall sing, And per-fect right-eous-ness.

Great is the Lord, our might-y God, And great-ly to be praised;
Up-on Thy glo-rious maj-es-ty And hon-or I will dwell,
Most gra-cious and com-pas-sion-ate Is God who reigns a-bove;

His great-ness is un-search-a-ble, A-bove all glo-ry raised.
And all Thy grand and glo-rious works And all Thy great-ness tell.
His wrath is ev-er slow to rise, Un-bounded is His love.

8

294
Hark! the Song of Jubilee

The kingdoms of this world are become the kingdoms of the Lord, and of His Christ.—Rev. 11: 15

JAMES MONTGOMERY, 1818   **THANKSGIVING 7. 7. 7. 7. D.**   WALTER B. GILBERT, 1829-1910

1. Hark! the song of ju - bi - lee, Loud as might-y thun - ders roar,
2. Hal - le - lu - jah! hark! the sound, From the depths un - to the skies,
3. He shall reign from pole to pole With il - lim - it - a - ble sway;

Or the full-ness of the sea When it breaks up - on the shore:
Wakes a - bove, be - neath, a - round All cre - a - tion's har - mo - nies;
He shall reign when, like a scroll, Yon - der heav'ns have passed a - way:

"Hal - le - lu - jah! for the Lord God Om - nip - o - tent shall reign;
See Je - ho - vah's ban - ner furled, Sheathed His sword; He speaks: 'tis done;
Then the end; be - neath His rod Man's last e - ne - my shall fall:

Hal - le - lu - jah!" let the word Ech - o round the earth and main.
And the king - doms of this world Are the king - doms of His Son.
Hal - le - lu - jah! Christ in God, God in Christ, is All in All.

218

Hallelujah, Praise Jehovah

295

PSALM 146

Psalter   BROCKLESBURY 8. 7. 8. 7.   CHARLOTTE A. BARNARD

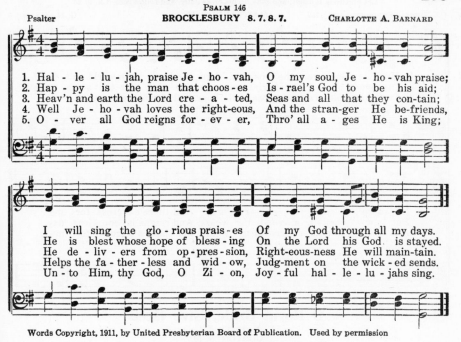

1. Hal - le - lu - jah, praise Je - ho - vah, O my soul, Je - ho - vah praise;
2. Hap - py is the man that choos - es Is - rael's God to be his aid;
3. Heav'n and earth the Lord cre - a - ted, Seas and all that they con-tain;
4. Well Je - ho - vah loves the right-eous, And the stran-ger He be-friends,
5. O - ver all God reigns for - ev - er, Thro' all a - ges He is King;

I will sing the glo - rious prais - es Of my God through all my days.
He is blest whose hope of bless - ing On the Lord his God is stayed.
He de - liv - ers from op - pres - sion, Right-eous-ness He will main-tain.
Helps the fa - ther - less and wid - ow, Judg-ment on the wick - ed sends.
Un - to Him, thy God, O Zi - on, Joy - ful hal - le - lu - jahs sing.

The Day of Wrath

296

For the great day of His wrath is come. — REV. 6: 17

THOMAS OF CELANO, 13th Cent. Lat.   **WINDHAM L. M.**   DANIEL READ, 1785

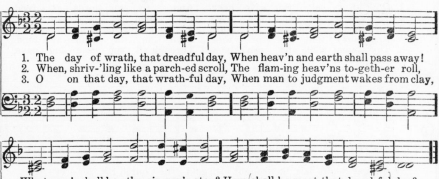

1. The day of wrath, that dreadful day, When heav'n and earth shall pass away!
2. When, shriv-'ling like a parch-ed scroll, The flam-ing heav'ns to-geth-er roll,
3. O on that day, that wrath-ful day, When man to judgment wakes from clay,

What pow'r shall be the sin-ner's stay? How shall he meet that dread-ful day?
And loud - er yet, and yet more dread, Swells the high trump that wakes the dead?
Be thou, O Christ, the sin-ner's stay, Tho' heav'n and earth shall pass a - way.

297 Must Jesus Bear the Cross Alone?

Let him deny himself, and take up his cross daily, and follow me.—LK. 9: 23

THOMAS SHEPHERD, 1665–1739 MAITLAND C. M. G. N. ALLEN

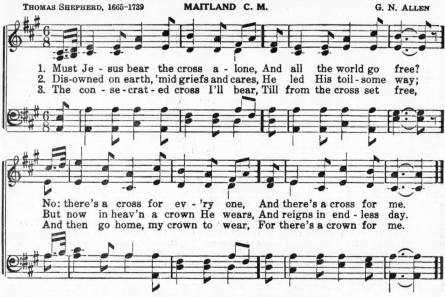

1. Must Je - sus bear the cross a - lone, And all the world go free?
2. Dis-owned on earth, 'mid griefs and cares, He led His toil - some way;
3. The con - se - crat - ed cross I'll bear, Till from the cross set free,

No: there's a cross for ev - 'ry one, And there's a cross for me.
But now in heav'n a crown He wears, And reigns in end - less day.
And then go home, my crown to wear, For there's a crown for me.

298 O Royal Bride, Give Heed

PSALM 45
GORTON S. M.

Psalter Arr. from LUDWIG VAN BEETHOVEN, 1807

1. O Roy - al Bride, give heed, And to my words at - tend;
2. Thy beau - ty and thy grace Shall then de - light the King;
3. En - throned in roy - al state, All glo - rious thou shalt dwell,
4. And they that hon - or thee Shall in thy train at - tend,
5. Thy name shall be pro - claimed Through all suc - ceed - ing days,

For Christ the King for - sake the world And ev - 'ry for - mer friend.
He on - ly is Thy right - ful Lord, To Him thy wor - ship bring.
With gar-ments fair, in-wrought with gold, The Church He lov - eth well.
And to the pal - ace of the King Shall joy - ful - ly as - cend.
And all the na - tions of the earth Shall give Thee end - less praise.

The Way of the Cross Leads Home

299

JESSIE BROWN POUNDS

CHAS. H. GABRIEL

1. I must needs go home by the way of the cross, There's no oth - er
2. I must needs go on in the blood-sprinkled way, The path that the
3. Then I bid fare-well to the way of the world, To walk in it

way but this; I shall ne'er get sight of the Gates of Light,
Sav - iour trod, If I ev - er climb to the heights sub - lime,
nev - er - more; For my Lord says "Come," and I seek my home

If the way of the cross I miss.
Where the soul is at home with God.
Where He waits at the o - pen door.

CHORUS

The way of the cross leads home, The way of the cross leads home; It is
leads home, leads home;

sweet to know, as I on - ward go, The way of the cross leads home.

300 If Ye Then Be Risen

GRANT COLFAX TULLAR

I. H. MEREDITH

With animation

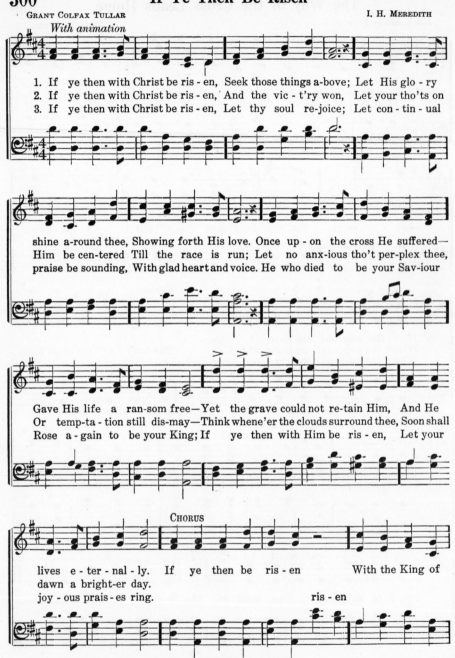

1. If ye then with Christ be ris-en, Seek those things a-bove; Let His glo-ry
2. If ye then with Christ be ris-en, And the vic-t'ry won, Let your tho'ts on
3. If ye then with Christ be ris-en, Let thy soul re-joice; Let con-tin-ual

shine a-round thee, Showing forth His love. Once up-on the cross He suffered—
Him be cen-tered Till the race is run; Let no anx-ious tho't per-plex thee,
praise be sounding, With glad heart and voice. He who died to be your Sav-iour

Gave His life a ran-som free—Yet the grave could not re-tain Him, And He
Or temp-ta-tion still dis-may—Think whene'er the clouds surround thee, Soon shall
Rose a-gain to be your King; If ye then with Him be ris-en, Let your

CHORUS

lives e-ter-nal-ly. If ye then be ris-en With the King of
dawn a bright-er day.
joy-ous prais-es ring. ris-en

Copyright, 1926, by I. H. Meredith. Renewal. Used by permission

222

If Ye Then Be Risen—Concluded

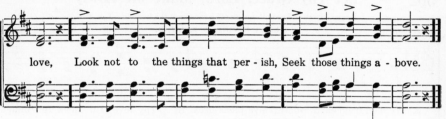

love,   Look not to   the things that per - ish, Seek those things a - bove.

Fade, Fade, Each Earthly Joy   301

But what things were gain to me, those I counted loss for Christ.—PHIL. 3: 7

JANE C. BONAR   LUNDIE   6. 4. 6. 4. 6. 6. 6. 4.   THEODORE E. PERKINS

1. Fade, fade, each earth-ly joy; Je - sus is   mine.   Break ev - 'ry
2. Tempt not my soul a - way; Je - sus is   mine.   Here would I
3. Fare - well, ye dreams of night; Je - sus is   mine.   Lost in this
4. Fare - well, mor-tal - i - ty; Je - sus is   mine.   Wel - come, e-

ten - der tie;   Je - sus   is mine. Dark is   the wil - der - ness,
ev - er stay;   Je - sus   is mine. Per - ish - ing things of clay,
dawn - ing bright, Je - sus   is mine. All that my soul has tried
ter - ni - ty;   Je - sus   is mine. Wel-come, O loved and blest,

Earth has no rest-ing place, Je - sus a - lone can bless; Je - sus is mine.
Born but for one brief day, Pass from my heart a - way; Je - sus is mine.
Left but a dis-mal void; Je - sus has sat - is - fied; Je - sus is mine.
Welcome, sweet scenes of rest, Welcome, my Saviour's breast; Je - sus is mine.

302 Let Thy Grace, Lord, Make Me Lowly

God resisteth the proud, but giveth grace unto the humble.—JAS. 4: 6

Anon.   LOVE DIVINE 8. 7. 8. 7. D.   GEO. F. LE JEUNE, 1887

1. Let Thy grace, Lord, make me low - ly, Hum - ble all my swell-ing pride;
2. Weaned from earth's de-lu - sive pleas-ures In Thy love I'll seek for mine:

Fall - en, guilt - y, and un - ho - ly, Great-ness from mine eyes I'll hide:
Placed in heav'n my no - bler treas-ures, Earth I qui - et - ly re - sign:

I'll for - bid my vain as - pir - ing, Nor at ear - ly hon - ors aim,
Thus the tran-sient world de - spis-ing, On the Lord my hopes re - ly;

No am - bi - tious heights de - sir - ing, Far a - bove my hum - ble claim.
Thus my joys from Him a - ris - ing, Like Him-self shall nev - er die.

Peace Through the Cross Shall Come

303

JESSIE BROWN POUNDS

From "Jerusalem's Gates Reopened"

1. Peace through the cross shall come, His peace to men;
2. Peace through the cross shall come, Come to a - bide;

As He has giv - en it, Give ye a - gain;
Deep in the hearts of men Hid - den, to guide;

CHORUS Duet

Peace, that our Christ may be Vic - tor o'er vic - to - ry,
Strong - er than pride of race, Strong - er than pomp of place,

Free, to make rul - ers free, Free through the cross.
Rul - ing by heav - en's grace, Peace through the cross.

304 Let There Be Light, Lord God of Hosts

Glory to God in the highest, and on earth peace, good will to men.—LK. 2: 9–14

MISSIONARY CHANT L. M.

WILLIAM MERRELL VORIES, 1908

HEINRICH C. ZEUNER, 1832

1. Let there be light, Lord God of Hosts! Let there be wis - dom on the earth! Let broad hu - man - i - ty have birth! Let there be deeds, in - stead of boasts.
2. With - in our pas - sioned hearts in - still The calm that end - eth strain and strife; Make us Thy min - is - ters of life; Purge us from lusts that curse and kill!
3. Give us the peace of vi - sion clear To see our broth - ers' good our own, To joy and suf - fer not a - lone: The love that cast - eth out all fear!
4. Let woe and waste of war - fare cease, That use - ful la - bor yet may build Its homes with love and vir - tue filled! God, give Thy way - ward chil - dren peace!

305 Lord, As to Thy Dear Cross We Flee

Be ye kind one to another.—EPH. 4: 32

JOHN HAMPDEN GURNEY, 1838

GREEN HILL C. M.

ALBERT L. PEACE, 1885

1. Lord, as to Thy dear cross we flee, And plead to be for - giv'n,
2. Let grace our self - ish - ness ex - pel, Our earth - li - ness re - fine;
3. Should friends mis - judge, or foes de - fame, Or breth - ren faith - less prove,
4. Kept peace - ful in the midst of strife, For - giv - ing and for - giv'n,

Lord, As to Thy Dear Cross—Concluded

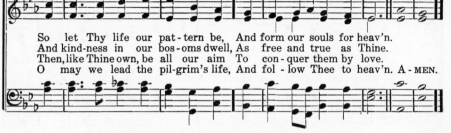

So let Thy life our pat-tern be, And form our souls for heav'n.
And kind-ness in our bos-oms dwell, As free and true as Thine.
Then, like Thine own, be all our aim To con-quer them by love.
O may we lead the pil-grim's life, And fol-low Thee to heav'n. A-MEN.

O Wherefore Do the Nations Rage 306

PSALM 2

Psalter   UXBRIDGE L. M.   LOWELL MASON

1. O where-fore do the na-tions rage, And kings and
2. Their strength is weak-ness in the sight Of Him Who
3. By God's de-cree His Son re-ceives The na-tions
4. Be wise, ye rul-ers of the earth, And serve the
5. De-lay not, lest His an-ger rise, And ye should

rul-ers strive in vain, A-gainst the Lord of
sits en-throned a-bove; He speaks, and judg-ments
for His her-it-age; The con-qu'ring Christ su-
Lord with god-ly fear; With rev-'rent joy con-
per-ish in your way; Lo, all that put their

earth and heav'n To o-ver-throw Mes-si-ah's reign?
fall on them Who tempt His wrath and scorn His love.
preme shall reign As King of kings, from age to age.
fess the Son While yet in mer-cy He is near.
trust in Him Are blest in-deed, and blest for aye.

307 We Know That God is On the Throne

MARK 11: 22

GEORGE O. WEBSTER

J. H. FILLMORE

1. We know that God is on the throne, Tho' strife and sin are here; And when the years have old-er grown, And men shall see more clear, The tu-mult and the strife will cease, And truth and right have sway; God speed for us the reign of peace, We hum-bly pray. Our God is on the throne, The com-ing days will show, And watch-ing o'er His own, As the

2. We know that God is on the throne, For we can clear-ly trace, As cen-tu-ries have come and gone, His pur-pos-es of grace; And tho' at times the mists ap-pear, And doubtings may a-rise, The dark'ning skies as quick-ly clear In glad sur-prise.

3. We know that God is on the throne, His pow'r can nev-er fail; And ere the years of time are flown, His Gos-pel shall pre-vail, And men shall live to serve in love, While each his place shall fill, The earth-life, like to that a-bove, In God's good-will. We know that God is on the throne,

REFRAIN

We Know That God is On the Throne—Concluded

a - ges flow; Our God is reign-ing still, And though we may not see,

Is work - ing out His ho - ly will To all e - ter - ni - ty.

What Grace, O Lord, and Beauty 308

Christ also suffered for us, leaving us an example.—I PET. 2: 21-23

EDWARD DENNY, 1839   **MARGUERITE C. M.**   EDWARD C. WALKER, 1876

1. What grace, O Lord, and beau - ty shone A - round Thy steps be - low;
2. For - ev - er on Thy bur-dened heart A weight of sor - row hung;
3. Thy foes might hate, de - spise, re - vile, Thy friends un-faith-ful prove;
4. Oh, give us hearts to love like Thee, Like Thee, O Lord, to grieve
5. One with Thy-self, may ev - 'ry eye In us, Thy breth-ren, see

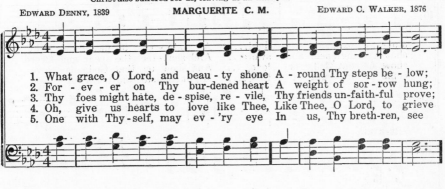

What pa - tient love was seen in all Thy life and death of woe!
Yet no un - gen - tle, murm'ring word Es - caped Thy si - lent tongue.
Un - wea - ried in for - give-ness still, Thy heart could on - ly love.
Far more for oth - ers' sins than all The wrongs that we re - ceive.
That gen - tle - ness and grace which spring From un - ion, Lord, with Thee.

309 We've a Story to Tell to the Nations

Go ye therefore and teach all nations.—MATT. 28: 19

MESSAGE P. M. Ref.

COLIN STERNE, 1896

Adapted from H. ERNEST NICHOL, 1896

1. We've a sto - ry to tell to the na - tions That shall turn their
2. We've a song to be sung to the na - tions, That shall lift their
3. We've a mes - sage to give to the na - tions, That the Lord who
4. We've a Sav - iour to show to the na - tions, Who the path of

hearts to the right, A sto - ry of truth and mer - cy, A
hearts to the Lord; A song that shall con - quer e - vil, And
reign - eth a - bove, Hath sent us His Son to save us, And
sor - row has trod, That all of the world's great peo - ples Might

sto - ry of peace and light,.... A sto - ry of peace and light.
shat - ter the spear and sword,.. And shat - ter the spear and sword.
show us that God is love,.... And show us that God is love.
come to the truth of God,.... Might come to the truth of God.

REFRAIN

For the dark-ness shall turn to dawn-ing, And the dawn-ing to noon-day bright,

And Christ's great kingdom shall come on earth, The king-dom of Love and Light.

One Sweetly Solemn Thought

310

Now is our salvation nearer than when we believed.—ROM. 13: 11

PHŒBE CARY, 1852

DULCE DOMUM S. M.

R. S. AMBROSE

1. One sweet-ly sol-emn thought Comes to me o'er and o'er,—
2. Near-er my Fa-ther's house, Where man-y man-sions be;
3. Near-er the bound of life Where bur-dens are laid down;
4. E'en now, per-chance, my feet Are slip-ping on the brink,

Near-er my home, to-day, am I Than e'er I've been be-fore.
Near-er to-day the great white throne, Near-er the crys-tal sea.
Near-er to leave the heav-y cross; Near-er to gain the crown.
And I, to-day, am near-er home,—Near-er than now I think.

Almighty Maker of My Frame

311

So teach us to number our days that we may apply our hearts unto wisdom.—Ps. 90: 12

ANNE STEELE, 1760

VENN. L. M.

G. J. ELVEY. Alt.

1. Al-might-y Mak-er of my frame! Teach me the meas-ure of my days,
2. My days are short-er than a span, A lit-tle point my life ap-pears;
3. Vain his am-bi-tion, noise and show; Vain are the cares which rack his mind;
4. O, be a no-ble por-tion mine! My God, I bow be-fore Thy throne;

Teach me to know how frail I am, And spend the rem-nant to Thy praise.
How frail at best is dy-ing man! How vain are all his hopes and fears!
He heaps up treas-ures mixed with woe, And dies and leaves them all be-hind.
Earth's fleeting treas-ure I re-sign, And fix my hopes on Thee a-lone.

312 A Few More Years Shall Roll

When a few years are come, then I shall go the way whence I shall not return.—Job 16: 22

HORATIUS BONAR, 1842   **THE PILGRIM. S. M. D.**   Arranged

1. A few more years shall roll,.... A few more sea-sons come;
2. A few more storms shall beat.... On this wild, rock-y shore;
3. A few more strug-gles here,... A few more part-ings o'er,
4. A few more meet-ings here.... Shall cheer us on our way;

And we shall lie with them that rest, A-sleep with-in the tomb.
And we shall be where tem-pests cease, And surg-es swell no more.
A few more toils, a few more tears, And we shall weep no more.
And we shall reach the end-less rest, Th' e-ter-nal Sab-bath day.

REFRAIN

Then oh, my Lord, pre-pare....... My soul for that great day;.......
Then oh,........ my Lord, pre-pare My soul........ for that great day;

Oh, wash me in Thy pre-cious blood, And take my sins a-way.

By Christ Redeemed

313

Ye do show the Lord's death till He come.—I COR. 11: 26

GEORGE L. RAWSON, 1857   IN MEMORIAM 8. 8. 8. 4.   FREDERICK C. MAKER

1. By Christ re-deemed, in Christ re - stored, We keep the mem - o-
2. His bod - y bro - ken in our stead Is shown in this me-
3. His fear - ful drops of ag - o - ny, His Life-blood shed for
4. And thus that dark be - tray - al night, With the last ad - vent
5. Un - til the trump of God be heard, Un - til the an - cient
6. O bless - ed hope! with this e - late, Let not our hearts be

ry a - dored, And show the death of our dear Lord, Un - til He come.
mo - rial bread; And so our fee - ble love is fed, Un - til He come.
us we see: The wine shall tell the mys - ter - y, Un - til He come.
we u - nite—The shame, the glo - ry, by this rite, Un - til He come.
graves be stirred, And with the great com-mand-ing word, The Lord shall come.
des - o - late, But strong in faith, in pa - tience wait, Un - til He come!

Bread of Heaven

314

Evermore give us this bread.—JOHN 6: 34

JOSIAH CONDER, 1824. Alt.   MOUNT ZION 7s. 6 l.   ARTHUR S. SULLIVAN, 1867

1. Bread of heav'n, on Thee we feed, For Thy flesh is meat in - deed; Ev - er may our souls be fed
2. Vine of heav'n, Thy blood supplies This blest cup of sac - ri - fice; Lord, Thy wounds our healing give,

With this true and liv-ing Bread; Day by day with strength supplied, Thro' the life of Him who died.
To Thy cross we look and live: Je - sus, may we ev - er be Graft-ed, root-ed, built on Thee.

315 Alas! and Did My Saviour Bleed?

In whom we have redemption through His blood.—Eph. 1: 7

ST. AGNES C. M.

Isaac Watts, 1707   John B. Dykes

1. A - las! and did my Sav - iour bleed? And did my Sov - 'reign die?
2. Was it for crimes that I have done, He groaned up - on the tree?
3. Well might the sun in dark - ness hide, And shut his glo - ries in,
4. Thus might I hide my blush - ing face While His dear cross ap - pears;
5. But drops of grief can ne'er re - pay The debt of love I owe;

Would He de - vote that sa - cred head For such a worm as I?
A - maz-ing pit - y! grace un-known! And love be - yond de - gree!
When God's own Son was cru - ci - fied For man, the crea - ture's sin.
Dis - solve my heart in thank - ful-ness, And melt mine eyes to tears.
Here, Lord, I give my - self a - way; 'Tis all that I can do.

Use also "Dundee" No. 370

316 Saw Ye My Saviour?

Saw ye Him whom my soul loveth?—S. S. 3: 3

ATONEMENT P. M.

1. Saw ye my Sav - iour, saw ye my Sav - iour, Saw ye my
2. He was ex - tend - ed, He was ex - tend - ed, Pain - ful - ly
3. Je - sus hung bleed-ing, Je - sus hung bleed - ing, Three dread-ful
4. Dark - ness pre - vail - ed, dark-ness pre - vail - ed, Dark-ness pre-

Sav - iour and God? Oh! He died on Cal - va - ry, To a -
nailed to the cross; Here He bowed His head and died, Thus my
hours...... in pain; And the sol - id rocks were rent, Thro' cre -
vailed o'er the land; And the sun re - fused to shine When His

234

Saw Ye My Savior—Concluded

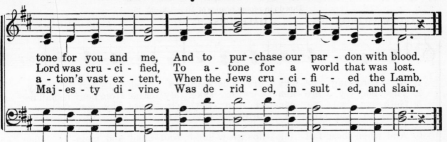

tone for you and me, And to pur-chase our par-don with blood.
Lord was cru-ci-fied, To a-tone for a world that was lost.
a-tion's vast ex-tent, When the Jews cru-ci-fi-ed the Lamb.
Maj-es-ty di-vine Was de-rid-ed, in-sult-ed, and slain.

"Till He Come"   317

Yet a little while, and He that shall come will come.—HEB. 10: 37

EDWARD H. BICKERSTETH, 1861   REYNOLDSTONE 7s. 6 l.   TIMOTHY R. MATTHEWS

1. "Till He come!" O let the words Lin-ger on the trem-bling chords;
2. When the wea-ry ones we love En-ter on their rest a-bove,
3. Clouds and con-flicts round us press: Would we have one sor-row less?
4. See, the feast of love is spread, Drink the wine, and break the bread:

Let the lit-tle while be-tween In their gold-en light be seen;
Seems the earth so poor and vast, All our life-joy o-ver-cast?
All the sharp-ness of the cross, All that tells the world is loss,
Sweet me-mo-rials,—till the Lord Call us round His heav'n-ly board;

Let us think how heav'n and home Lie be-yond that 'Till He come.'
Hush, be ev-'ry mur-mur dumb: It is on-ly 'Till He come.'
Death and dark-ness, and the tomb, On-ly whis-per 'Till He come.'
Some from earth, from glo-ry some, Sev-ered on-ly 'Till He come.'

318 According to Thy Gracious Word

This do in remembrance of Me.—Lk. 22: 19

JAMES MONTGOMERY, 1825   DALEHURST C. M.   ARTHUR COTTMAN, 1874

1. Ac - cord - ing to Thy gra-cious Word, In meek hu - mil - i - ty,
2. Thy bod - y, bro - ken for my sake, My bread from heav'n shall be;
3. Geth-sem - a - ne can I for - get? Or there Thy con - flict see,
4. When to the cross I turn mine eyes, And rest on Cal - va - ry,
5. Re - mem - ber Thee, and all Thy pains, And all Thy love to me:
6. And when these fail - ing lips grow dumb, And mind and mem - 'ry flee,

This will I do, my dy - ing Lord, I will re - mem - ber Thee.
Thy tes - ta - men - tal cup I take, And thus re - mem - ber Thee.
Thine ag - o - ny and blood - y sweat, And not re - mem - ber Thee?
O Lamb of God, my Sac - ri - fice, I must re - mem - ber Thee.
Yea, while a breath, a pulse re - mains Will I re - mem - ber Thee.
When Thou shalt in Thy king-dom come, Je - sus, re - mem - ber me.

319 Blest Feast of Love Divine

That ye may eat and drink at my table in my kingdom.—Lk. 22: 29, 30

EDWARD DENNY, 1839   ST. ANDREW S. M.   JOSEPH BARNBY, 1866

1. Blest feast of love di - vine! 'Tis grace that makes us free
2. That blood which flowed for sin, In sym - bol here we see,
3. O, if this glimpse of love Be so di - vine - ly sweet,

To feed up - on this bread and wine, In mem - 'ry, Lord, of Thee.
And feel the bless - ed pledge with - in That we are loved by Thee.
What will it be, O Lord, a - bove, Thy gladd'ning smile to meet?

Happy Day

Happy is that people whose God is the Lord.—Ps. 144: 15

PHILIP DODDRIDGE. Publ., 1755   **L. M.**   From E. F. RIMBAULT

1. O hap-py day that fixed my choice On Thee, my Sav-iour and my God!
2. O hap-py bond that seals my vows To Him who mer-its all my love;
3. 'Tis done, the great trans-ac-tion's done; I am my Lord's and He is mine;
4. Now rest, my long-di-vid-ed heart, Fixed on this bliss-ful cen-ter, rest;
5. High heav'n that heard the sol-emn vow, That vow re-newed shall dai-ly hear,

Well may this glow-ing heart re-joice, And tell its rap-tures all a-broad.
Let cheer-ful an-thems fill His house, While to that sa-cred shrine I move.
He drew me and I fol-lowed on, Charmed to confess the voice di-vine.
Nor ev-er from thy Lord de-part, With Him of ev-'ry good pos-sessed.
Till in life's lat-est hour I bow, And bless in death a bond so dear.

REFRAIN

Hap-py day, hap-py day, When Je-sus washed my sins a-way;

He taught me how to watch and pray, And live re-joic-ing ev-'ry day:

Hap-py day, hap-py day, When Je-sus washed my sins a-way.

321 Baptized Into Our Saviour's Death

So many of us as were baptized into Jesus Christ were baptized into His death.—ROM. 6: 3

PHILIP DODDRIDGE, Publ., 1755

EVAN C. M.

LOWELL MASON
Arr. from W. H. HAVERGAL

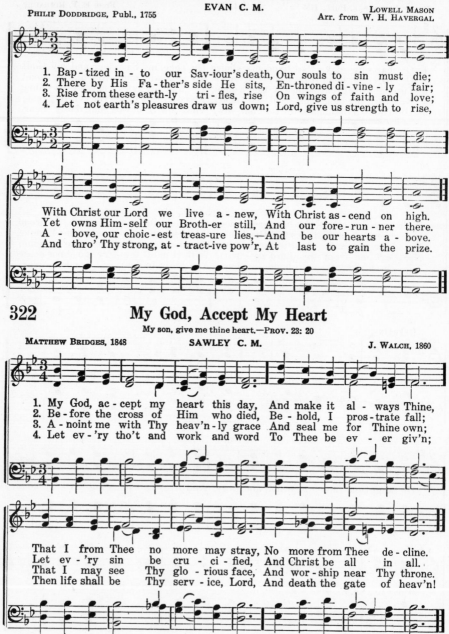

1. Bap - tized in - to our Sav-iour's death, Our souls to sin must die;
2. There by His Fa - ther's side He sits, En-throned di - vine - ly fair;
3. Rise from these earth-ly tri - fles, rise On wings of faith and love;
4. Let not earth's pleasures draw us down; Lord, give us strength to rise,

With Christ our Lord we live a - new, With Christ as - cend on high.
Yet owns Him-self our Broth-er still, And our fore-run - ner there.
A - bove, our choic - est treas-ure lies,—And be our hearts a - bove.
And thro' Thy strong, at - tract-ive pow'r, At last to gain the prize.

322 My God, Accept My Heart

My son, give me thine heart.—PROV. 23: 20

MATTHEW BRIDGES, 1848

SAWLEY C. M.

J. WALCH, 1860

1. My God, ac - cept my heart this day, And make it al - ways Thine,
2. Be - fore the cross of Him who died, Be - hold, I pros-trate fall;
3. A - noint me with Thy heav'n-ly grace And seal me for Thine own;
4. Let ev - 'ry tho't and work and word To Thee be ev - er giv'n;

That I from Thee no more may stray, No more from Thee de - cline.
Let ev - 'ry sin be cru - ci - fied, And Christ be all in all.
That I may see Thy glo - rious face, And wor - ship near Thy throne.
Then life shall be Thy serv - ice, Lord, And death the gate of heav'n!

We Bless the Name of Christ, the Lord

323

For thus it becometh us to fulfill all righteousness.—MATT. 3: 15

S. F. COFFMAN, 1926   **RETREAT L. M.**   THOMAS HASTINGS, 842

1. We bless the name of Christ, the Lord, We bless Him for His ho-ly Word,
2. We fol-low Him with pure de-light To sanc-ti-fy His sa-cred rite;
3. Bap-tized in God,—the Fa-ther, Son And Ho-ly Spir-it,—Three in One,
4. By grace we "Ab-ba, Fa-ther," cry; By grace the Com-fort-er comes nigh;

Who loved to do His Fa-ther's will And all His right-eous-ness ful-fill.
And thus our faith with wa-ter seal To prove o-be-dience that we feel.
With conscience free, we rest in God, In love and peace, thro' Je-sus' blood.
And for Thy grace our love shall be For-ev-er, on-ly, Lord, for Thee.

O Lord, While We Confess

324

The answer of a good conscience toward God.—I PET. 3: 21

MARY P. BOWLY   **MARLOW C. M.**   JOHN CHETHAM

1. O Lord, while we con-fess the worth Of this the out-ward seal,
2. Death to the world we here a-vow, Death to each flesh-ly lust;
3. Bap-tized in-to the Fa-ther's name, We'd walk as sons of God;
4. Bap-tized in-to the Ho-ly Ghost, We'd keep His tem-ple pure,

Do Thou the truths here-in set forth, To ev-'ry heart re-veal.
New-ness of life our call-ing now, A ris-en Lord our trust.
Bap-tized in Christ, we own Thy claim, As ran-somed by Thy blood.
And make Thy grace our on-ly boast, And by Thy strength en-dure.

325 Extol the Love of Christ

He riseth from supper and took a towel and girded Himself.—Jn. 13: 3-5.

S. F. Coffman, 1925

VARINA C. M. D.

Geo. F. Root

1. Ex - tol the love of Christ, ye saints, And sing His won - drous worth,
2. Ex - tol the love which sought to show The Fa-ther's bound-less grace;
3. The Lord and Mas - ter hum - bly served To glo - ri - fy the meek;
4. Let poor, vain man ex - am - ple take And from his pride re - pent;

Whose love, like God, e - ter - nal is In heav - en and on earth.
The Son, from Fa-ther's bos - om come,—Be - held the Fa - ther's face:—
His heav'n-ly glo - ry shared with those Who would His fa - vor seek.
For Christ far great-er is than man, Or serv - ant that is sent.

From God He brought His bless - ing rare; To God He did as - cend.
In serv - ile gar - ments clothed up - on, With hum - ble serv - ice meet,
Lord, teach Thy saints in Thee to know The full - ness of Thy love,
Ex - am - ple, wor - thy, Christ has giv'n, And hap - py shall they be

And con - stant in His heav'n - ly love He loved un - to the end.
The Mas - ter loved as none could love And washed His serv-ants' feet.
The fel - low - ship Thy serv - ice taught, Thy glo - ry, bright, a - bove.
Who wash each oth - er's feet, and love As deep and true as He.

Behold, Where, in a Mortal Form

326

For it pleased the Father that in Him should all fullness dwell.— COL. 1: 19

WILLIAM ENFIELD, 1771   ST. SAVIOUR C. M.   FREDERICK G. BAKER, 1876

1. Be - hold, where, in a mor - tal form, Ap - pears each grace di - vine;
2. To spread the rays of heav'n - ly light, To give the mourn-er joy,
3. Low - ly in heart to all, His friends A friend and serv - ant found;
4. Be Christ our pat - tern and our guide! His im - age may we bear!

The vir - tues, all in Je - sus met, With mild - est ra - diance shine.
To preach glad ti - dings to the poor, Was His di - vine em - ploy.
He washed their feet, He wiped their tears, And healed each bleeding wound.
O may we tread His ho - ly steps, His joy and glo - ry share. A - MEN.

Christ, in the Night He Was Betrayed

327

I have given you an example, that ye should do as I have done to you.—JN. 13: 15

HEBRON L. M.   LOWELL MASON, 1830

1. Christ in the night He was be-trayed For us a plain ex - am - ple laid;
2. The pas-chal feast was there prepared, And Lord and serv-ants mu-tual shared;
3. He rose and laid His gar-ments by, When towel and wa-ter were bro't nigh;
4. So aft - er He had washed their feet, Re-sumed His gar-ment, took His seat,
5. "Ex - am - ple give I un - to you, As I have done so ye should do,

He to a priv - ate room re - tired With those He aft - er-wards in-spired.
Be - fore He suf - fered 'twas His will This great de - sire He should ful - fill.
To prove His love di - vine - ly sweet, He stooped to wash His serv-ants' feet.
He asked them if they now had tho't What les - son plain He here had taught.
And if ye then My serv-ants be, O - bey My Word and fol - low Me."

328

Love's Consecration

I then, your Lord and Master, have washed your feet.—Jn. 13: 13, 14

S. B. McManus, 1902   **C. M.**   A. B. Kolb, 1902

1. Love con - se - crates the hum - blest act, And sanc - ti - fies each deed,
2. When in the shad - ow of the cross, Christ bowed and washed the feet
3. "Ye call Me Lord and Mas - ter, all, Yet I would hum - bly bow
4. "As I have done this un - to you, My breth - ren, here this night,
5. Love serves, yet will - ing stoops to serve, What Christ in love so true,

It sheds a ben - e - dic - tion sweet, And hal - lows ev - 'ry need.
Of His dis - ci - ples, 'twas a sign Of His great love com - plete.
And con - se - crate this low - ly deed, As ye be - hold Me now.
Thus would I have you do to each When I have passed from sight."
Hath free - ly done for one and all,—Shall we not glad - ly do?

329

All Praise to Our Redeeming Lord

Keep the unity of the Spirit in the bonds of peace.— Eph. 4: 3; Rom. 16: 16

Charles Wesley   **DEDHAM C. M.**   Wm. Gardiner

1. All praise to our re - deem - ing Lord, Who joins us by His grace,
2. He bids us build each oth - er up; And, gath-ered in - to one,
3. The kiss of peace to each we give—A pledge of Chris - tian love;
4. And if our fel - low - ship be - low, In Je - sus is so sweet,

And bids us, each to each re - stored, To - geth-er seek His face.
To our high call-ing's glo - rious hope, We hand in hand go on.
In love, while here on earth we'll live, In love we'll dwell a - bove.
What height of rap-ture shall we know When round His throne we meet.

242

When Christ Beheld in Sin's Dark Night

330

The marriage of the Lamb is come and His wife hath made herself ready.— Rev. 19: 7

S. F. Coffman, 1911   BARTHOLDI L. M.   Felix Mendelssohn-Bartholdy

1. When Christ be-held, in sin's dark night, His bride, deceived, en-slaved and lost;
2. Oh, bride, He gave His life for thee, His blood thy cleansing hath se-cured;
3. Thy plight-ed faith to Him, thy Lord, Thy bri - dal veil doth ev - er show;
4. Thy mod-est ways are His de - light, By hum - ble grac - es art thou known;
5. Ex - alt - ed by such heav'nly grace, The Church in pa-tience shall a - bide,

Com-pas-sion bro't a sav - ing light, And paid the ransom's aw - ful cost.
Let all thy gar-ments ho - ly be; Thy pure heart nev-er be al-lured.
Thy hus-band, He: thy law, His Word: None oth-er law or serv - ice know.
An heir of glo - ry, this thy right, To share with Christ a roy - al throne.
And wait to see His glo - rious face When Christ shall come to own His bride.

Let Saints On Earth in Concert Sing

331

Of whom the whole family in heaven and earth are named.— Eph. 3: 15

Charles Wesley   BROWN C. M.   William B. Bradbury, 1844

1. Let saints on earth in con - cert sing With those whose work is done;
2. One fam - i - ly, we dwell in Him, One Church, a - bove, be - neath;
3. E'en now to their e - ter - nal home There pass some spir - its blest;
4. Je - sus, be Thou our con-stant Guide; Then, when the word is giv'n,

For all the serv - ants of our King In heav'n and earth are one.
Tho' now di - vid - ed by the stream, The nar - row stream of death.
While oth - ers to the mar - gin come, Wait-ing their call to rest.
Bid Jor - dan's nar-row stream di - vide, And bring us safe to heav'n.

332

Lo, What a Pleasing Sight

That ye may be perfectly joined together.—I Cor. 1: 10

Isaac Watts, 1719   GERAR S. M.   Lowell Mason

1. Lo, what a pleas-ing sight Are breth-ren that a-gree! How
2. All in their sta-tions move, And each per-forms his part In
3. Formed for the pur-est joys, By one de-sire pos-sessed, One
4. No bliss can e-qual theirs, Where such af-fec-tions meet; While
5. 'Tis the same pleas-ure fills The breast in worlds a-bove, Where

blest are all whose hearts u-nite In bonds of pi-e-ty.
all the cares of life and love, With sym-pa-thiz-ing heart.
aim the zeal of all em-ploys, To make each oth-er blest.
praise de-vout, and min-gled prayers Make their com-mun-ion sweet.
joy, like morn-ing dew, dis-tils, And all the air is love.

333

How Pleasant and How Good

PSALM 133

Psalter   INVITATION C. M.   Arranged from Wallace

1. How pleas-ant and how good it is When breth-ren in the Lord
2. Such love is like a-noint-ing oil In con-se-cra-tion poured;
3. To those who dwell in broth-er-hood The Lord His bless-ing sends,

In one an-oth-er's joy de-light And dwell in sweet ac-cord.
Such love is like the morn-ing dew, With sweet re-fresh-ment stored.
He crowns them with the crown of life, Of life that nev-er ends.

Words Copyright, 1911, by United Presbyterian Board of Publication. Used by permission

The Church's One Foundation

For other foundation can no man lay.— I COR. 3: 11

SAMUEL J. STONE, 1865   AURELIA 7. 6. 7. 6. D.   SAMUEL S. WESLEY, 1864

1. The Church's one Foun - da - tion Is Je - sus Christ her Lord;
2. E - lect from ev - 'ry na - tion, Yet one o'er all the earth,
3. 'Mid toil and trib - u - la - tion, And tu - mult of her war,
4. Yet she on earth hath un - ion With God the Three in One,

She is His new cre - a - tion By wa - ter and the Word:
Her char - ter of sal - va - tion One Lord, one faith, one birth;
She waits the con - sum - ma - tion Of peace for - ev - er - more;
And mys - tic, sweet com - mun - ion With those whose rest is won:

From heav'n He came and sought her To be His ho - ly Bride;
One ho - ly name she bless - es, Par - takes one ho - ly food,
Till with the vi - sion glo - rious Her long - ing eyes are blest,
O hap , py ones and ho - ly! Lord, give us grace that we

With His own blood He bought her, And for her life He died.
And to one hope she press - es, With ev - 'ry grace en - dued.
And the great Church vic - to - rious Shall be the Church at rest.
Like them, the meek and low - ly, On high may dwell with Thee.

335 Glorious Things of Thee Are Spoken

Glorious things are spoken of thee, O city of God.—Ps. 87: 1-3

JOHN NEWTON, 1779   AUSTRIAN HYMN 8. 7. 8. 7. D.   FRANZ JOSEPH HAYDN

1. Glo-rious things of thee are spo-ken, Zi - on, cit - y of our God;
2. See the streams of liv - ing wat-ers, Springing from e - ter - nal Love,
3. Round each hab - i - ta - tion hov'ring, See the cloud and fire ap - pear
4. Sav - iour, if of Zi - on's cit - y I, through grace, a mem - ber am,

He whose word can - not be bro-ken Formed thee for His own a - bode:
Well sup - ply thy sons and daughters, And all fear of want re-move:
For a glo - ry and a cov'ring, Show-ing that the Lord is near:
Let the world de - ride or pit - y, I will glo - ry in Thy name:

On the Rock of A - ges found-ed, What can shake thy sure re - pose?
Who can faint while such a riv - er Ev - er flows their thirst to assuage;
Thus de - riv - ing from their ban - ner Light by night and shade by day,
Fad - ing is the world-ling's pleas-ure, All his boast - ed pomp and show;

With sal - va - tion's walls sur-round-ed, Thou mayst smile at all thy foes.
Grace which, like the Lord the Giv - er, Nev - er fails from age to age?
Safe they feed up - on the man - na Which He gives them when they pray.
Sol - id joys and last - ing treas-ure None but Zi - on's chil - dren know.

O Where Are Kings and Empires Now 336

I lay in Zion a stone for a foundation stone.—ISA. 28: 16

A. C. COXE, 1839 ST. ANNE. C. M. W. CROFT, 1708

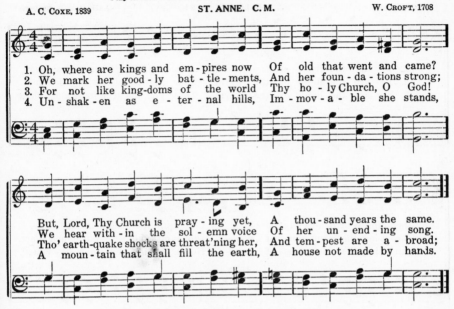

1. Oh, where are kings and em - pires now Of old that went and came?
2. We mark her good - ly bat - tle - ments, And her foun - da - tions strong;
3. For not like king-doms of the world Thy ho - ly Church, O God!
4. Un - shak - en as e - ter - nal hills, Im - mov - a - ble she stands,

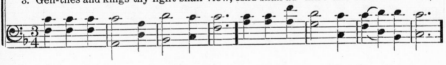

But, Lord, Thy Church is pray - ing yet, A thou - sand years the same.
We hear with - in the sol - emn voice Of her un - end - ing song.
Tho' earth-quake shocks are threat'ning her, And tem - pest are a - broad;
A moun - tain that shall fill the earth, A house not made by hands.

Zion, Awake, Thy Strength Renew 337

Awake; put on thy strength, O Zion.—ISA. 52: 1

WM. SHRUBSOLE, JR., 1795 HESPERUS L. M. HENRY BAKER, 1866

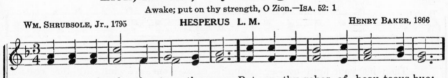

1. Zi - on, a - wake, thy strength renew; Put on thy robes of beau-teous hue;
2. Church of our God, a - rise and shine, Bright with the beam of truth di - vine;
3. Gen-tiles and kings thy light shall view, And shall ad - mire and love thee too;—

And let th'ad-mir-ing world be - hold The King's fair daughter clothed in gold.
Then shall thy ra-diance stream a - far, Wide as the hea - then na - tions are.
They come, like clouds a - cross the sky, As doves that to their win - dows fly.

338 ## Ye Are the Light of the World

MATT. 5: 16

R. J. CRAIG   THE LIGHT 7s. 8 l.   J. D. BRUNK, by per.

1. Ye are the light of the world, Driv - ing the dark-ness a - way,
2. Ye are the light of the world, Caus - ing the clouds to de - part,
3. Ye are the light of the world; Thro' you the true light must shine,

Shed-ding your beams on the lost, Chang-ing their night in - to day.
Throw-ing the sun - shine of peace Down on the poor bur-dened heart.
Call - ing the lost sons of men Home to the Fa - ther di - vine.

Then let your light ev - er shine, Show - ing the right way to go;
Then let your light ev - er shine; Loved ones are pant - ing for rest;
Then let your light ev - er shine, Hal - low the name that is love;

Glad - ly the lost ones we'll see— God's bound-less love they will know.
Sun-shine their souls will re - vive, Lift - ing them up to the blest.
You will each shine as a star, Fixed in the or - bit a - bove.

I Love Thy Kingdom, Lord

Behold, I have graven thee upon the palms of my hands.—Isa. 49: 16

TIMOTHY DWIGHT, 1800   BEALOTH S. M. D.   LOWELL MASON

1. I love Thy king-dom, Lord, The house of Thine a-bode—
2. For her my tears shall fall, For her my prayers as-cend;
3. Je-sus, Thou Friend di-vine, Our Sav-iour and our King,

The Church our blest Re-deem-er saved With His own pre-cious blood.
To her my cares and toils be giv'n Till toils and cares shall end.
Thy hand from ev-'ry snare and foe Shall great de-liv-'rance bring.

I love Thy Church, O God, Her walls be-fore Thee stand,
Be-yond my high-est joy I prize her heav'n-ly ways,
Sure as Thy truth shall last, To Zi-on shall be giv'n

Dear as the ap-ple of Thine eye, And grav-en on Thy hand.
Her sweet com-mun-ion, sol-emn vows, Her hymns of love and praise.
The bright-est glo-ries earth can yield, And bright-er bliss of heav'n.

249

9

340

On the Mountain's Top Appearing

How beautiful upon the mountains are the feet of them that bring good tidings.—Isa. 52: 7

THOS. KELLY, 1803. Alt.   ZION 8. 7. 8. 7. 4. 7. 4. 7.   THOS. HASTINGS

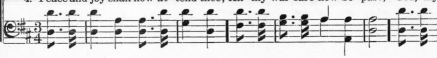

1. On the mountain's top ap-pear-ing, Lo! the sa-cred her-ald stands, Welcome
2. Has thy night been long and mournful? Have thy friends unfaithful proved? Have thy
3. God, thy God, will now re-store thee; He Him-self ap-pears thy friend; All thy
4. Peace and joy shall now at-tend thee; All thy war-fare now be past; God, thy

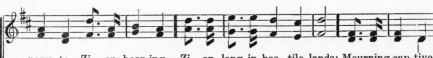

news to Zi-on bear-ing— Zi-on, long in hos-tile lands; Mourning cap-tive,
foes been proud and scorn-ful, By thy sighs and tears unmoved? Cease thy mourning,
foes shall flee be-fore thee; Here their boasts and triumphs end. Great de-liv-'rance
Sav-iour, will de-fend thee; Vic-to-ry is thine at last; All thy con-flicts

God Himself will loose thy bands; Mourning captive, God Himself will loose thy bands.
Zi-on still is well-be-loved; Cease thy mourning, Zi-on still is well-be-loved.
Zi-on's King will sure-ly send; Great de-liv'rance Zi-on's King will sure-ly send.
End in ev-er-last-ing rest; All thy con-flicts End in ev-er-last-ing rest.

341

Zion Stands With Hills Surrounded

As the mountains round about Jerusalem.—Ps. 125: 2

THOS. KELLY, 1806   MOUNT ZION 8. 7. 8. 7. 8. 7.   JOHN H. SPIELMAN, 1881

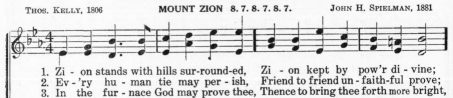

1. Zi-on stands with hills sur-round-ed, Zi-on kept by pow'r di-vine;
2. Ev-'ry hu-man tie may per-ish, Friend to friend un-faith-ful prove;
3. In the fur-nace God may prove thee, Thence to bring thee forth more bright,

Zion Stands With Hills Surrounded—Concluded

All her foes shall be con-found-ed, Tho' the world in arms com-bine;
Mothers cease their own to cher-ish; Heav'n and earth at last re - move;
But can nev - er cease to love thee; Thou art pre-cious in His sight:

Hap - py Zi - on, hap - py Zi - on, What a fa - vored lot is thine!
But no chan-ges, but no chan-ges Can at - tend Je - ho-vah's love.
God is with thee, God is with thee, God, thine ev - er - last-ing light.

City of God, How Broad and Far   342

The joy of the whole earth is Mount Zion.—Ps. 48: 1, 2

SAMUEL JOHNSON, 1861   NOX PRAECESSIT C. M.   J. BAPTISTE CALKIN, 1875

1. Cit - y of God, how broad and far Out-spread thy walls sub-lime!
2. One ho - ly Church, one ar - my strong, One stead-fast high in - tent,
3. How pure - ly hath thy speech come down From man's pri - me - val youth;
4. How gleam thy watch-fires thro' the night With nev - er - faint-ing ray!
5. In vain the surg - e's an - gry shock, In vain the drift - ing sands;

The true thy char-tered free - men are Of ev - 'ry age and clime.
One work - ing band, one har - vest-song, One King Om - nip - o - tent!
How grand - ly hath thine em - pire grown Of free-dom, love, and truth!
How rise thy tow'rs, se - rene and bright, To meet the dawn - ing day!
Un - harmed up - on th' e - ter - nal Rock Th' e - ter - nal cit - y stands.

343 People of the Living God

Thy people shall be my people, and thy God my God.—RUTH 1: 16–17

JAMES MONTGOMERY, 1829   **ENNIUS 7s. 8 l.**   From Harmonia Sacra

1. Peo - ple of the liv - ing God, I have sought the world a - round;
2. Lone - ly I no lon - ger roam Like the cloud, the wind, the wave;
3. Tell me not of gain and loss, Ease, en - joy-ment, pomp, and pow'r;

Paths of sin and sor - row trod, Peace and com - fort no - where found:
Where you dwell shall be my home, Where you die shall be my grave;
Wel - come pov - er - ty and cross, Shame, re-proach, af - flic - tion's hour.

Now to you my spir - it turns, — Turns a fu - gi - tive un - blest;
Mine the God whom you a - dore; Your Re-deem - er shall be mine;
"Fol - low Me"—I know Thy voice; Je - sus, Lord, Thy steps I see;

Breth - ren, where your al - tar burns, Oh, re - ceive me in - to rest.
Earth can fill my soul no more,—Ev - ' ry i - dol I re - sign.
Now I take Thy yoke by choice, Light Thy bur - den now to me.

Lord, in Thy Presence

There am I in the midst of them.—MATT. 18: 20

344

EVAN C. M.

LOWELL MASON
Arr. from W. H. HAVERGAL

1. Lord, in Thy pres-ence here we meet, May we in Thee be found!
2. With har-mo-ny Thy serv-ants bless, That we may own to Thee,
3. May Zi-on's good be kept in view, And bless our fee-ble aim,

O make the place di-vine-ly sweet, And let Thy grace a-bound.
How good, how sweet, how pleas-ant 'tis When brethren all a-gree.
That all we un-der-take to do, May glo-ri-fy Thy name.

Jesus, From Whom All Blessings Flow

That He might present it to Himself a glorious church.—EPH. 5: 25-27

345

CHARLES WESLEY

DUKE STREET L. M.

JOHN HATTON, c. 1793

1. Je-sus, from whom all bless-ings flow, Great Builder of Thy Church be-low,
2. The few that tru-ly call Thee Lord, And wait Thy sanc-ti-fy-ing word,
3. O let them all Thy mind ex-press, Stand forth Thy chosen wit-ness-es,
4. In them let all man-kind be-hold How Christians lived in days of old,

If now Thy Spir-it move my breast, Hear, and ful-fill Thine own re-quest.
And Thee their ut-most Sav-iour own, U-nite and per-fect them in one.
Thy pow'r un-to sal-va-tion show, And per-fect ho-li-ness be-low.
Might-y their en-vious foes to move, A prov-erb of re-proach—and love.

346 Enter, Jesus Bids Thee Welcome

Let us run with patience the race that is set before us.—HEB. 12: 1, 2

CORINTH 8. 7. 8. 7. 8. 7.

SIDNEY DYER, 1883

"Essay on the Church
Plain Chant," 1872

1. En - ter, Je - sus bids thee wel-come In the full - ness of His grace;
2. Tri - als hard may oft be - set thee, Cross-es fill the path you trace,
3. Welcome then to joys and sor-rows, Ev - 'ry foe and dan - ger face;

With this hand of love we give thee In our hearts the warm-est place:
But a vic-tor's palm a - waits thee; Slack-en not thy heav'nward pace:
God is with us, we shall tri-umph,—Hal - le - lu - jah to His grace!

Hence to - geth - er, Hence to - geth - er, Let us run the Chris - tian race.
Firm to - geth - er, Firm to - geth - er, Let us run the Chris - tian race.
O what glo - ry, O what glo - ry Crowns the bless-ed Chris - tian race!

347 Children of the Heavenly King

Fear not, little flock.—LK. 12: 32

PLEYEL'S HYMN 7. 7. 7. 7.

JOHN CENNICK, 1742

Arr. from IGNAZ J. PLEYEL, 1790

1. Chil - dren of the heav'n-ly King, As ye jour - ney, sweet-ly sing;
2. We are trav - 'ling home to God In the way the fa - thers trod;
3. Lift your eyes, ye sons of light, Zi - on's cit - y is in sight;
4. Fear not, breth-ren; joy - ful stand On the bor - ders of your land;
5. Lord, o - be - dient-ly we go, Glad - ly leav - ing all be - low;

Children of the Heavenly King—Concluded

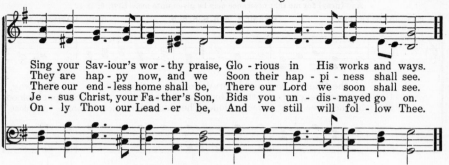

Sing your Sav-iour's wor-thy praise, Glo-rious in His works and ways.
They are hap-py now, and we Soon their hap-pi-ness shall see.
There our end-less home shall be, There our Lord we soon shall see.
Je-sus Christ, your Fa-ther's Son, Bids you un-dis-mayed go on.
On-ly Thou our Lead-er be, And we still will fol-low Thee.

How Pleasant, How Divinely Fair

348

My soul longeth, even fainteth for the courts of the Lord.—Ps. 84: 1-7

ISAAC WATTS, 1719   WARRINGTON L. M.   RALPH HARRISON, 1784

1. How pleas-ant, how di-vine-ly fair, O Lord of
2. Blest are the saints that sit on high, A-round Thy
3. Blest are the souls that find a place With-in the

hosts, Thy dwell-ings are! With strong de-sire my spir-it
throne of maj-es-ty; Thy bright-est glo-ries shine a-
tem-ple of Thy grace: Here they be-hold Thy gen-tle

faints To meet th' as-sem-blies of Thy saints.
bove, And all their work is praise and love.
rays, And seek Thy face, and learn Thy praise.

349 Lord of the Church

And (pray) for me that utterance may be given unto me.—EPH. 6: 18-20

EDWARD OSLER, 1836   BREMEN 8. 8. 6. 8. 8. 6.   THOS. HASTINGS, 1836

1. Lord of the Church, we humbly pray For those who guide us in Thy way,
2. Help them to preach the truth of God, Re-demp-tion thro' the Saviour's blood;
3. So may they live to Thee a-lone; Then hear the welcome word,—"Well done!"

And speak Thy ho-ly Word: With love di-vine their hearts in-spire,
Nor let the Spir-it cease On all the Church His gifts to show'r;
And take their crown a-bove; En-ter in-to their Mas-ter's joy,

And touch their lips with hallowed fire, And need-ful strength af-ford.
To them a mes-sen-ger of pow'r, To us, of life and peace.
And all e-ter-ni-ty em-ploy In praise, and bliss, and love. A-MEN.

350 Let Zion's Watchmen All Awake

They watch for your souls as they that must give account.—HEB. 13: 17

PHILIP DODDRIDGE, 1736   ARMENIA C. M.   SILVANUS BILLINGS POND

1. Let Zi-on's watchmen all a-wake And take th' a-larm they give,
2. 'Tis not a cause of small im-port, The pas-tor's care de-mands,
3. They watch for souls, for which the Lord Did heav'n-ly bliss fore-go!
4. Lord, let Thy serv-ants, as they preach, Thy great sal-va-tion see;

Let Zion's Watchmen All Awake—Concluded

Now let them from the mouth of God Their sol - emn charge re - ceive.
But what might fill an an - gel's heart, And filled a Sav-iour s hands.
For souls, which must for-ev - er live, In rap - tures, or in woe.
And watch Thou dai - ly o'er their souls, That they may watch for Thee.

Hail to the Brightness 351

Then shall thy light break forth as the morning.—ISA. 58: 8

THOS. HASTINGS, 1830 WESLEY 11. 10. 11. 10. LOWELL MASON, 1833

1. Hail to the bright-ness of Zi - on's glad morn-ing! Joy to the
2. Hail to the bright-ness of Zi - on's glad morn-ing, Long by the
3. Lo! in the des - ert rich flow-ers are spring-ing, Streams ev - er
4. See, from all lands—from the isles of the o - cean,—Praise to Je-

lands that in dark - ness have lain! Hushed be the ac - cents of
proph - ets of Is - rael fore - told! Hail to the mil - lions from
co - pious are glid - ing a - long; Loud from the moun - tain - tops
ho - vah as - cend - ing on high; Fallen are the en - gines of

sor - row and mourn-ing; Zi - on in tri - umph be - gins her mild reign.
bond-age re - turn-ing, Gen - tiles and Jews the blest vi - sion be - hold.
ech - oes are ring - ing, Wastes rise in ver - dure and min - gle in song.
war and com - mo - tion, Shouts of sal - va - tion are rend - ing the sky.

352 Lord, When At Thy Command

I have planted, Apollos watered; but God giveth the increase. —I Cor. 3: 6

LEOMINSTER. S. M. D.

Geo. William Martin, 1862
Har. by Arthur S. Sullivan, 1874

Charles Wesley

Slowly

1. Lord, when at Thy com - mand, The Word of life we sow,
2. Now then the cease - less show'r Of Gos - pel bless - ings send,

Wa - tered by Thy al - might - y hand, The seed shall sure - ly grow:
And let the soul - con - vert - ing pow'r Thy min - is - ters at - tend.

The vir - tue of Thy grace A large in - crease shall give,
On mul - ti - tudes con - fer The heart - re - new - ing love,

And mul - ti - ply the faith - ful race Who to Thy glo - ry live.
And by the joy of grace pre - pare For full - er joys a - bove.

Pass Me Not, O Gentle Saviour

Whom have I in heaven but Thee.—Ps. 73: 25

FANNY J. CROSBY   8. 5. 8. 5.   Ref.   W. H. DOANE, 1870

1. Pass me not, O gen - tle Sav - iour,   Hear my hum - ble cry;
2. Let me at a throne of mer - cy   Find a sweet re - lief;
3. Trust-ing on - ly in Thy mer - it,   Would I seek Thy face;
4. Thou the spring of all my com - fort,   More than life for me,

While on oth - ers Thou art call - ing,   Do not pass me by.
Kneel-ing there in deep con - tri - tion,   Help my un - be - lief.
Heal my wound-ed, bro - ken spir - it,   Save me by Thy grace.
Whom have I on earth be - side Thee?   Whom in heav'n but Thee?

REFRAIN

Sav - iour, Sav - iour, Hear my hum - ble cry, While on

oth - ers Thou art call - ing,   Do not pass me by.

354 I Need Thee Every Hour

Mine eyes are ever toward the Lord.—Ps. 25: 15

ANNIE S. HAWKS, 1872

ROBERT LOWRY

1. I need Thee ev-'ry hour, Most gra-cious Lord; No ten-der voice like
2. I need Thee ev-'ry hour, Stay Thou near by; Temp-ta-tions lose their
3. I need Thee ev-'ry hour, In joy or pain; Come quick-ly and a-
4. I need Thee ev-'ry hour, Teach me Thy will; And Thy rich prom-is-
5. I need Thee ev-'ry hour, Most Ho-ly One; Oh, make me Thine in-

REFRAIN

Thine Can peace af-ford.
pow'r When Thou art nigh.
bide, Or life is vain.   I need Thee, oh, I need Thee; Ev-'ry hour I
es In me ful-fill.
deed, Thou bless-ed Son.

need Thee; O bless me now, my Sav-iour! I come to Thee.

355 As Pants the Hart

As the hart panteth after the water-brooks, so panteth my soul after Thee, O God.—Ps. 42: 1

TATE AND BRADY, 1696-98   BEATITUDO C.M.   JOHN B. DYKES, 1875

1. As pants the hart for cool-ing streams When heat-ed in the chase,
2. For Thee, my God, the liv-ing God, My thirst-y soul doth pine;
3. Why rest-less, why cast down, my soul? Trust God; and He'll em-ploy
4. Why rest-less, why cast down, my soul? Hope still; and thou shalt sing

As Pants the Hart—Concluded

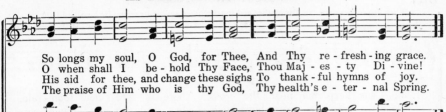

So longs my soul, O God, for Thee, And Thy re-fresh-ing grace.
O when shall I be-hold Thy Face, Thou Maj-es-ty Di-vine!
His aid for thee, and change these sighs To thank-ful hymns of joy.
The praise of Him who is thy God, Thy health's e-ter-nal Spring.

We Would See Jesus

356

JN. 12: 21

Anna B. WARNER, 1858 · FELIX 11. 10. 11. 10. · FELIX MENDELSSOHN-BARTHOLDY

1. We would see Je-sus; for the shad-ows length-en A-cross this
2. We would see Je-sus, the great rock foun-da-tion Where-on our
3. We would see Je-sus: oth-er lights are pal-ing, Which for long
4. We would see Je-sus: this is all we're need-ing; Strength, joy, and

lit-tle land-scape of our life; We would see Je-sus, our weak
feet were set by sov-'reign grace: Nor life nor death, with all their
years we have re-joiced to see; The bless-ings of our pil-grim-
will-ing-ness come with the sight; We would see Je-sus, dy-ing,

faith to strength-en, For the last wea-ri-ness, the fi-nal strife.
ag-i-ta-tion, Can thence re-move us, if we see His face.
age are fail-ing; We would not mourn them, for we go to Thee.
ris-en, plead-ing; Then wel-come day, and fare-well mor-tal night.

357 Near the Cross

When Jesus therefore saw His mother and the disciple standing by whom He loved.—JN. 19: 26

FANNY J. CROSBY   7. 6. 7. 6. Ref.   W. H. DOANE, 1869

1. Je - sus, keep me near the cross, There a pre - cious foun - tain,
2. Near the cross, a trem - bling soul, Love and mer - cy found me,
3. Near the cross! O Lamb of God, Bring its scenes be - fore me;
4. Near the cross I'll watch and wait, Hop - ing, trust - ing ev - er,

Free to all, a heal - ing stream, Flows from Cal - v'ry's moun - tain.
There the Bright and Morn - ing Star Shed His beams a - round me.
Help me walk from day to day, With its shad - ows o'er me.
Till I reach the gold - en strand, Just be - yond the riv - er.

REFRAIN

In the cross, in the cross Be my glo - ry ev - er,

Till my rap - tured soul shall find Rest be - yond the riv - er.

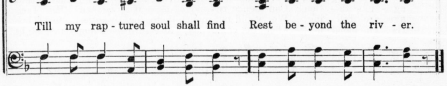

O God, the Rock of Ages

He shall set me upon a rock.—Ps. 27: 5

EDWARD H. BICKERSTETH, 1870   GREENLAND 7. 6. 7. 6. D.   Arr. from J. MICHAEL HAYDN

1. O God, the Rock of A - ges, Who ev - er - more hast been,
   What time the tem - pest ra - ges, Our dwell - ing - place se - rene;
   Be - fore Thy first cre - a - tions, O Lord, the same as now,
   To end - less gen - er - a - tions The ev - er - last - ing Thou!

2. Our years are like the shad - ows On sun - ny hills that lie,
   Or grass - es in the mead - ows That blos - som but to die:
   A sleep, a dream, a sto - ry By stran - gers quick - ly told,
   An un - re - main - ing glo - ry Of things that soon are old.

3. O Thou, who canst not slum - ber, Whose light grows nev - er pale,
   Teach us a - right to num - ber Our years be - fore they fail:
   On us Thy mer - cy light - en, On us Thy good - ness rest,
   And let Thy Spir - it bright - en The hearts Thy - self hast blessed.

4. Lord, crown our faith's en - deav - or With beau - ty and with grace,
   Till, clothed in light for - ev - er, We see Thee face to face:
   A joy no lan - guage meas - ures; A foun - tain brim - ming o'er;
   An end - less flow of pleas - ures; An o - cean with - out shore.

359 More Love to Thee

To know the love of Christ which passeth knowledge.—EPH. 3: 19

ELIZABETH P. PRENTISS, 1869 6. 4. 6. 4. 6. 6. 4. 4. W. H. DOANE, 1869

1. More love to Thee, O Christ, More love to Thee! Hear Thou the
2. Once earth-ly joy I craved, Sought peace and rest; Now Thee a-
3. Let sor-row do its work, Send grief and pain; Sweet are Thy
4. Then shall my lat-est breath Whis-per Thy praise; This be the

prayer I make, On bend-ed knee; This is my ear-nest plea,
lone I seek, Give what is best: This all my prayer shall be,
mes-sen-gers, Sweet their re-frain, When they can sing with me,
part-ing cry My heart shall raise, This still its prayer shall be,

More love, O Christ, to Thee, More love to Thee, More love to Thee!

360 O Thou In All Thy Might

The Lord thy God in the midst of thee is mighty.—ZEPH. 3: 17

FREDERICK L. HOSMER, 1876 BOARDMAN C. M. L. DEVEREUX
Arr. by GEORGE KINGSLEY

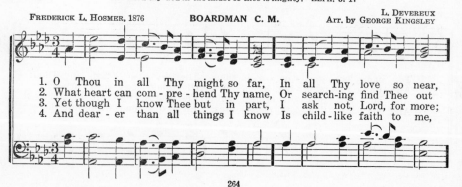

1. O Thou in all Thy might so far, In all Thy love so near,
2. What heart can com-pre-hend Thy name, Or search-ing find Thee out
3. Yet though I know Thee but in part, I ask not, Lord, for more;
4. And dear-er than all things I know Is child-like faith to me,

O Thou in All Thy Might—Concluded

Be - yond the range of sun and star, And yet be - side us here.
Who art with - in, a quick'ning Flame, A Pres - ence round a - bout?
E - nough for me to know Thou art, To love Thee and a - dore.
That makes the dark - est way I go An o - pen path to Thee.

As Thirsts the Hart 361

My soul thirsteth for God, for the living God.—Ps. 42: 2

Psalter   BELOIT L. M.   CARL G. REISSIGER

1. As thirsts the hart for wa - ter brooks, So thirsts my
2. Far from the courts of God, my tears Have been my
3. Tho' troub - les surge, yet through the day The Lord His
4. O why art thou cast down, my soul, And why so

soul, O God, for Thee; It seeks for God, and ev - er
food by night and day, While con-stant-ly with bit - ter
gra - cious help will give, And in the night my heart shall
troub - led shouldst thou be? Hope thou in God, and Him ex-

looks And longs the liv - ing God to see.
sneers, Where is thy God, the scoff - ers say.
pray And sing to Him in Whom I live.
tol, Who gives His sav - ing help to me.

362 I Could Not Do Without Thee

Without me ye can do nothing,—Jn. 15: 5

FRANCES R. HAVERGAL, 1873   MAGDALENA 7. 6. 7. 6. D.   JOHN STAINER

1. I could not do without Thee, O Saviour of the lost,
Whose precious blood redeemed me At such tremendous cost:
Thy righteousness, Thy pardon, Thy precious blood must be
My only hope and comfort, My glory and my plea.

2. I could not do without Thee, I cannot stand alone,
I have no strength or goodness, No wisdom of my own:
But Thou, beloved Saviour, Art all in all to me,
And weakness will be power If leaning hard on Thee.

3. I could not do without Thee, For O, the way is long,
And I am often weary, And sigh replaces song:
How could I do without Thee? I do not know the way;
Thou knowest and Thou leadest, And wilt not let me stray.

4. I could not do without Thee, No other friend can read
The spirit's strange, deep longings, Interpreting its need:
No human heart could enter Each dim recess of mine,
And soothe and hush and calm it, O blessed Lord, like Thine.

O Jesus, I Have Promised

Lo, I am with you always.—MATT. 28: 20

JOHN E. BODE, 1868   ANGEL'S STORY 7.6.7.6. D.   ARTHUR H. MANN, 1883

1. O Je - sus, I have prom - ised To serve Thee to the end;
2. O let me feel Thee near me, The world is ev - er near;
3. O let me hear Thee speak - ing In ac - cents clear and still,
4. O Je - sus, Thou hast prom - ised To all who fol - low Thee

Be Thou for - ev - er near me, My Mas - ter and my Friend:
I see the sights that daz - zle, The tempt - ing sounds I hear:
A - bove the storms of pas - sion, The mur - murs of self - will:
That where Thou art in glo - ry There shall Thy serv - ant be;

I shall not fear the bat - tle If Thou art by my side,
My foes are ev - er near me, A - round me and with - in;
O speak to re - as - sure me, To has - ten or con - trol;
And, Je - sus, I have prom - ised To serve Thee to the end;

Nor wan - der from the path - way If Thou wilt be my Guide.
But, Je - sus, draw Thou near - er, And shield my soul from sin.
O speak, and make me lis - ten, Thou Guard-ian of my soul.
O give me grace to fol - low My Mas - ter and my Friend. A-MEN.

364

O Love That Casts Out Fear

Perfect love casteth out fear.—I Jn. 4: 18

HORATIUS BONAR, 1861 · ST. DENYS 6. 6. 6. 6. · FRANK S. SPINNEY, 1850-1888

1. O love that casts out fear, O love that casts out sin,
2. True sun-light of the soul, Sur-round me as I go;
3. Great love of God, come in, Well-spring of heav'n-ly peace;
4. Love of the liv-ing God, Of Fa-ther, and of Son,

Tar - ry no more with-out, But come and dwell with - in.
So shall my way be safe, My feet no stray - ing know.
Thou liv-ing wa-ter, come, Spring up, and nev - - er cease.
Love of the Ho - ly Ghost, Fill Thou each need - - y one. A - MEN.

365

O For a Heart to Praise My God

I will praise Thee, O Lord, with my whole heart.—Ps. 9: 1

CHARLES WESLEY, 1742 · SOLITUDE C. M. · A. J. SHOWALTER

1. Oh, for a heart to praise my God, A heart from sin set free!
2. A heart re-signed, sub - mis-sive, meek, My dear Re-deem-er's throne;
3. A heart in ev - 'ry thought re-newed, And full of love di-vine,
4. An hum-ble, low - ly, con-trite heart, Be - liev-ing, true, and clean,
5. Thy na-ture, gra - cious Lord, im-part, Come quick-ly from a - bove,

A heart that's sprin-kled with the blood So free-ly shed for me.
Where on - ly Christ is heard to speak, Where Je - sus reigns a - lone.
Per - fect, and right, and pure, and good,—A cop - y, Lord, of Thine.
Which nei-ther life nor death can part From Him that dwells with - in.
Write Thy new name up - on my heart, Thy new, best name of Love.

Eternal Source of Joys Divine

366

Thou art my God, I will praise Thee.—Ps. 118: 20

ST. NICHOLAS C. M.

WILLIAM H. HAVERGAL

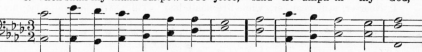

1. E - ter - nal Source of joys di - vine, To Thee my soul as - pires;
2. My Hope, my Trust, my Life, my Lord, As - sures me of Thy love;
3. Then shall my thank-ful pow'rs re - joice, And tri - umph in my God,

Oh, could I say, "The Lord is mine," 'Tis all my soul de - sires.
Oh, speak the kind, trans-port-ing word, And bid my fears re - move.
Till heav'n-ly rap - ture tune my voice, To spread Thy praise a - broad.

O For a Closer Walk With God

367

That ye might walk worthy of the Lord with all pleasing.—Col. 1: 10

WILLIAM COWPER, 1769   **ELIZABETHTOWN C. M.**   GEORGE KINGSLEY, 1838

1. Oh, for a clos - er walk with God, A calm and heav'n-ly frame!
2. Where is the bless - ed - ness I knew When first I saw the Lord?
3. The dear - est i - dol I have known, What-e'er that i - dol be,
4. So shall my walk be close with God, Calm and se - rene my frame;

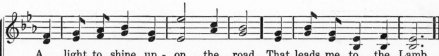

A light to shine up - on the road That leads me to the Lamb.
Where is the soul - re - fresh-ing view Of Je - sus and His Word?
Help me that i - dol to de - throne And wor - ship on - ly Thee.
So pur - er light shall mark the road That leads me to the Lamb.

Use also "Dalehurst" No. 420

368 Nearer, Still Nearer

Let us draw near with a true heart in full assurance of faith.—Heb. 10: 22

C. H. M.   Mrs. C. H. Morris

1. Near-er, still near-er, close to Thy heart, Draw me, my Sav-iour, so
2. Near-er, still near-er, noth-ing I bring, Naught as an of-f'ring to
3. Near-er, still near-er, Lord, to be Thine, Sin, with its fol-lies, I
4. Near-er, still near-er, while life shall last, Till safe in glo-ry my

pre-cious Thou art; Fold me, O fold me close to Thy breast, Shel-ter me
Je-sus my King, On-ly my sin-ful, now con-trite heart; Grant me the
glad-ly re-sign, All of its pleasures, pomp and its pride; Give me but
an-chor is cast, Thro' end-less a-ges, ev-er to be, Near-er, my

safe in that "Ha-ven of Rest," Shel-ter me safe in that "Ha-ven of Rest."
cleansing Thy blood doth impart, Grant me the cleansing Thy blood doth impart.
Je-sus, my Lord cru-ci-fied, Give me but Je-sus, my Lord cru-ci-fied.
Sav-iour, still near-er to Thee, Near-er, my Sav-iour, still near-er to Thee

369 Nearer, My God, to Thee

Draw nigh to God.—Jas. 4: 8

Mrs. Sarah F. Adams, 1840   BETHANY 6. 4. 6. 4. 6. 6. 6. 4.   Lowell Mason

1. Near-er, my God, to Thee, Near-er to Thee; E'en though it
2. Tho' like a wan-der-er, Day-light all gone, Dark-ness be
3. There let the way ap-pear, Steps up to heav'n; All that Thou
4. Then with my wak-ing tho'ts Bright with Thy praise, Out of my
5. Or if on joy-ful wing, Cleav-ing the sky, Caught up to

Nearer, My God, to Thee—Concluded

be   a cross That rais - eth me;   Still all my song shall be,
o - ver me, My   rest a   stone,   Yet in   my dreams I'd be,
send - est me In   mer - cy giv'n;   An - gels to beck - on me,
sto - ny griefs Beth - el I'll raise;   So by   my woes to be,
meet my King, Swift - ly I   fly,   Still all my song shall be

Near - er, my God, to Thee, Near - er, my God, to Thee, Near - er to Thee.

Above the Trembling Elements   370

Thy mercy, O Lord, is in the heavens.—Ps. 36: 5

Mrs. Anna L. Price, 1890   DUNDEE C. M.   Scotch Psalter, 1615

Slowly

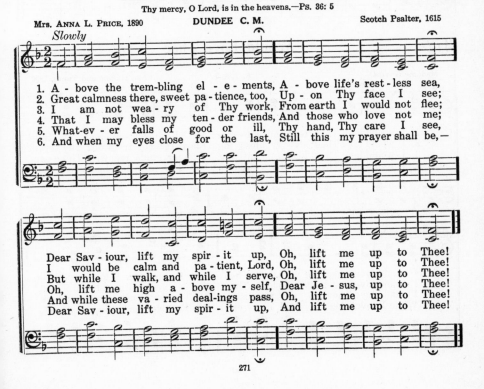

1. A - bove the trem-bling el - e - ments, A - bove life's rest - less sea,
2. Great calmness there, sweet pa - tience, too, Up - on Thy face I   see;
3. I   am not wea - ry of Thy work, From earth I would not flee;
4. That I may bless my ten - der friends, And those who love not me;
5. What-ev - er falls of good or ill, Thy hand, Thy care I see,
6. And when my eyes close for the last, Still this my prayer shall be,—

Dear Sav - iour, lift my spir - it up, Oh, lift me up to Thee!
I   would be calm and pa - tient, Lord, Oh, lift me up to Thee!
But while I walk, and while I serve, Oh, lift me up to Thee!
Oh, lift me high a - bove my - self, Dear Je - sus, up to Thee!
And while these va - ried deal-ings pass, Oh, lift me up to Thee!
Dear Sav - iour, lift my spir - it up, And lift me up to Thee!

271

371

Father, I Stretch My Hands to Thee

I stretch my hands unto Thee.—Ps. 143: 6

CHARLES WESLEY   AZMON C. M.   Arr. from CARL. G. GLÄSER

1. Fa - ther, I stretch my hands to Thee, No oth - er help I know;
2. What did Thy on - ly Son en - dure, Be - fore I drew my breath!
3. O Je - sus, could I this be - lieve, I now should feel Thy pow'r;
4. Au - thor of faith, to Thee I lift My wea - ry, long - ing eyes;

If Thou with - draw Thy - self from me, Ah, whith - er shall I go?
What pain, what la - bor to se - cure My soul from end - less death!
Now my poor soul Thou wouldst re - trieve, Nor let me wait one hour.
O may I now re - ceive that gift, My soul with - out it dies.

372

I Would Love Thee

I would love Thee, O Lord, my strength.—Ps. 18: 1

Madame GUYON   8. 7. 8. 7.   From Hymns and Tunes, 1890

1. I would love Thee, God and Fa - ther! My Re - deem - er, and my King!
2. I would love Thee; ev - 'ry bless - ing Flows to me from out Thy throne;
3. I would love Thee; look up - on me, Ev - er guide me with Thine eye:
4. I would love Thee; I have vowed it; On Thy love my heart is set;

I would love Thee; for with - out Thee Life is but a bit - ter thing.
I would love Thee;—he who loves Thee Nev - er feels him - self a - lone.
I would love Thee; if not nour - ished By Thy love, my soul would die.
While I love Thee, I will nev - er My Re - deem - er's blood for - get.

Jesus, Lover of My Soul

Who loved me and gave Himself for me.—GAL. 2: 20

CHARLES WESLEY, 1740　　　　REFUGE　7. 7. 7. 7. D.　　　　JOSEPH P. HOLBROOK

1. Je - sus, lov - er of my soul, Let me to Thy bos - om fly,
2. Oth - er ref - uge have I none, Hangs my help - less soul on Thee;
3. Thou, O Christ, art all I want; More than all in Thee I find;
4. Plenteous grace with Thee is found, Grace to par - don all my sin;

While the near - er wa - ters roll, While the tem - pest still is high:
Leave, oh, leave me not a - lone, Still sup - port and com-fort me.
Raise the fall - en, cheer the faint, Heal the sick, and lead the blind.
Let the heal - ing streams abound; Make and keep me pure with-in.

Hide me, O my Sav - iour, hide, Till the storm of life is past;
All my trust on Thee is stayed, All my help from Thee I bring;
Just and ho - ly is Thy name, I am all un - right-eous-ness;
Thou of life the foun - tain art, Free - ly let me take of Thee;

Safe in - to the ha - ven guide, O re - ceive my soul at last.
Cov - er my de - fense-less head With the shad - ow of Thy wing.
False, and full of sin, I am, Thou art full of truth and grace.
Spring Thou up with-in my heart, Rise to all e - ter - ni - ty.

374

Jesus, Lover of My Soul

He is my refuge and my fortress.—Ps. 91

CHARLES WESLEY, 1740   HOLLINGSIDE 7. 7. 7. 7. D.   JOHN B. DYKES, 1861

1. Je - sus, lov - er of my soul, Let me to Thy bos - om fly,
2. Oth - er ref - uge have I none; Hangs my help-less soul on Thee;
3. Thou, O Christ, art all I want; More than all in Thee I find;
4. Plenteous grace with Thee is found, Grace to par - don all my sin;

While the near - er wa - ters roll, While the tem - pest still is high:
Leave, oh, leave me not a - lone, Still sup - port and com - fort me.
Raise the fall - en, cheer the faint, Heal the sick, and lead the blind.
Let the heal - ing streams a - bound; Make and keep me pure with - in.

Hide me, O my Sav - iour, hide, Till the storm of life is past;
All my trust on Thee is stayed, All my help from Thee I bring;
Just and ho - ly is Thy name, I am all un - right-eous-ness;
Thou of life the foun - tain art, Free - ly let me take of Thee;

Safe in - to the ha - ven guide, O re - ceive my soul at last.
Cov - er my de-fense - less head With the shad-ow of Thy wing.
False, and full of sin, I am, Thou art full of truth and grace.
Spring Thou up with - in my heart, Rise to all e - ter - ni - ty. A - MEN.

Jesus, Lover of My Soul

The Lord is my refuge.—Ps. 91: **9**

CHARLES WESLEY, 1740 MARTYN 7. 7. 7. 7. D. S. B. MARSH, 1798-1875

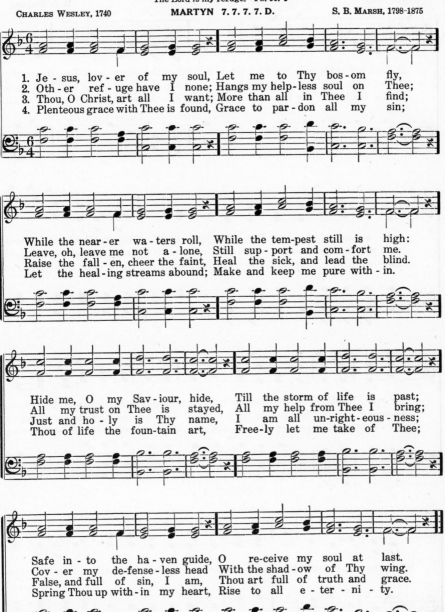

1. Je - sus, lov - er of my soul, Let me to Thy bos - om fly,
2. Oth - er ref - uge have I none; Hangs my help-less soul on Thee;
3. Thou, O Christ, art all I want; More than all in Thee I find;
4. Plenteous grace with Thee is found, Grace to par - don all my sin;

While the near - er wa - ters roll, While the tem-pest still is high:
Leave, oh, leave me not a - lone, Still sup - port and com - fort me.
Raise the fall - en, cheer the faint, Heal the sick, and lead the blind.
Let the heal - ing streams abound; Make and keep me pure with - in.

Hide me, O my Sav - iour, hide, Till the storm of life is past;
All my trust on Thee is stayed, All my help from Thee I bring;
Just and ho - ly is Thy name, I am all un-right-eous - ness;
Thou of life the foun-tain art, Free-ly let me take of Thee;

Safe in - to the ha - ven guide, O re-ceive my soul at last.
Cov - er my de-fense - less head With the shad - ow of Thy wing.
False, and full of sin, I am, Thou art full of truth and grace.
Spring Thou up with - in my heart, Rise to all e - ter - ni - ty.

376 When the Shadows Flee

JAMES ROWE   E. O. SELLERS

1. Smil-ing skies will bend a - bove us, When the shad - ows flee; Hearts now
2. Fet - ters nev - er - more will bind us, When the shad - ows flee; This dark
3. We shall view our home su - per - nal, When the shad - ows flee; We shall

cold a - gain will love us, When the shad-ows flee; We shall lose our care and
vale will be be - hind us, When the shad-ows flee; There will be no tem-pest
meet our King e - ter - nal, When the shad-ows flee; There, where death will reach us

sor - row, Troub-le nev - er - more to bor-row, On that bless-ed, peaceful mor-row,
sweeping, — In our lov-ing Father's keeping We shall wake, where none are weeping,
nev - er, There, where naught our hearts shall sever, We shall dwell with Christ for-ev-er,

CHORUS

When the shad - ows flee. With e - ter - nal day be - fore us, And our Sav - iour

When the Shadows Flee—Concluded

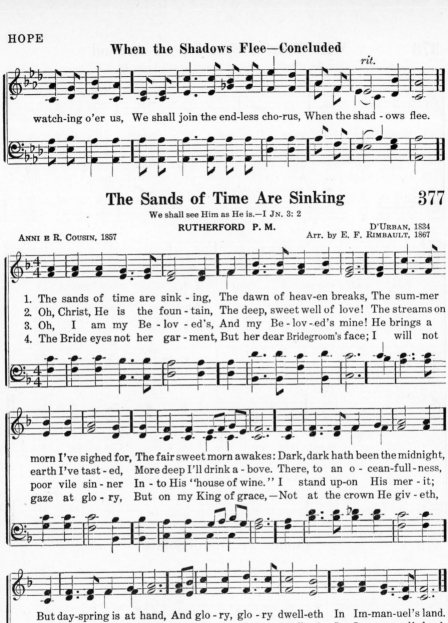

watch-ing o'er us, We shall join the end-less cho-rus, When the shad-ows flee.

The Sands of Time Are Sinking   377

We shall see Him as He is.—I Jn. 3: 2

RUTHERFORD P. M.

ANNIE R. COUSIN, 1857

D'URBAN, 1834
Arr. by E. F. RIMBAULT, 1867

1. The sands of time are sink-ing, The dawn of heav-en breaks, The sum-mer
2. Oh, Christ, He is the foun-tain, The deep, sweet well of love! The streams on
3. Oh, I am my Be-lov-ed's, And my Be-lov-ed's mine! He brings a
4. The Bride eyes not her gar-ment, But her dear Bridegroom's face; I will not

morn I've sighed for, The fair sweet morn awakes: Dark, dark hath been the midnight,
earth I've tast-ed, More deep I'll drink a-bove. There, to an o-cean-full-ness,
poor vile sin-ner In-to His "house of wine." I stand up-on His mer-it;
gaze at glo-ry, But on my King of grace,—Not at the crown He giv-eth,

But day-spring is at hand, And glo-ry, glo-ry dwell-eth In Im-man-uel's land.
His mer-cy doth ex-pand, And glo-ry, glo-ry dwell-eth In Im-man-uel's land.
I know no oth-er stand, Not e'en where glory dwell-eth In Im-man-uel's land.
But on His pierc-ed hand: The Lamb is all the glo-ry Of Im-man-uel's land.

378 With Tearful Eyes I Look Around

Him that cometh unto Me, I will in no wise cast out.—Jn. 6: 37

CHARLOTTE ELLIOTT   COME TO ME L. M.   J. D. BRUNK, 1902

1. With tear-ful eyes I look a - round, Life seems a
2. It tells me of a place of rest; It tells me
3. When na - ture shud - ders, loth to part From all I
4. "Come, for all else must fail and die; Earth is no
5. O voice of mer - cy! voice of love! In con - flict,

dark and storm - y sea; Yet, 'midst the gloom, I
where my soul may flee; Oh! to the wea - ry,
love, en - joy, and see; When a faint chill steals
rest - ing - place for thee; To heav'n di - rect thy
grief, and ag - o - ny, Sup - port me, cheer me

hear a sound, A heav'n - ly whis - per, "Come to Me."
faint, op - pressed, How sweet the bid - ding, "Come to Me."
o'er my heart, A sweet voice ut - ters, "Come to Me."
weep - ing eye, I am thy por - tion, "Come to Me."
from a - bove! And gen - tly whis - per, "Come to Me."

379 Come, Ye Disconsolate

To heal the broken-hearted.—Lk. 4: 18

THOMAS MOORE, 1816   11. 10. 11. 10. P. M.   SAMUEL WEBBE
Alt. by THOMAS HASTINGS

1. Come, ye dis - con - so - late, wher-e'er ye lan - guish, Come to the
2. Joy of the des - o - late, light of the stray - ing, Hope of the
3. Here see the bread of life; see wa-ters flow - ing Forth from the

Come, Ye Disconsolate—Concluded

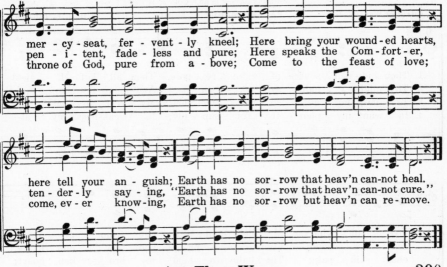

mer - cy - seat, fer - vent - ly kneel; Here bring your wound - ed hearts,
pen - i - tent, fade - less and pure; Here speaks the Com - fort - er,
throne of God, pure from a - bove; Come to the feast of love;

here tell your an - guish; Earth has no sor - row that heav'n can-not heal.
ten - der - ly say - ing, "Earth has no sor - row that heav'n can-not cure."
come, ev - er know - ing, Earth has no sor - row but heav'n can re - move.

Art Thou Weary   380

Come unto Me, all ye that labor and are heavy laden.—MATT. 11: 28

BULLINGER 8. 5. 8. 3.

STEPHEN, THE SABAITE, 8th cen. Greek
Tr. by JOHN M. NEALE, 1862

ETHELBERT M. BULLINGER, 1877

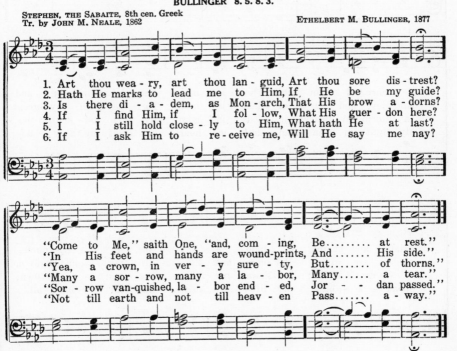

1. Art thou wea - ry, art thou lan - guid, Art thou sore dis - trest?
2. Hath He marks to lead me to Him, If He be my guide?
3. Is there di - a - dem, as Mon - arch, That His brow a - dorns?
4. If I find Him, if I fol - low, What His guer - don here?
5. I I still hold close - ly to Him, What hath He at last?
6. If I ask Him to re - ceive me, Will He say me nay?

"Come to Me," saith One, "and, com - ing, Be........ at rest."
"In His feet and hands are wound-prints, And....... His side."
"Yea, a crown, in ver - y sure - ty, But........ of thorns."
"Many a sor - row, many a la - bor, Many...... a tear."
"Sor - row van-quished, la - bor end - ed, Jor - - dan passed."
"Not till earth and not till heav - en Pass....... a - way."

279

381 Thou Hidden Source of Calm Repose

Christ is all, and in all.—COL. 3: 11

CHARLES WESLEY, 1749 PATER OMNIUM L. M. 6l. H. J. E. HOLMES

1. Thou hid-den source of calm re-pose, Thou all-suf-fi-cient
2. Thy might-y name sal-va-tion is, And keeps my hap-py
3. Je-sus, my all in all Thou art; My rest in toil, my
4. In want my plen-ti-ful sup-ply; In weak-ness my al-

love di-vine, My help and ref-uge from my foes,
soul a-bove: Com-fort it brings, and pow'r, and peace,
ease in pain; The balm to heal my bro-ken heart;
might-y pow'r; In bonds my per-fect lib-er-ty;

Se-cure I am whiie Thou art mine: And lo! from sin, and
And joy, and ev-er-last-ing love: To me, with Thy great
In storm my peace; in loss my gain; My joy be-neath the
My light in Sa-tan's dark-est hour; In grief my joy un-

grief, and shame, I hide me, Je--sus, in Thy name.
name, are giv'n Par-don, and ho--li-ness, and heav'n.
ty-rant's frown; In shame my glo--ry and my crown.
speak-a-ble; My life in death,— my all in all.

280

I Heard the Voice of Jesus Say

382

If any man thirst, let him come unto Me and drink.—Jn. 7: 37

HORATIUS BONAR, 1846   **8. 6. 8. 6. D.**   J. D. BRUNK, 1911

1. I heard the voice of Je - sus say, "Come un - to Me and rest;
2. I heard the voice of Je - sus say, "Be - hold, I free - ly give
3. I heard the voice of Je - sus say, "I am this dark world's Light;

Lay down, thou wea - ry one, lay down Thy head up - on My breast!"
The liv - ing wa - ter; thirst - y one, Stoop down and drink and live!"
Look un - to Me, thy morn shall rise And all thy day be bright!"

I came to Je - sus as I was, Wea - ry and worn and sad;
I came to Je - sus, and I drank Of that life - giv - ing stream:
I looked to Je - sus, and I found In Him my Star, my Sun;

I found in Him a rest - ing place, And He has made me glad.
My thirst was quenched, my soul re - vived, And now I live in Him.
And in that light of life I'll walk Till all my jour - ney's done.

Used by permission

10

383 He Leadeth Me

I being in the way, the Lord led me.—GEN. 24: 27

JOSEPH H. GILMORE, 1862   L. M. D.   WILLIAM B. BRADBURY, 1864

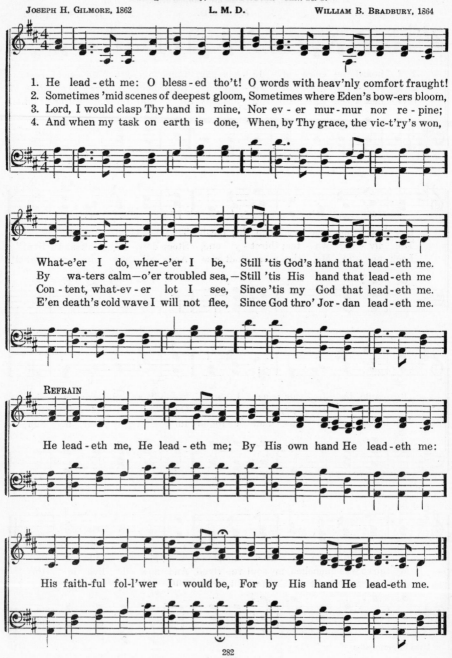

1. He lead-eth me: O bless-ed tho't! O words with heav'nly comfort fraught!
2. Sometimes 'mid scenes of deepest gloom, Sometimes where Eden's bow-ers bloom,
3. Lord, I would clasp Thy hand in mine, Nor ev-er mur-mur nor re-pine;
4. And when my task on earth is done, When, by Thy grace, the vic-t'ry's won,

What-e'er I do, wher-e'er I be, Still 'tis God's hand that lead-eth me.
By wa-ters calm—o'er troubled sea,—Still 'tis His hand that lead-eth me
Con-tent, what-ev-er lot I see, Since 'tis my God that lead-eth me.
E'en death's cold wave I will not flee, Since God thro' Jor-dan lead-eth me.

REFRAIN

He lead-eth me, He lead-eth me; By His own hand He lead-eth me:

His faith-ful fol-l'wer I would be, For by His hand He lead-eth me.

In Heavenly Love Abiding

384

If ye keep My commandments, ye shall abide in My love.—Jn. 15: 10

ANNA L. WARING, 1850 AURELIA 7. 6. 7. 6. D. SAMUEL S. WESLEY, 1864

1. In heav'n-ly love a-bid-ing, No change my heart shall fear,
2. Wher-ev-er He may guide me, No want shall turn me back;
3. Green pas-tures are be-fore me, Which yet I have not seen;

And safe is such con-fid-ing, For noth-ing chang-es here:
My Shep-herd is be-side me, And noth-ing can I lack;
Bright skies will soon be o'er me, Where dark-est clouds have been:

The storm may roar with-out me; My heart may low be laid;
His wis-dom ev-er wak-eth, His sight is nev-er dim;
My hope I can-not meas-ure; My path to life is free:

But God is round a-bout me, And can I be dis-mayed?
He knows the way He tak-eth, And I will walk with Him.
My Sav-iour has my treas-ure, And He will walk with me.

385 All the Way My Saviour Leads Me

The Lord alone did lead him.—DEUT. 32: 12

FANNY J. CROSBY, 1875   ROBERT LOWRY

1. All the way my Sav-iour leads me; What have I to ask be-side?
2. All the way my Sav-iour leads me; Cheers each wind-ing path I tread;
3. All the way my Sav-iour leads me; Oh, the full-ness of His love!

Can I doubt His ten-der mer-cy, Who thro' life has been my guide?
Gives me grace for ev-'ry tri-al; Feeds me with the liv-ing bread;
Per-fect rest to me is prom-ised In my Fa-ther's house a-bove;

Heav'n-ly peace, di-vin-est com-fort, Here by faith in Him to dwell!
Though my wea-ry steps may fal-ter, And my soul a-thirst may be,
When my spir-it, clothed im-mor-tal, Wings its flight to realms of day,

For I know, what-e'er be-fall me, Je-sus do-eth all things well;
Gush-ing from the Rock be-fore me, Lo! a spring of joy I see;
This my song thro' end-less a-ges,— Je-sus led me all the way;

All the Way My Saviour Leads Me—Concluded

For I know, what-e'er be - fall me, Je - sus do - eth all things well.
Gush-ing from the Rock be - fore me, Lo! a spring of joy I see.
This my song thro' end - less a - ges,— Je - sus led me all the way.

To Thy Pastures, Fair and Large — 386

The Lord is my Shepherd, I shall not want.— Ps. 23: 1

JAMES MERRICK, 1765   **HENDON 7s. 5 l.**   ABRAHAM H. C. MALAN

1. To Thy pas - tures, fair and large, Heav'n - ly Shep - herd,
2. When I faint with sum - mer's heat, Thou shalt guide my
3. Safe the drear - y vale I tread, By the shades of
4. Con - stant to my lat - est end, Thou my foot - steps

lead Thy charge; And my couch with ten - d'rest care, Midst the
wea - ry feet To the streams, that, still and slow, Thro' the
death o'er - spread, With Thy rod and staff sup - plied— This my
shalt at - tend; Thou shalt bid Thy hal - lowed dome Yield me

spring-ing grass pre - pare, Midst the spring-ing grass pre - pare.
ver - dant mead-ows flow, Thro' the ver - dant mead - ows flow.
guard, and that my guide, This my guard, and that my guide.
an e - ter - nal home, Yield me an e - ter - nal home.

387

Rock of Ages

And that Rock was Christ.—I Cor. 10: 4

A. M. TOPLADY, 1776   TOPLADY 7s. 6 l.   THOMAS HASTINGS, 1830

1. Rock of A - ges, cleft for me, Let me hide my - self in Thee;
2. Not the la - bor of my hands Can ful - fill the law's de-mands;
3. Noth-ing in my hands I bring, Sim - ply to Thy cross I cling;
4. While I draw this fleet - ing breath, When my heart-strings break in death,

Let the wa - ter and the blood, From Thy riv - en side which flowed,
Could my zeal no res - pite know, Could my tears for - ev - er flow,
Nak - ed, come to Thee for dress; Help - less, look to Thee for grace;
When I soar to worlds un-known, See Thee on Thy judg-ment throne,

Be of sin the doub - le cure; Cleanse me from its guilt and pow'r.
All for sin could not a - tone, Thou must save, and Thou a - lone.
Foul, I to the foun-tain fly, Wash me, Sav - iour, or I die.
Rock of A - ges, cleft for me, Let me hide my - self in Thee.

388

O Holy Saviour

The Lord is my portion, saith my soul, therefore will I hope in Him.—Lam. 3: 24

CHARLOTTE ELLIOTT, 1836   FLEMMING 8. 8. 8. 6.   FRIEDRICH F. FLEMMING

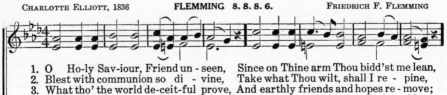

1. O Ho-ly Sav-iour, Friend un - seen, Since on Thine arm Thou bidd'st me lean,
2. Blest with communion so di - vine, Take what Thou wilt, shall I re - pine,
3. What tho' the world de-ceit-ful prove, And earthly friends and hopes re-move,
4. Tho' faith and hope are oft-en tried, I ask not, need not, aught be - side;

O Holy Saviour—Concluded

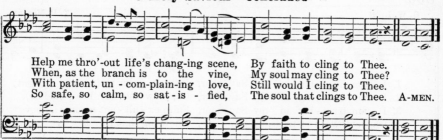

Help me thro'-out life's chang-ing scene, By faith to cling to Thee.
When, as the branch is to the vine, My soul may cling to Thee?
With patient, un - com-plain-ing love, Still would I cling to Thee.
So safe, so calm, so sat-is - fied, The soul that clings to Thee. A-MEN.

My Faith Looks Up to Thee

389

Looking unto Jesus.—HEB. 12: 2

RAY PALMER

OLIVET 6. 6. 4. 6. 6. 6. 4.

LOWELL MASON

1. My faith looks up to Thee, Thou Lamb of Cal - va - ry,
2. May Thy rich grace im - part Strength to my faint - ing heart,
3. While life's dark maze I tread, And griefs a - round me spread,
4. When ends life's tran - sient dream, When death's cold, sul - len stream

Sav - iour di - vine! Now hear me while I pray, Take all my
My zeal in - spire; As Thou hast died for me, Oh, may my
Be Thou my guide; Bid dark - ness turn to day, Wipe sor-row's
Shall o'er me roll, Blest Sav - iour, then, in love, Fear and dis-

guilt a - way; Oh, let me from this day Be whol - ly Thine!
love to Thee Pure, warm, and change-less be, A liv - ing fire!
tears a - way, Nor let me ev - er stray From Thee a - side.
trust re - move; Oh, bear me safe a - bove, A ran - somed soul!

390 I Am Trusting in My Saviour

G. W. LYON

T. B. MOSLEY

1. I am trust-ing in my Sav-iour, With a calm and stead-y light;
2. I am trust-ing in my Sav-iour, Oh, how sad my life would be,
3. I am trust-ing in my Sav-iour, Faith ex-ult-ant mounts a-bove
4. Oh, how sweet to trust my Sav-iour, Know-ing that He is a friend,

Hope is shin-ing on my path-way, Mak-ing all things fair and bright.
But for Thy dear pres-ence, Sav-iour, And to know I'm led by Thee.
This dark world and all its pas-sions To the realms of end-less love.
Who will cheer me thro' life's jour-ney, And be with me to the end.

REFRAIN

I am trusting, trusting, trusting,........ I am trusting day by day;......
wholly trusting, day by day;

I am trust-ing in my Sav-iour,...... To go with me all the way.
bless-ed Sav-iour,

How Gentle God's Commands

His commandments are not grievous.—I Jn. 5: 3

DENNIS S. M.

PHILIP DODDRIDGE

JOHANN G. NAEGELI
Adapted by L. MASON, 1845

391

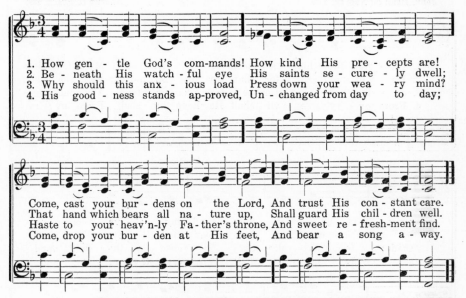

1. How gen - tle God's com-mands! How kind His pre - cepts are!
2. Be - neath His watch - ful eye His saints se - cure - ly dwell;
3. Why should this anx - ious load Press down your wea - ry mind?
4. His good - ness stands ap-proved, Un - changed from day to day;

Come, cast your bur - dens on the Lord, And trust His con - stant care.
That hand which bears all na - ture up, Shall guard His chil - dren well.
Haste to your heav'n-ly Fa - ther's throne, And sweet re - fresh-ment find.
Come, drop your bur - den at His feet, And bear a song a - way.

My God, My Father,—Blissful Name

They that know Thy name will put their trust in Thee.—Ps. 9: 10

392

ANNE STEELE, 1760

JERUSALEM C. M.

T. WORSLEY STANIFORTH, 1866

1. My God, my Fa - ther,—bliss-ful name,—O may I call Thee mine!
2. This on - ly can my fears con - trol, And bid my sor - rows fly;
3. What-e'er Thy prov - i - dence de - nies, I calm - ly would re - sign;
4. What-e'er Thy sa - cred will or - dains, O give me strength to bear,

May I with sweet as - sur - ance claim A por - tion so di - vine!
What harm can ev - er reach my soul, Be - neath my Fa-ther's eye?
For Thou art good and just and wise; O bend my will to Thine.
And let me know my Fa - ther reigns, And trust His ten - der care.

393 Unto the Hills Around

PSALM 121

LUX BEATA 10. 4. 10. 4. 10. 10.

JOHN, DUKE OF ARGYLL, 1870　　　　　ALBERT L. PEACE, 1885

1. Un - to the hills a - round do I lift up My long - ing
2. He will not suf - fer that thy foot be moved: Safe shalt thou
3. Je - ho - vah is Him - self thy keep - er true, Thy change - less
4. From ev - 'ry e - vil shall He keep thy soul, From ev - 'ry

eyes: O whence for me shall my sal - va - tion come,
be. No care - less slum - ber shall His eye - lids close,
shade; Je - ho - vah thy de - fense on thy right hand
sin: Je - ho - vah shall pre - serve thy go - ing out,

From whence a - rise? From God the Lord doth come my cer - tain
Who keep - eth thee. Be - hold, our God, the Lord, He slum - b'reth
Him - self hath made. And thee no sun by day shall ev - er
Thy com - ing in. A - bove thee watch - ing, He whom we a -

aid, From God the Lord, who heav'n and earth hath made.
ne'er, Who keep - eth Is - rael in His ho - ly care.
smite; No moon shall harm thee in the si - lent night.
dore Shall keep thee hence - forth, yea, for - ev - er - more.

Call Jehovah Thy Salvation

PSALM 91

JAMES MONTGOMERY, 1822   MOULTRIE 8. 7. 8. 7. D.   GERARD F. COBB, 1838-1904

1. Call Je - ho - vah thy sal - va - tion, Rest be-neath th' Al-might-y's shade,
2. From the sword at noon - day wast-ing, From the noi - some pes - ti - lence,
3. Since, with pure and firm af - fec - tion Thou on God hast set thy love,

In His se - cret hab - i - ta - tion Dwell, and nev - er be dis - mayed:
In the depth of mid-night blast-ing, God shall be thy sure de - fense:
With the wings of His pro - tec - tion He will shield thee from a - bove:

There no tu - mult shall a - larm thee, Thou shalt dread no hid - den snare;
He shall charge His an - gel le - gions Watch and ward o'er thee to keep;
Thou shalt call on Him in troub - le, He will heark - en, He will save;

Guile nor vi - o - lence can harm thee, In e - ter - nal safe-guard there.
Tho' thou walk thro' hos - tile re - gions, Tho' in des - ert wilds thou sleep.
Here for grief re - ward thee doub - le, Crown with life be - yond the grave.

395 Safe in the Arms of Jesus

Underneath are the everlasting Arms.—DEUT. 33: 27

FANNY J. CROSBY, 1868   7. 6. 7. 6.   12 l.   W. H. DOANE, 1870

1. Safe in the arms of Je - sus, Safe on His gen - tle breast,
2. Safe in the arms of Je - sus, Safe from cor - rod - ing care,
3. Je - sus, my heart's dear ref - uge, Je - sus has died for me;

REF.—*Safe in the arms of Je - sus, Safe on His gen - tle breast,*

There by His love o'er - shad - ed, Sweet-ly my soul shall rest.
Safe from the world's temp-ta - tions, Sin can - not harm me there.
Firm on the Rock of A - ges Ev - er my trust shall be.

There by His love o'er - shad - ed, Sweet - ly my soul shall rest.

Hark! 'tis the voice of an - gels, Borne in a song to me,
Free from the blight of sor - row, Free from my doubts and fears;
Here let me wait with pa - tience, Wait till the night is o'er;

D. C. REFRAIN

O - ver the fields of glo - ry, O - ver the jas - per sea......
On - ly a few more tri - als, On - ly a few more tears!....
Wait till I see the morn - ing Break on the gold - en shore....

God Moves in a Mysterious Way 396

How unsearchable are His judgments, and His ways past finding out.—Rom. 11: 33

WILLIAM COWPER, 1774   **DUNFERMLINE C. M.**   Scottish Psalter, 1615

1. God moves in a mys - te - rious way, His won - ders to per - form;
2. Ye fear - ful saints, fresh cour - age take; The clouds ye so much dread
3. Judge not the Lord by fee - ble sense, But trust Him for His grace;
4. His pur - pos - es will ri - pen fast, Un - fold - ing ev - 'ry hour;
5. Blind un - be - lief is sure to err, And scan His work in vain;

He plants His foot-steps in the sea, And rides up - on the storm.
Are big with mer - cy, and shall break In bless-ings on your head.
Be - hind a frown-ing prov - i - dence He hides a smil - ing face.
The bud may have a bit - ter taste, But sweet will be the flow'r.
God is His own in - ter - pret - er, And He will make it plain.

God is the Refuge of His Saints 397

PSALM 46

ISAAC WATTS, 1719   **WARD L. M.**   Arr. by LOWELL MASON

1. God is the ref - uge of His saints, When storms of sharp dis-tress in - vade;
2. Let mountains from their seats be hurled Down to the deep, and bur - ied there,
3. There is a stream whose gen-tle flow Sup-plies the cit - y of our God,
4. That sacred stream, Thy ho - ly word, Our grief al - lays, our fear con - trols:

Ere we can of - fer our complaints, Be - hold Him pres - ent with His aid.
Con - vul-sions shake the sol - id world, Our faith shall nev - er yield to fear.
Life, love, and joy, still glid - ing thro', And wa-t'ring our di - vine a - bode.
Sweet peace Thy prom-is-es af - ford, And give new strength to faint-ing souls.

398 Blessed Assurance

He is faithful that promised.—HEB. 10: 23

FANNY J. CROSBY

MRS. JOSEPH F. KNAPP, 1873

1. Bless-ed as-sur-ance, Je-sus is mine! Oh, what a fore-taste of
2. Per-fect sub-mis-sion, per-fect de-light, Vi-sions of rap-ture now
3. Per-fect sub-mis-sion, all is at rest, I in my Sav-iour am

glo-ry di-vine! Heir of sal-va-tion, pur-chase of God,
burst on my sight; An-gels de-scend-ing bring from a-bove,
hap-py and blest; Watch-ing and wait-ing, look-ing a-bove,

REFRAIN

Born of His Spir-it, washed in His blood.
Ech-oes of mer-cy, whis-pers of love. This is my sto-ry,
Filled with His good-ness, lost in His love.

this is my song, Prais-ing my Sav-iour all the day long; This is my

sto-ry, this is my song, Prais-ing my Sav-iour all the day long.

Father, Lead Us

ALICE JEAN CLEATOR

GEORGE C. HUGG

With spirit

1. O Fa - ther, lead us Gen - tly by the hand, Thro' sun and
2. When we would fal - ter Or when we would stray, O Fa - ther,

shad - ow Of the fu - ture land! Dim and un - trav - eled Lies the
lead us All a - long our way! Help us to ev - er Clos - er

way be - fore: O Fa - ther, lead us, Lead us ev - er - more!
walk to Thee, Thro' ways of dark-ness Where we can - not see!

CHORUS

Fears oft af - fright us! Doubt-ings walk be - fore!

O heav'n - ly Fa - ther, lead us, Now, and ev - er - more.

400

Guide Me, O Thou Great Jehovah

Thou hast guided them in Thy strength unto Thy holy habitation.—Ex. 15: 13

WILLIAM WILLIAMS, 1745. Welch   SEGUR 8. 7. 8. 7. 4. 7.   J. P. HOLBROOK, 1822-1888

1. Guide me, O   Thou great Je-ho - vah, Pil-grim thro' this bar-ren land:
2. O - pen Thou the crys-tal foun-tain, Whence the healing streams do flow;
3. When I   tread the verge of Jor - dan, Bid my anx - ious fears sub-side;

I   am weak, but Thou art might-y;   Hold me with Thy pow'r-ful hand!
Let the fi - ery, cloud-y pil - lar Lead me all   my jour-ney through:
Death of death and hell's de-struc-tion, Land me safe on Ca-naan's side:

Bread of heav-en, Bread of heaven, Feed me till   I want no more.
Strong Deliv'rer, Strong Deliv'rer, Be Thou still my strength and shield.
Songs of prais-es, Songs of praises, I   will ev - er give to Thee. A - MEN.

401

Gently, Lord, O Gently Lead Us

For Thy name's sake lead me.—Ps. 31: 3

THOMAS HASTINGS   SARDIS 8. 7. 8. 7.   LUDWIG VAN BEETHOVEN

1. Gen - tly, Lord, O   gen - tly lead us   Thro' this lone - ly vale of tears,
2. When temp-ta-tion's darts as - sail us, When in   de - vious paths we stray,
3. In   the hour of pain and an-guish, In   the hour when death draws near,
4. When this mor - tal life is   end - ed, Bid us   in Thine arms to rest,

Gently, Lord, O Gently Lead Us—Concluded

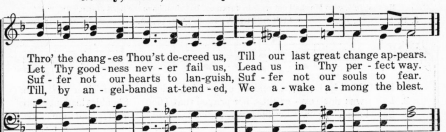

Thro' the chang-es Thou'st de-creed us, Till our last great change ap-pears.
Let Thy good-ness nev - er fail us, Lead us in Thy per - fect way.
Suf - fer not our hearts to lan-guish, Suf - fer not our souls to fear.
Till, by an - gel-bands at-tend - ed, We a - wake a - mong the blest.

Lead Us, O Father, in the Paths of Peace   402

I will instruct thee and teach thee in the way which thou shalt go.—Ps. 32: 8

WILLIAM H. BURLEIGH   ELLERS 10. 10. 10. 10.   EDWARD J. HOPKINS, 1869

1. Lead us, O Fa - ther, in the paths of peace; With - out Thy
2. Lead us, O Fa - ther, in the paths of truth; Un - helped by
3. Lead us, O Fa - ther, in the paths of right; Blind - ly we
4. Lead us, O Fa - ther, to Thy heav'n-ly rest, How - ev - er

guid - ing hand we go a - stray, And doubts ap - pall, and sor-rows
Thee, in er - ror's maze we grope, While pas - sion stains, and fol - ly
stum - ble when we walk a - lone, In - volved in shad - ows of a
rough and steep the path may be, Thro' joy or sor - row, as Thou

still in - crease: Lead us thro' Christ the true and liv - ing way.
dims our youth, And age comes on, un - cheered by faith and hope.
dark-some night, On - ly with Thee we jour - ney safe - ly on.
deem-est best, Un - til our lives are per - fect - ed in Thee.

403 **Lead, Kindly Light**

He that followeth Me shall not walk in darkness, but shall have the light of life.—JN. 8: 12

J. H. NEWMAN, 1832   LUX BENIGNA 10. 4. 10. 4. 10. 10.   JOHN B. DYKES

1. Lead, kind-ly Light, a-mid th' en-cir-cling gloom, Lead Thou me on;
2. I was not ev-er thus, nor prayed that Thou Shouldst lead me on;
3. So long Thy pow'r has blest me, sure it still Will lead me on

The night is dark, and I am far from home; Lead Thou me on:
I loved to choose and see my path; but now Lead Thou me on.
O'er moor and fen, o'er crag and tor-rent, till The night is gone;

Keep Thou my feet; I do not ask to see........
I loved the gar-ish day, and, spite of fears,.....
And with the morn those an-gel-fac-es smile......

The dis-tant scene,—one step e-nough for me.
Pride ruled my will: re-mem-ber not past years.
Which I have loved long since, and lost a-while.

Just As Seemeth Good to Thee

Just and true are Thy ways, Thou King of saints.—REV. 15: 3

IDA L. REED

GEORGE C. HUGG

Fervently

1. Choose my path, O bless-ed Sav-iour, Let me, trust-ing, lean on Thee;
2. Let Thy wis-dom guide me ev - er, For I dare not trust my own;
3. Life is full of cares per-plex - ing, And a - lone I lose the way;

Or - der Thou life's joys and du - ties, Just as seem-eth good to Thee.
Lead Thou me in ten - der mer - cy, Leave me not to walk a - lone.
Keep me near to Thee, dear Sav - iour, Choose for me the path, I pray.

REFRAIN

Just as seem - eth good to Thee, Just as seem - eth good to Thee;

Or - der Thou my steps, dear Sav-iour, Just as seem - eth good to Thee.

405 I Gave My Life For Thee

FRANCES R. HAVERGAL, 1852|

P. P. BLISS

1. I gave my life for thee,...... My pre - cious blood I shed,
2. My Fa-ther's house of light,...... My glo - ry - cir - cled throne
3. I suf - fered much for thee,...... More than thy tongue can tell,
4. And I have brought to thee,...... Down from my home a - bove,

That thou might'st ransomed be,....... And quick-ened from the dead;
I left, for earth - ly night, ... For wan-d'rings sad and lone:
Of bit - t'rest ag - o - ny,....... To res - cue thee from hell;
Sal - va - tion full and free,...... My par - don and my love;

f
I gave, I gave my life for thee, What hast thou giv'n for me?
I left, I left it all for thee, Hast thou left aught for me?
I've borne, I've borne it all for thee, What hast thou borne for me?
I bring, I bring rich gifts to thee, What hast thou brought to me?

f
I gave, I gave my life for thee, What hast thou giv'n for me?
I left, I left it all for thee, Hast thou left aught for me?
I've borne, I've borne it all for thee, What hast thou borne for me?
I bring, I bring rich gifts to thee, What hast thou brought to me?

I Am Thine, O Lord

Whose I am, and whom I serve.—ACTS 27. 23

FANNY J. CROSBY, 1875   **DRAW ME NEARER P. M.**   W. H. DOANE

1. I am Thine, O Lord; I have heard Thy voice, And it told Thy
2. Con - se - crate me now to Thy serv - ice, Lord, By the pow'r of
3. O the pure de - light of a sin - gle hour That be - fore Thy
4. There are depths of love that I can - not know Till I cross the

1. love to me; But I long to rise in the arms of faith, And be
2. grace di - vine; Let my soul look up with a stead-fast hope, And my
3. throne I spend, When I kneel in prayer, and with Thee, my God, I com-
4. nar - row sea; There are heights of joy that I may not reach Till I

REFRAIN

1. clos - er drawn to Thee.
2. will be lost in Thine.
3. mune as friend with friend.
4. rest in peace with Thee.

Draw me near - - er, near - er, bless - ed

near - er, near - er,

Lord, To the cross where Thou hast died; Draw me near - er,

near - er, near - er, bless - ed Lord, To Thy pre - cious bleed - ing side.

407 Something For Thee

SYLVANUS D. PHELPS   ROBERT LOWRY

1. Sav - iour, Thy dy - ing love Thou gav - est me, Nor should I
2. At the blest mer - cy seat, Plead - ing for me, My fee - ble
3. Give me a faith - ful heart, Like - ness to Thee, That each de -
4. All that I am and have, Thy gifts so free, In joy, in

aught with-hold, Dear Lord, from Thee: In love my soul would bow, My heart ful -
faith looks up, Je - sus, to Thee; Help me the cross to bear, Thy won-drous
part - ing day Henceforth may see Some work of love be - gun, Some deed of
grief, thro' life, Dear Lord, for Thee! And when Thy face I see, My ran-somed

fill its vow, Some of - f'ring bring Thee now, Some - thing for Thee.
love de - clare, Some song to raise, or prayer, Some - thing for Thee.
kind - ness done, Some wan-d'rer sought and won, Some - thing for Thee.
soul shall be, Thro' all e - ter - ni - ty, Some - thing for Thee.

408 Thy Life Was Given For Me

I lay down my life for the sheep.—JN. 10: 15

FRANCES R. HAVERGAL, 1858   DEVOTION 6s. 6 l.   JOHN H. GOWER, 1895

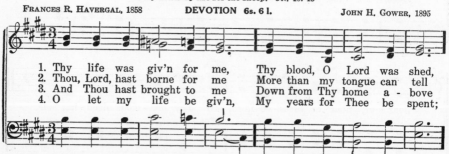

1. Thy life was giv'n for me, Thy blood, O Lord was shed,
2. Thou, Lord, hast borne for me More than my tongue can tell
3. And Thou hast brought to me Down from Thy home a - bove
4. O let my life be giv'n, My years for Thee be spent;

Thy Life Was Given For Me—Concluded

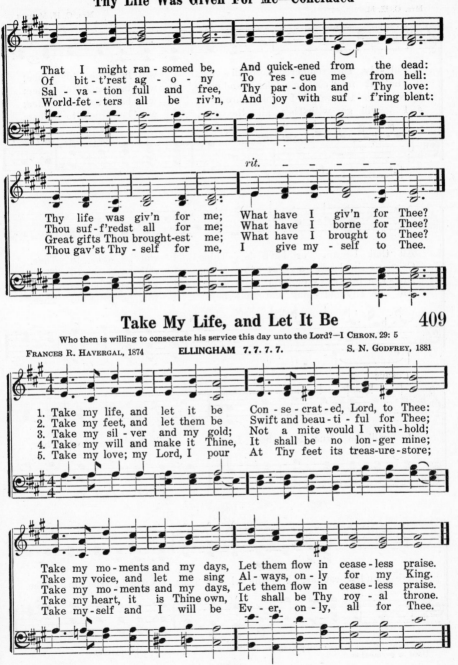

That I might ran - somed be, And quick-ened from the dead:
Of bit - t'rest ag - o - ny To res - cue me from hell:
Sal - va - tion full and free, Thy par - don and Thy love:
World-fet - ters all be riv'n, And joy with suf - f'ring blent:

rit.

Thy life was giv'n for me; What have I giv'n for Thee?
Thou suf - f'redst all for me; What have I borne for Thee?
Great gifts Thou brought-est me; What have I brought to Thee?
Thou gav'st Thy - self for me, I give my - self to Thee.

Take My Life, and Let It Be   409

Who then is willing to consecrate his service this day unto the Lord?—I CHRON. 29: 5

FRANCES R. HAVERGAL, 1874   ELLINGHAM 7. 7. 7. 7.   S. N. GODFREY, 1881

1. Take my life, and let it be   Con - se - crat - ed, Lord, to Thee:
2. Take my feet, and let them be   Swift and beau - ti - ful for Thee;
3. Take my sil - ver and my gold;   Not a mite would I with - hold;
4. Take my will and make it Thine,   It shall be no lon - ger mine;
5. Take my love; my Lord, I pour   At Thy feet its treas - ure - store;

Take my mo - ments and my days, Let them flow in cease - less praise.
Take my voice, and let me sing Al - ways, on - ly for my King.
Take my mo - ments and my days, Let them flow in cease - less praise.
Take my heart, it is Thine own, It shall be Thy roy - al throne.
Take my - self and I will be Ev - er, on - ly, all for Thee.

303

410 I Will Be True to Thee

Mrs. C. H. M.

Mrs. C. H. MORRIS

1. Ful - ly sur - ren-dered, Lord di - vine, I will be true to Thee;
2. Tho' it may cost me friends and home, I will be true to Thee;
3. Now to the world I bid fare - well, I will be true to Thee;
4. I will go with Thee all the way, I will be true to Thee;

All that I am or have is Thine, I will be true to Thee.
Cause me in lands a - far to roam, I will be true to Thee.
Bro - ken for - ev - er its deep spell, I will be true to Thee.
All of Thy bid - ding will o - bey, I will be true to Thee.

CHORUS

I will be true to Thee, Lord, I will be true to Thee;

Where Thou lead-est me, I will fol - low Thee, I will be true to Thee.

Give of Your Best to the Master

It is good for a man that he bear the yoke in his youth.—LAM. 3: 27

H. B. G.

Mrs. CHARLOTTE BARNARD

1. Give of your best to the Mas - ter; Give of the strength of your youth;
2. Give of your best to the Mas - ter; Give Him first place in your heart;
3. Give of your best to the Mas - ter; Naught else is wor - thy His love;

REF.—*Give of your best to the Mas - ter; Give of the strength of your youth;*

FINE

Throw your soul's fresh, glowing ar - dor In - to the bat - tle for truth.
Give Him first place in your serv - ice; Con - se - crate ev - - 'ry part.
He gave Him - self for your ran - som; Gave up His glo - ry a - bove;

Clad in sal - va - tion's full ar - mor, Join in the bat - tle for truth.

Je - sus has set the ex - am - ple; Daunt-less was He, young and brave;
Give, and to you shall be giv - en; God His be - lov - ed Son gave;
Laid down His life with - out mur - mur, You from sin's ru - in to save;

rall. D. C.

Give Him your loy - al de - vo - tion, Give Him the best that you have....
Grate - ful - ly seek - ing to serve Him, Give Him the best that you have....
Give Him your heart's ad - o - ra - tion, Give Him the best that you have....

412 Father, I Know That All My Life

So teach us to number our days that we may apply our hearts unto wisdom.—Ps. 90: 12

ANNA L. WARING, 1846   SLINGSBY 8. 6. 8. 6. 8. 6.   JOHN B. DYKES, 1867

1. Fa - ther, I know that all my life Is por-tioned out for me;
2. Wher-ev - er in the world I am, In what-so-e'er es - tate,
3. I ask Thee for the dai - ly strength, To none that ask de - nied;
4. In serv - ice which Thy will ap - points There are no bonds for me;

The chang - es that are sure to come, I do not fear to see:
I have a fel - low - ship with hearts To keep and cul - ti - vate;
A mind to blend with out-ward life, While keep-ing at Thy side;
My in - most heart is taught the truth That makes Thy chil - dren free;—

I ask Thee for a pres - ent mind, In - tent on pleas - ing Thee.
A work of low - ly love to do For Him on whom I wait.
Con-tent to fill a lit - tle space, If Thou be glo - ri - fied.
A life of self-re-nounc-ing love Is one of lib - er - ty. A - MEN.

413 Thine Forever! God of Love

My sheep . . . shall never perish.—JN. 10: 27, 28

MRS. MARY F. MAUDE, 1847   ST. GURON 7. 7. 7. 7.   C. J. DICKENSON

1. Thine for - ev - er! God of love, Hear us from Thy throne a - bove,
2. Thine for - ev - er! Lord of life, Shield us thro' our earth - ly stife,
3. Thine for - ev - er! O how blest They who find in Thee their rest!
4. Thine for - ev - er! Thou our Guide, All our wants by Thee sup - plied,

Thine Forever! God of Love—Concluded

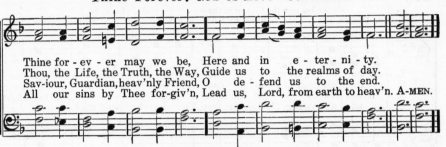

Thine for - ev - er may we be, Here and in e - ter - ni - ty.
Thou, the Life, the Truth, the Way, Guide us to the realms of day.
Sav-iour, Guardian, heav'nly Friend, O de - fend us to the end.
All our sins by Thee for-giv'n, Lead us, Lord, from earth to heav'n. A-MEN.

How Shall I Follow Him   414

What things were gain to me, those I counted loss for Christ.—PHIL. 3: 8

JOSIAH CONDER   GERMANY L. M.   LUDWIG VAN BEETHOVEN

1. How shall I fol - low Him I serve? How shall I
2. Lord, should my path through suf - f'ring lie, For - bid it
3. O let me think how Thou didst leave Un - tast - ed
4. To faint, to grieve, to die for me! Thou cam - est
5. Yes! I would count them all but loss, To gain the

cop - y Him.... I love? Nor from those bless - ed
I should e'er.... re - pine; Still let me turn to
ev - 'ry pure.... de - light, To fast, to faint, to
not Thy - self.... to please: And, dear as earth - ly
no - tice of...... Thine eye: Flesh shrinks and trem - bles

foot - steps swerve, Which lead me to His seat a - bove?
Cal - va - ry, Nor heed my griefs, re - mem - b'ring Thine.
watch, to grieve, The toil - some day, the home - less night:—
com - forts be, Shall I not love Thee more than these?
at the cross, But Thou canst give the vic - - to - ry.

415 Just As I Am, Thine Own to Be

Remember now thy Creator in the days of thy youth.—Eccl. 12: 1

MARIANNE HEARN, 1887   JUST AS I AM 8. 8. 8. 6.   JOSEPH BARNBY, 1893

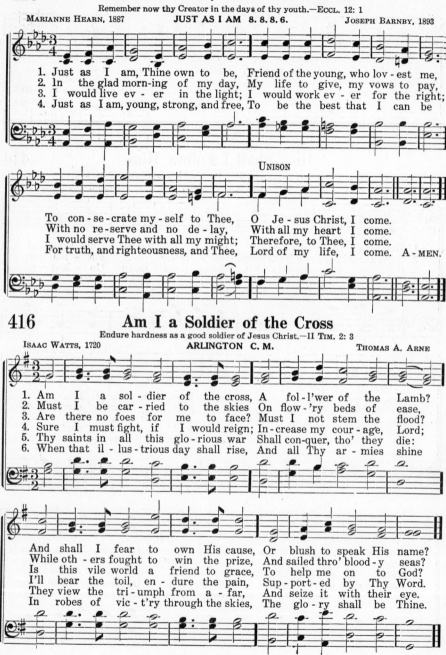

1. Just as I am, Thine own to be, Friend of the young, who lov-est me,
2. In the glad morn-ing of my day, My life to give, my vows to pay,
3. I would live ev - er in the light; I would work ev - er for the right;
4. Just as I am, young, strong, and free, To be the best that I can be

UNISON

To con - se - crate my-self to Thee, O Je - sus Christ, I come.
With no re - serve and no de - lay, With all my heart I come.
I would serve Thee with all my might; Therefore, to Thee, I come.
For truth, and righteousness, and Thee, Lord of my life, I come. A - MEN.

416 Am I a Soldier of the Cross

Endure hardness as a good soldier of Jesus Christ.—II TIM. 2: 3

ISAAC WATTS, 1720   ARLINGTON C. M.   THOMAS A. ARNE

1. Am I a sol - dier of the cross, A fol - l'wer of the Lamb?
2. Must I be car - ried to the skies On flow - 'ry beds of ease,
3. Are there no foes for me to face? Must I not stem the flood?
4. Sure I must fight, if I would reign; In-crease my cour - age, Lord;
5. Thy saints in all this glo - rious war Shall con-quer, tho' they die:
6. When that il - lus - trious day shall rise, And all Thy ar - mies shine

And shall I fear to own His cause, Or blush to speak His name?
While oth - ers fought to win the prize, And sailed thro' blood - y seas?
Is this vile world a friend to grace, To help me on to God?
I'll bear the toil, en - dure the pain, Sup - port - ed by Thy Word.
They view the tri - umph from a - far, And seize it with their eye.
In robes of vic - t'ry through the skies, The glo - ry shall be Thine.

I'll Live For Him

Being made free from sin, and become servants to God.—ROM. 6: 22

R. E. HUDSON   8. 8. 8. 6. D.   C. R. DUNBAR

1. My life, my love I give to Thee, Thou Lamb of God, who died for me;
2. I now be-lieve Thou dost re-ceive, For Thou hast died that I might live;
3. Oh, Thou who died on Cal-va-ry To save my soul and make me free,

Oh, may I ev - er faith - ful be, My Sav - iour and my God!
And now hence-forth I'll trust in Thee, My Sav - iour and my God!
I'll con - se - crate my life to Thee, My Sav - iour and my God!

REFRAIN

I'll live for Him who died for me, How hap - py then my life shall be!

I'll live for Him who died for me, My Sav - iour and my God!

418 In the Hour of Trial

When He hath tried me, I shall come forth as gold.—JOB. 23: 10

JAMES MONTGOMERY, 1834   PENITENCE 6. 5. 6. 5. D.   SPENCER LANE. 1879

1. In the hour of tri - al, Je - sus, plead for me;
2. With its witch-ing pleas - ures Would this vain world charm,
3. If with sore af - flic - tion Thou in love chas - tise,
4. When in dust and ash - es To the grave I sink,

Lest by base de - ni - al I de - part from Thee;
Or its sor - did treas - ures Spread to work me harm,
Pour Thy ben - e - dic - tion On the sac - ri - fice;
While heav'n's glo-ry flash - es O'er the shelv - ing brink,

When Thou seest me wav - er, With a look re - call,......
Bring to my re - mem - brance Sad Geth - sem - a - ne,.......
Then, up - on Thine al - tar Free - ly of - fered up,.......
On Thy truth re - ly - ing Thro' that mor - tal strife,....

Nor for fear or fa - vor Suf - fer me to fall.
Or, in dark - er sem - blance, Cross-crowned Cal - va - ry.
Tho' the flesh may fal - ter, Faith shall drink the cup.
Lord, re - ceive me, dy - ing, To e - ter - nal life.

My God and Father, While I Stray

419

Not my will, but Thine be done.—Lk. 22: 42

CHARLOTTE ELLIOTT, 1834   TROYT'S CHANT 8.8.8.4.   ARTHUR H. D. TROYT, 1857

1. My God and Father, while I stray Far from my home in life's rough way,
2. What though in lonely grief I sigh For friends beloved, no lon-ger nigh,
3. Let but my fainting heart be blest With Thy sweet Spirit for its guest,
4. Renew my will from day to day; Blend it with Thine, and take a-way
5. Then, when on earth I breathe no more The prayer oft mixed with tears before,

O teach me from my heart to say, "Thy will be done."
Submissive still would I re-ply, "Thy will be done."
My God, to Thee I leave the rest; Thy will be done.
All that now makes it hard to say, "Thy will be done."
I'll sing upon a hap-pier shore, "Thy will be done." A-MEN.

Out of the Depths

420

Out of the depths have I cried unto Thee, O Lord.—Ps. 131

ELIZABETH E. MARCY   DALEHURST C. M.   ARTHUR COTTMAN, 1874

1. Out of the depths to Thee I cry, Whose faint-ing foot-steps trod
2. Thou Man of grief, who once a-part Didst all our sor-rows bear,—
3. Is this the con-se-crat-ed dow'r, Thy cho-sen ones ob-tain,
4. Then, O my soul, in si-lence wait; Faint not, O fal-t'ring feet;
5. Let faith tran-scend the pass-ing hour, The tran-sient pain and strife,

The paths of our hu-man-i-ty, In-car-nate Son of God!
The trem-bling hand, the faint-ing heart, The ag-o-ny, and prayer!
To know Thy res-ur-rec-tion pow'r, Thro' fel-low-ship of pain?
Press on-ward to that blest es-tate, In right-eous-ness com-plete.
Up-raised by an im-mor-tal pow'r,—The pow'r of end-less life.

421

Prince of Peace, Control My Will

Thou wilt keep him in perfect peace whose mind is stayed on Thee.—Isa. 26: 3

MARY A. S. BARBER   ALETTA 7. 7. 7. 7.   WILLIAM B. BRADBURY

1. Prince of Peace, con - trol my will; Bid this strug-gling heart be still;
2. Thou hast bought me with Thy blood, O - pened wide the gate to God:
3. May Thy will, not mine, be done; May Thy will and mine be one;
4. Sav - iour, at Thy feet I fall, Thou my life, my God, my all!

Bid my fears and doubt - ings cease, Hush my spir - it in - to peace.
Peace I ask, but peace must be, Lord, in be - ing one with Thee.
Chase these doubtings from my heart, Now Thy per - fect peace im - part.
Let Thy hap - py serv - ant be One for - ev - er - more with Thee.

422

Jesus, Saviour, Pilot Me

So He brought them unto their desired haven.—Ps. 107: 30

EDWARD HOPPER, 1818-1888   PILOT 7s. 6 l.   JOHN E. GOULD

FINE

1. Je - sus, Sav - iour, pi - lot me O - ver life's tem - pes - tuous sea;
D. C.—*Chart and com - pass came from Thee, Je - sus, Sav - iour, pi - lot me.*
2. As a moth - er stills her child, Thou canst hush the o - cean wild;
D. C.—*Won-drous Sov - 'reign of the sea, Je - sus, Sav - iour, pi - lot me.*
3. When at last I near the shore, And the fear - ful break-ers roar
D. C.—*May I hear Thee say to me, "Fear not, I will pi - lot thee!"*

D. C.

Un-known waves be-fore me roll, Hid - ing rocks and treach'rous shoal;
Boist'rous waves o - bey Thy will When Thou say'st to them, "Be still!"
'Twixt me and the peace-ful rest, Then, while lean - ing on Thy breast,

312

Saviour, Like a Shepherd Lead Us

He calleth His own sheep by name, and leadeth them out.—Jn. 10: 3

DOROTHY A. THRUPP, 1830   BRADBURY 8. 7. 8. 7. D.   WILLIAM B. BRADBURY

1. Sav - iour, like a shep-herd lead us,   Much we need Thy ten-d'rest care;
2. We are Thine, do Thou be - friend us,   Be the guard-ian of our way;
3. Thou hast prom-ised to re - ceive us,   Poor and sin - ful tho' we be;
4. Ear - ly let us seek Thy fa - vor,   Ear - ly let us do Thy will;

In Thy pleas-ant pas-tures feed us,   For our use Thy folds pre - pare;
Keep Thy flock, from sin de - fend us,   Seek us when we go a - stray;
Thou hast mer - cy to re - lieve us,   Grace to cleanse, and pow'r to free;
Bless-ed Lord and on - ly Sav - iour,   With Thy love our bos-oms fill:

Bless - ed Je - sus! Bless - ed Je - sus! Thou hast bought us, Thine we are,
Bless - ed Je - sus! Bless - ed Je - sus! Hear, O hear us, when we pray,
Bless - ed Je - sus! Bless - ed Je - sus! We will ear - ly turn to Thee,
Bless - ed Je - sus! Bless - ed Je - sus! Thou hast loved us, love us still,

Bless - ed Je - sus! Bless - ed Je - sus! Thou hast bought us, Thine we are.
Bless - ed Je - sus! Bless - ed Je - sus! Hear, O hear us, when we pray.
Bless - ed Je - sus! Bless - ed Je - sus! We will ear - ly turn to Thee.
Bless - ed Je - sus! Bless - ed Je - sus! Thou hast loved us, love us still.

313

424 What Wait I For But Thee

PSALM 39

Psalter   DULCE DOMUM S. M.   R. S. AMBROSE

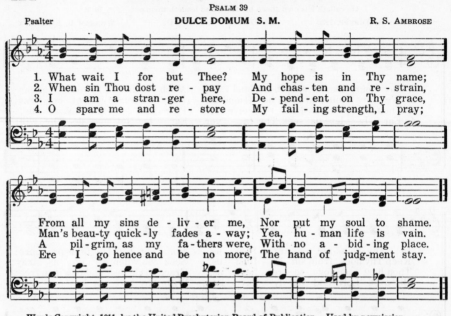

1. What wait I for but Thee? My hope is in Thy name;
2. When sin Thou dost re - pay And chas - ten and re - strain,
3. I am a stran-ger here, De - pend-ent on Thy grace,
4. O spare me and re - store My fail - ing strength, I pray;

From all my sins de - liv-er me, Nor put my soul to shame.
Man's beau-ty quick-ly fades a - way; Yea, hu - man life is vain.
A pil-grim, as my fa-thers were, With no a - bid-ing place.
Ere I go hence and be no more, The hand of judg-ment stay.

Words Copyright, 1911, by the United Presbyterian Board of Publication. Used by permission

425 Father, Whate'er of Earthly Bliss

No good thing will He withold from them that walk uprightly.—Ps. 84: 11

NAOMI C. M.

ANNE STEELE, 1760   JOHANN G. NAEGELI
               Arr. by LOWELL MASON, 1836

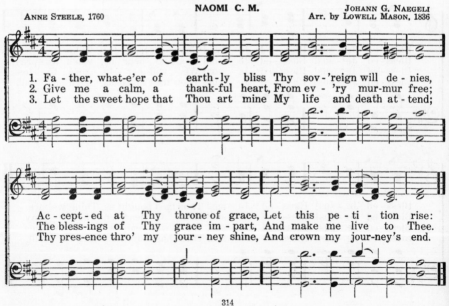

1. Fa - ther, what-e'er of earth-ly bliss Thy sov-'reign will de - nies,
2. Give me a calm, a thank-ful heart, From ev - 'ry mur-mur free;
3. Let the sweet hope that Thou art mine My life and death at - tend;

Ac - cept-ed at Thy throne of grace, Let this pe - ti - tion rise;
The bless-ings of Thy grace im - part, And make me live to Thee.
Thy pres-ence thro' my jour - ney shine, And crown my jour-ney's end.

My Jesus, As Thou Wilt

426

For even Christ pleased not Himself.—Rom. 15: 3

RESIGNATION

BENJAMIN SCHMOLK, 1716
Tr. by JANE BORTHWICK, 1854

JEWETT 6. 6. 6. 6. D.

CARL M. VON WEBER, 1821
Arr. by JOSEPH P. HOLBROOK, 1862

1. My Je - sus, as Thou wilt; Oh, may Thy will be mine;
2. My Je - sus, as Thou wilt; Tho' seen thro' many a tear,
3. My Je - sus, as Thou wilt; All shall be well for me;

In - to Thy hand of love I would my all re - sign:
Let not my star of hope Grow dim or dis - ap - pear:
Each chang-ing fu - ture scene I glad - ly trust with Thee:

Thro' sor - row or thro' joy, Con - duct me as Thine own,
Since Thou on earth hast wept And sor - rowed oft a - lone,
Straight to my home a - bove I trav - el calm - ly on,

rit.

And help me still to say, "My Lord, Thy will be done."
If I must weep with Thee, My Lord, Thy will be done.
And sing in life or death,— My Lord, Thy will be done.

315

427 Jesus, I My Cross Have Taken

Come, take up the cross, and follow me.—Mk. 10: 21

DISCIPLE 8. 7. 8. 7. D.

Henry F. Lyte, 1825

Arr. from Mozart
By Lowell Mason

1. Je - sus, I   my cross have tak - en,   All   to leave and   fol - low Thee;
2. Let the world de - spise and leave me,   They have left my   Sav - iour too;
3. Man may troub-le   and   dis - tress me, 'Twill but drive me   to Thy breast;

Na - ked, poor, de-spised, for - sak - en,   Thou, from hence, my   all shalt be.
Hu - man hearts and looks de - ceive me; Thou art   not   like them un - true;
Life with tri - als   hard may press me; Heav'n will bring me   sweet - er   rest.

Per - ish ev - 'ry fond am - bi - tion,   All I've sought, or hoped, or known;
And while Thou shalt smile up - on   me,   God of   wis - dom, love, and might,
Oh, 'tis not   in   grief to harm me,   While Thy love is   left   to   me;

Yet, how rich is   my con-di - tion! God and heav'n are   still my own.
Foes may hate and friends may shun me; Show Thy face and   all   is bright.
Oh, 'twere not in joy to charm me, Were that joy   un-mixed with Thee.

Thy Way, Not Mine, O Lord   428

Working in you that which is well-pleasing in His sight.—HEB. 13: 20, 21

HORATIUS BONAR, 1857   HOLY GUIDE 6. 6. 6. 6.   UZZIAH C. BURNAP, 1895

1. Thy way, not mine, O Lord, How - ev - er dark it be!
2. Smooth let it be or rough, It will be still the best;
3. The king - dom that I seek Is Thine; so let the way
4. Choose Thou for me my friends, My sick - ness or my health;
5. Not mine, not mine the choice, In things or great or small;

Lead me by Thine own hand; Choose out the path for me.
Wind - ing or straight, it leads Right on - ward to Thy rest.
That leads to it be Thine, Else I must sure - ly stray.
Choose Thou my cares for me, My pov - er - ty or wealth.
Be Thou my guide, my strength, My wis - dom and my all. A - MEN.

Used by permission of The Presbyterian Board of Publication and Sabbath-School Work

My Gracious Lord, I Own Thy Right   429

For all things come of Thee, and of Thine own have we given Thee.— I CHRON. 29: 14

PHILIP DODDRIDGE, Pub. 1755   HOLBORN HILL L. M.   ST. ALBAN'S Tune Book

1. My gra-cious Lord, I own Thy right To ev - 'ry serv - ice I can pay,
2. What is my be - ing but for Thee, Its sure sup-port, its no - blest end?
3. 'Tis to my Sav - iour I would live, To Him who for my ran - som died;
4. His work my hoar - y age shall bless, When youthful vig - or is no more;

And call it my su - preme de - light To hear Thy dic - tates, and o - bey.
'Tis my de - light Thy face to see, And serve the cause of such a Friend.
Nor could all world-ly hon - or give Such bliss as crowns me at His side.
And my last hour of life con - fess His dy - ing love, His sav - ing pow'r.

430 O Sometimes the Shadows Are Deep

Who is a rock, save our God.—Ps. 18: 31

E. JOHNSON

THE ROCK OF REFUGE

WILLIAM G. FISCHER

1. O some-times the shad-ows are deep, And rough seems the path to the goal,
2. O some-times how long seems the day, And sometimes how wea-ry my feet;
3. O near to the Rock let me keep, If bless-ings or sor-rows pre-vail;

And sorrows, sometimes how they sweep Like tempests down o - ver the soul!
But toil - ing in life's dust-y way, The Rock's blessed shadow, how sweet!
Or climb - ing the moun-tain way steep, Or walk-ing the shad-ow - y vale.

REFRAIN

O then to the Rock let me fly,
let me fly,
To the Rock that is

high - er than I;
is high - er than I;
O then to the Rock let me

fly,
let me fly,
To the Rock that is high - er than I.

318

The Name of Jesus

W. C. Martin

E. S. Lorenz

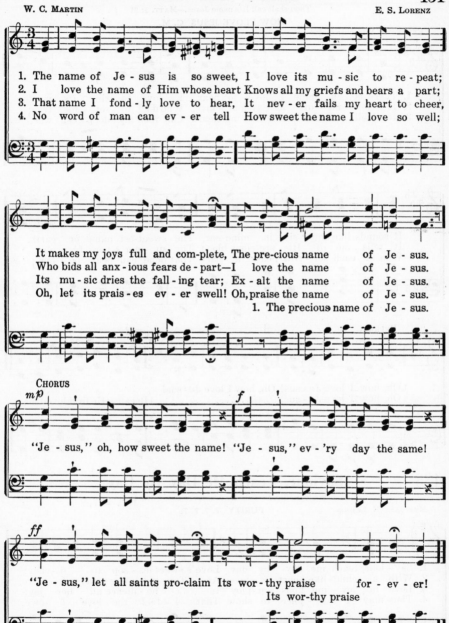

1. The name of Je-sus is so sweet, I love its mu-sic to re-peat;
2. I love the name of Him whose heart Knows all my griefs and bears a part;
3. That name I fond-ly love to hear, It nev-er fails my heart to cheer,
4. No word of man can ev-er tell How sweet the name I love so well;

It makes my joys full and com-plete, The pre-cious name of Je-sus.
Who bids all anx-ious fears de-part—I love the name of Je-sus.
Its mu-sic dries the fall-ing tear; Ex-alt the name of Je-sus.
Oh, let its prais-es ev-er swell! Oh, praise the name of Je-sus.

1. The precious name of Je-sus.

CHORUS

mp

"Je-sus," oh, how sweet the name! "Je-sus," ev-'ry day the same!

ff

"Je-sus," let all saints pro-claim Its wor-thy praise for-ev-er!

Its wor-thy praise

432 There is a Name I Love to Hear

Thou shalt call His name Jesus.—MATT. 1: 21

HOW I LOVE JESUS C. M.

FREDERICK WHITFIELD, 1855

1. There is a name I love to hear, I love to sing its worth;
2. It tells me of a Sav-iour's love, Who died to set me free;
3. It tells of One whose lov-ing heart Can feel my deep-est woe,

It sounds like mu-sic in mine ear, The sweet-est name on earth.
It tells me of His pre-cious blood, The sin-ner's per-fect plea.
Who in each sor-row bears a part, That none can bear be-low.

REFRAIN

{ Oh, how I love Je-sus! Oh, how I love Je-sus!
{ Oh, how I love Je-sus! (*Omit*.................) Because He first loved me.

433 Saviour, Teach Me Day By Day

We love Him, because He first loved us.—I JN. 4: 19

Miss JANE E. LEESON   **PURITY 7. 7. 7. 7.**

1. Sav-iour, teach me day by day Love's sweet les-son to o-bey;
2. With a child-like heart of love, At Thy bid-ding may I move,
3. Love in lov-ing finds em-ploy—In o-be-dience all her joy;
4. Thus may I re-joice to show That I feel the love I owe;

320

Saviour, Teach Me Day By Day—Concluded

Sweet - er les - son can - not be: Lov - ing Him who first loved me.
Prompt to serve and fol - low Thee— Lov - ing Him who first loved me.
Ev - er new that joy will be: Lov - ing Him who first loved me.
Sing - ing till Thy face I see, Of His love who first loved me.

O Love That Will Not Let Me Go 434

I will never leave thee, nor forsake thee.—HEB. 13: 5

GEORGE MATHESON, 1842-1906   8. 8. 8. 8. 6.   ALBERT L. PEACE

1. O love that will not let me go,.... I rest my wea - ry
2. O light that fol - l'west all my way,.. I yield my flick-'ring
3. O joy that seek - est me thro' pain,.. I can - not close my
4. O cross that lift - est up my head,.. I dare not ask to

soul in Thee; I give Thee back the life I owe,.... That
torch to Thee; My heart re - stores its bor-rowed ray, ... That
heart to Thee; I trace the rain - bow thro' the rain,.... And
hide from Thee; I lay in dust life's glo - ry dead, ... And

in Thine o - cean depths its flow May rich - er, full - er be.
in Thy sun-shine's glow, its day May bright-er, fair - er be.
feel the prom - ise is not vain That morn shall tear - less be.
from the ground there blossoms red Life that shall end - less be.

435 **Jesus, My Lord, My God, My All**

If we love one another, His love is perfected in us.—I JN. 4: 12

HENRY COLLINS, 1854   ST. CHRYSOSTOM 8s. 6 l.   JOSEPH BARNBY, 1872

1. Je - sus, my Lord, my God, my All, Hear me, blest Sav - iour,
2. Je - sus, too late I Thee have sought, How can I love Thee
3. Je - sus, what didst Thou find in me That Thou hast dealt so
4. Je - sus, of Thee shall be my song; To Thee my heart and

when I call; Hear me, and from Thy dwell - ing place Pour
as I ought? And how ex - tol Thy match-less fame, The
lov - ing - ly? How great the joy that Thou hast bought, So
soul be - long: All that I have or am is Thine; And

down the rich - es of Thy grace: Je - sus, my Lord, I
glo - rious beau - ty of Thy name? Je - sus, my Lord, I
far ex - ceed - ing hope or thought! Je - sus, my Lord, I
Thou, blest Sav - iour, Thou art mine: Je - sus, my Lord, I

Thee a - dore; O make me love Thee more and more.
Thee a - dore; O make me love Thee more and more.
Thee a - dore; O make me love Thee more and more.
Thee a - dore; O make me love Thee more and more. A - MEN.

I Know I Love Thee Better, Lord

Behold, the half was not told me.—I Kgs. 10: 7

FRANCES R. HAVERGAL

R. E. HUDSON

1. I know I love Thee bet-ter, Lord, Than an-y earth-ly joy;
2. I know that Thou art near-er still Than an-y earth-ly throng;
3. O Sav-iour, pre-cious Sav-iour mine! What will Thy pres-ence be,

For Thou hast giv-en me the peace Which noth-ing can de-stroy.
And sweet-er is the thought of Thee, Than an-y love-ly song.
If such a life of joy can crown Our walk on earth with Thee?

REFRAIN

The half has nev-er yet been told yet been told Of

love so full and free! The half has nev-er yet been

told, yet been told, The blood— it cleans-eth me! cleans-eth me!

Copyright, 1881, by R. E. Hudson

323

437 I Want to Love Him More

F. L. SNYDER   HOWARD E. SMITH

1. There is a sto-ry ev-er new, I'll tell it o'er and o'er,
2. The Prince of life, yet as a babe, He came in days of yore,
3. The sto-ry ev-er sweet-er grows, How on the cross He bore
4. O, how He suf-fered on the tree, No love like that be-fore;

How Je-sus gave His life for me; I want to love Him more.
To bring good-will and peace to men; I want to love Him more.
My sins, and by His stripes I'm healed; I want to love Him more.
I know and feel I love Him, yet I want to love Him more.

REFRAIN

I want to love Him more,   I want to love Him more;
      love Him more,   love Him more;

He did so ver-y much for me, I want to love Him more.
                                        love Him more.

Alone With Thee

438

Mary, which sat at Jesus' feet, and heard His words.—Lk. 10: 39

LIDA SHIVERS LEECH   **L. M. D.**   J. D. BRUNK

1. A - lone with Thee, 'tis wondrous sweet, To sit con - fid - ing at Thy feet;
2. A - lone with Thee for one brief hour, To be be - yond the tempter's pow'r;
3. A - lone with Thee, O let me be, Till all Thy beau - ty I shall see;

And in the sun - shine of Thy smile, Be lost to earth - ly things, a - while.
Be-neath the shad - ow of Thy cross, Earth's vain al-lure-ments seem as dross.
And from my life each day shall shine The im - age of Thy love di - vine.

REFRAIN

A - lone with Thee, 'tis won-drous sweet, To sit con - fid - ing at Thy feet;

To look in - to Thy face di - vine, And know that I'm a child of Thine.

Copyright, 1927, by Mrs. John D. Brunk. Used by permission

439

O Love Divine

Christ hath suffered for us in the flesh.—I Pet. 4: 1, 2

OLIVER WENDELL HOLMES, 1859   **ABENDS L. M.**   HERBERT S. OAKELEY, 1874

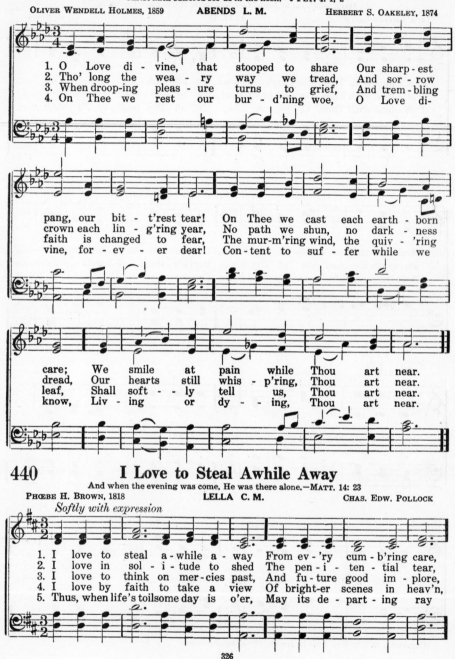

1. O Love di - vine, that stooped to share Our sharp - est
2. Tho' long the wea - ry way we tread, And sor - row
3. When droop-ing pleas - ure turns to grief, And trem - bling
4. On Thee we rest our bur - d'ning woe, O Love di -

pang, our bit - t'rest tear! On Thee we cast each earth - born
crown each lin - g'ring year, No path we shun, no dark - ness
faith is changed to fear, The mur-m'ring wind, the quiv - 'ring
vine, for - ev - er dear! Con - tent to suf - fer while we

care; We smile at pain while Thou art near.
dread, Our hearts still whis - p'ring, Thou art near.
leaf, Shall soft - - ly tell us, Thou art near.
know, Liv - ing or dy - - ing, Thou art near.

440

I Love to Steal Awhile Away

And when the evening was come, He was there alone.—MATT. 14: 23

PHŒBE H. BROWN, 1818   **LELLA C. M.**   CHAS. EDW. POLLOCK

Softly with expression

1. I love to steal a - while a - way From ev - 'ry cum - b'ring care,
2. I love in sol - i - tude to shed The pen - i - ten - tial tear,
3. I love to think on mer - cies past, And fu - ture good im - plore,
4. I love by faith to take a view Of bright - er scenes in heav'n,
5. Thus, when life's toilsome day is o'er, May its de - part - ing ray

I Love to Steal Awhile Away—Concluded

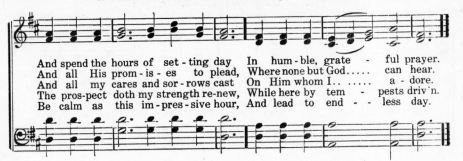

And spend the hours of set-ting day In hum-ble, grate - ful prayer.
And all His prom-is-es to plead, Where none but God..... can hear.
And all my cares and sor-rows cast On Him whom I...... a - dore.
The pros-pect doth my strength re-new, While here by tem - pests driv'n.
Be calm as this im-pres-sive hour, And lead to end - - less day.

O Master, Let Me Walk With Thee   441

Enoch walked with God.—GEN. 5: 24

WASHINGTON GLADDEN, 1879   MARYTON L. M.   H. PERCY SMITH, 1874

1. O Mas - ter, let me walk with Thee In low - ly
2. Help me the slow of heart to move By some clear,
3. Teach me Thy pa - tience; still with Thee In clos - er,
4. In hope that sends a shin - ing ray Far down the

paths of serv - ice free; Tell me Thy se - cret,
win - ning word of love; Teach me the way - ward
dear - er com - pa - ny, In work that keeps faith
fu - ture's broad - 'ning way, In peace that on - ly

help me bear The strain of toil, the fret of care.
feet to stay, And guide them in the home-ward way.
sweet and strong, In trust that tri - umphs o - - ver wrong,
Thou canst give; With Thee, O Mas - ter, let me live.

442

Begin the Day With God

I have set the Lord always before me.—Ps. 16: 8

LISBON S. M.

DANIEL READ

1. Be - gin the day with God, Kneel down to Him in prayer,
2. O - pen the book of God, And read a por - tion there,
3. Go through the day with God, What - e'er thy work may be;
4. Con - verse in mind with God; Thy spir - it heav'n-ward raise,
5. Con - clude the day with God; Thy sins to Him con - fess,

Lift up thine heart to His a - bode, And seek His love to share.
That it may hal - low all thy tho'ts, And sweet-en all thy care.
Wher-e'er thou art, at home, a - broad, He still is near to thee.
Ac - knowl-edge ev - 'ry good be-stowed, And of - fer grate-ful praise.
Trust in the Lord's a - ton - ing blood, And plead His right-eous - ness.

443

Walk in the Light

Walk as children of light.—Eph. 5: 8

MANOAH C. M.

BERNARD BARTON, 1826

From F. JOSEPH HAYDN
Arr. in HENRY W. GREATOREX's Collection, Boston, 1851

1. Walk in the light! so shalt thou know That fel - low-ship of love
2. Walk in the light! and thou shalt find Thy heart made tru - ly His
3. Walk in the light! and thou shalt own Thy dark-ness passed a - way,
4. Walk in the light! thy path shall be Peace-ful, se - rene and bright:

His Spir - it on - ly can be - stow Who reigns in light a - bove.
Who dwells in cloud-less light en-shrined, In whom no dark-ness is.
Be - cause that light hath on thee shone In which is per - fect day.
For God, by grace, shall dwell in thee, And God Him-self is light.

Follow the Path of Jesus

444

Follow His steps.—I PET. 2: 21

BOUND BROOK   7. 6. 7. 5. D.   From Hymns and Tunes, 1890

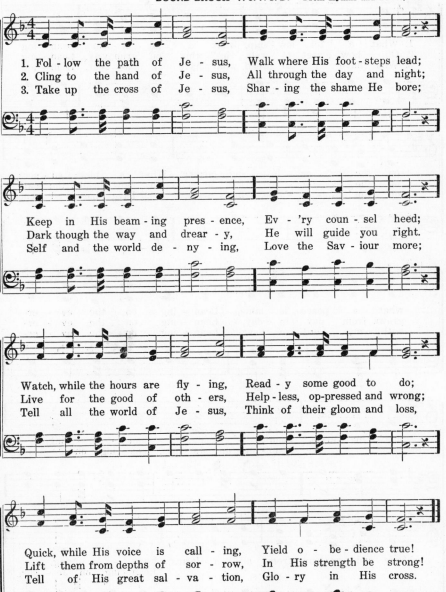

1. Fol - low the path of Je - sus, Walk where His foot - steps lead;
2. Cling to the hand of Je - sus, All through the day and night;
3. Take up the cross of Je - sus, Shar - ing the shame He bore;

Keep in His beam - ing pres - ence, Ev - 'ry coun - sel heed;
Dark though the way and drear - y, He will guide you right.
Self and the world de - ny - ing, Love the Sav - iour more;

Watch, while the hours are fly - ing, Read - y some good to do;
Live for the good of oth - ers, Help - less, op-pressed and wrong;
Tell all the world of Je - sus, Think of their gloom and loss,

Quick, while His voice is call - ing, Yield o - be - dience true!
Lift them from depths of sor - row, In His strength be strong!
Tell of His great sal - va - tion, Glo - ry in His cross.

445 Leaning On the Everlasting Arms

E. A. Hoffman

A. J. Showalter

1. What a fel-low-ship, what a joy di-vine, Lean-ing
2. Oh, how sweet to walk in this pil-grim way, Lean-ing
3. What have I to dread, what have I to fear, Lean-ing

on the ev-er-last-ing arms; What a bless-ed-ness,
on the ev-er-last-ing arms; Oh, how bright the path
on the ev-er-last-ing arms; I have bless-ed peace

what a peace is mine, Lean-ing on the ev-er-
grows from day to day, Lean-ing on the ev-er-
with my Lord so near, Lean-ing on the ev-er-

REFRAIN

last-ing arms. Lean - - ing, lean - - ing,
Lean-ing on Je-sus, lean-ing on Je-sus,

Safe and se-cure from all a-larms; Lean - - ing,
Lean-ing on Je-sus,

Leaning On the Everlasting Arms—Concluded

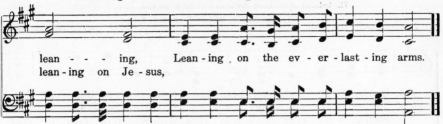

lean - - - ing, Lean-ing on the ev-er-last-ing arms.
lean-ing on Je-sus,

Abide With Me, I Need Thee   446

To-day I must abide at thy house.—Lk. 19: 5

EMMA G. DIETRICK   10s. 4l.   CHAS. EDW. POLLOCK

Slow

1. A - bide with me, I need Thee ev - 'ry day, To lead me
2. Be with me, Lord, wher - e'er my path may lead, Ful - fill Thy
3. A - bide with me, my Lord, and when at last This earth and

safe through all the wea - ry way; When storms sur - round and
Word, sup - ply my ev - 'ry need; Help me to live each
all its wea - ry cares are past, I'll pray no more that

on - ly clouds I see, Lord, be my com - fort and a - bide with me!
day more close to Thee, And oh, dear Lord, I pray, a - bide with me!
Thou a - bide with me, For then, at last, I shall a - bide with Thee!

331

447 O Lamb of God, Still Keep Me

The beloved of the Lord shall dwell in safety by Him —DEUT. 33: 12

ST. GEORGE'S, BOLTON 7. 6. 7. 6. D.

JAMES G. DECK, 1842. Alt.

JAMES WALCH, 1875

1. O Lamb of God, still keep me Near to Thy wound - ed side;
2. 'Tis on - ly in Thee hid - ing, I feel my life se - cure;
3. Soon shall my eyes be - hold Thee With rap - ture, face to face;

'Tis on - ly there in safe - ty And peace I can a - bide.
On - ly in Thee a - bid - ing, The con - flict can en - dure:
One half hath not been told me Of all Thy pow'r and grace;

What foes and snares sur - round me, What doubts and fears with - in!
Thine arm the vic - t'ry gain - eth O'er ev - 'ry hate - ful foe;
Thy beau - ty, Lord, and glo - ry, The won - ders of Thy love,

Thy grace that sought and found me A - lone can keep me clean.
Thy love my heart sus - tain - eth In all its cares and woe.
Shall be the end - less sto - ry Of all Thy saints a - bove.

With Me Abide

Abide with us, for it is toward evening.—LK. 24: 29

G. P. HOTT

8. 6. 8. 6. D. Ref.

WILL H. RUEBUSH

1. With me a - bide, the morn - ing hour Fades swift - ly in - to
2. With me a - bide, the noon - day hour Calls me in tones of
3. With me a - bide, the eve - ning falls A - bout life's qui - et

noon; Life's gold - en hues, like spar - kling dews, Will
love; I glad - ly hear when Thou art near To
way; If near my side Thou wilt a - bide, With

REFRAIN

van - ish, oh, so soon. A - bide with me, a-
whis - per from a - bove. A - bide with me,
joy shall end the day.

bide with me, I need Thee all the while, To
a - bide with me,

cres - cen - do *dim - in - u - en - do*

fill and still my rest - less heart, My life to rec - on - cile.

449 Fresh From the Throne of Glory

There is a river, the streams whereof shall make glad the city of God.—Ps. 46: 4

HORATIUS BONAR, 1868   RIVER OF LIFE P. M.   ROBERT LOWRY

1. Fresh from the throne of glo - ry, Bright in its crys - tal gleam,
2. Stream full of life and glad - ness, Spring of all health and peace,
3. Riv - er of God, I greet thee, Not now a - far, but near,

Bursts out the liv - ing foun - tain, Swells on the liv - ing stream:
No harps by thee hang si - lent, Nor hap - py voi - ces cease:
My soul to thy still wa - ters Hastes in its thirst - ings here:

Bless - ed riv - er, Let me ev - er Feast my eyes on thee,....
Tran - quil riv - er, Let me ev - er Sit and sing by thee,....
Ho - ly riv - er, Let me ev - er Drink of on - ly thee,....

Bless - ed riv - er, Let me ev - er Feast my eyes on thee.
Tran - quil riv - er, Let me ev - er Sit and sing by thee.
Ho - ly riv - er, Let me ev - er Drink of on - ly thee.

334

In the Cross of Christ I Glory

God forbid that I should glory, save in the cross of our Lord Jesus Christ.—GAL. 6: 14

JOHN BOWRING, 1825

RATHBUN 8. 7. 8. 7.

I. CONKEY

1. In the cross of Christ I glo - ry, Tow - 'ring o'er the wrecks of time;
2. When the woes of life o'er - take me, Hopes de - ceive and fears an - noy,
3. When the sun of bliss is beam - ing Light and love up - on my way,
4. Bane and bless - ing, pain and pleas - ure, By the cross are sanc - ti - fied;

All the light of sa - cred sto - ry, Gath - ers round its head sub - lime.
Nev - er shall the cross for - sake me; Lo! it glows with peace and joy.
From the cross the ra - diance streaming, Adds more lus - ter to the day.
Peace is there that knows no meas - ure, Joys that thro' all time a - bide.

Thou Art My Portion

Thou art my portion, O Lord.—Ps. 119: 57

BOARDMAN C. M.

ISAAC WATTS, 1719

L. DEVEREUX
Arr. by GEORGE KINGSLEY

1. Thou art my por - tion, O my God; Soon as I know Thy way,
2. I choose the path of heav'n - ly truth, And glo - ry in my choice;
3. Thy pre - cepts and Thy heav'n - ly grace I set be - fore mine eyes;
4. Now I am Thine, for - ev - er Thine; O save Thy serv - ant, Lord;

My heart makes haste t' o - bey Thy Word, And suf - fers no de - lay.
Not all the rich - es of the earth Could make me so re - joice.
Thence I de - rive my dai - ly strength, And there my com - fort lies.
Thou art my shield, my hid - ing - place; My hope is in Thy Word.

452   When Peace, Like a River

H. G. SPAFFORD

P. P. BLISS

1. When peace, like a riv - er, at - tend - eth my way,
2. Though Sa - tan should buf - fet, though tri - als should come,
3. My sin— O the bliss of this glo - ri - ous thought—
4. O Lord, haste the day when my faith shall be sight,

When sor - rows like sea bil - lows roll; What - ev - er my
Let this blest as - sur - ance con - trol, That Christ hath re-
My sin— not in part, but the whole, Is nailed to His
The clouds be rolled back as a scroll, The trump shall re-

lot, Thou hast taught me to say, It is well, it is
gard - ed my help - less es - tate, And hath shed His own
cross and I bear it no more— Praise the Lord, praise the
sound, and the Lord shall de - scend, "E - ven so"— It is

REFRAIN

well with my soul.   It is well............... with my
blood for my soul.
Lord, O my soul!
well with my soul.   It is well

When Peace Like a River—Concluded

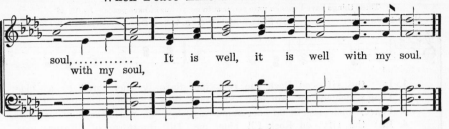

soul,........... It is well, it is well with my soul.
with my soul,

O How Happy Are They

453

If ye know these things, happy are ye if ye do them.—Jn. 13: 17

CHARLES WESLEY, 1749   6. 6. 9. 6. 6. 9.

1. Oh, how hap - py are they Who their Sav - iour o - bey, And have
2. 'Twas a heav - en be - low My Re - deem - er to know, And the
3. Je - sus all the day long Was my joy and my song; Oh, that
4. Now my rem - nant of days Would I spend in His praise, Who has

laid up their treas - ures a - bove! Oh, what tongue can ex - press The sweet
an - gels could do noth-ing more, Than to fall at His feet, And the
more His sal - va - tion might see! "He hath loved me," I cried, "He hath
died, me from death to re - deem; Whether man - y or few, All my

com - fort and peace Of a soul in its ear - li - est love.
sto - ry re - peat, And the lov - er of sin - ners a - dore.
suf - fered and died, To re - deem such a reb - el as me!"
days are His due— May they all be de - vot - ed to Him.

454 In the Rifted Rock

These things have I spoken unto you that in me ye might have peace.—JN. 16: 33

MARY D. JAMES   SWEETLY RESTING 8. 7. 8. 7. D.   WILLIAM W. BENTLY

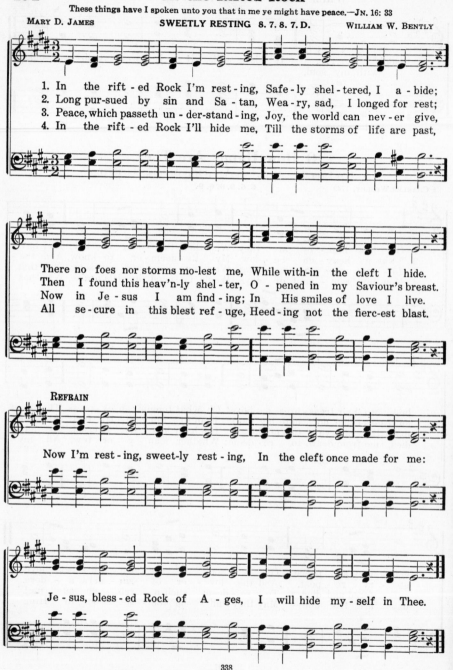

1. In the rift - ed Rock I'm rest - ing, Safe - ly shel - tered, I a - bide;
2. Long pur-sued by sin and Sa - tan, Wea - ry, sad, I longed for rest;
3. Peace, which passeth un - der-stand - ing, Joy, the world can nev - er give,
4. In the rift - ed Rock I'll hide me, Till the storms of life are past,

There no foes nor storms mo-lest me, While with-in the cleft I hide.
Then I found this heav'n-ly shel - ter, O - pened in my Saviour's breast.
Now in Je - sus I am find - ing; In His smiles of love I live.
All se - cure in this blest ref - uge, Heed-ing not the fierc-est blast.

REFRAIN

Now I'm rest - ing, sweet-ly rest - ing, In the cleft once made for me:

Je - sus, bless - ed Rock of A - ges, I will hide my - self in Thee.

338

Peace, Perfect Peace

455

My peace I give unto you.—JN. 14: 27

EDWARD H. BICKERSTETH, 1875 PAX TECUM 10. 10. Arr. by CHARLES J. VINCENT, 1876

GEORGE T. CALDBECK

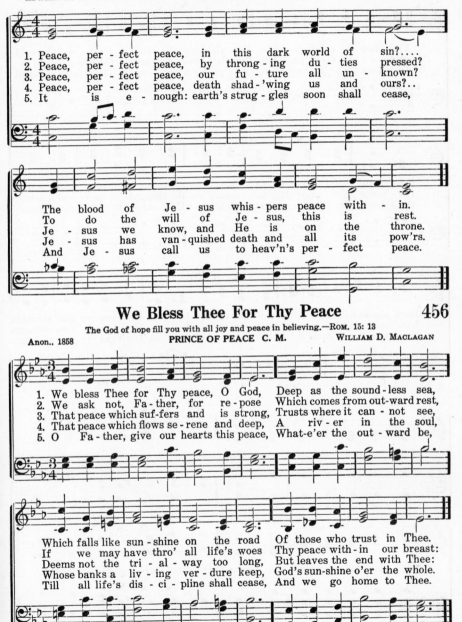

1. Peace, per - fect peace, in this dark world of sin?....
2. Peace, per - fect peace, by throng - ing du - ties pressed?
3. Peace, per - fect peace, our fu - ture all un - known?
4. Peace, per - fect peace, death shad - 'wing us and ours?..
5. It is e - nough: earth's strug - gles soon shall cease,

The blood of Je - sus whis - pers peace with - in.
To do the will of Je - sus, this is rest.
Je - sus we know, and He is on the throne.
Je - sus has van - quished death and all its pow'rs.
And Je - sus call us to heav'n's per - fect peace.

We Bless Thee For Thy Peace

456

The God of hope fill you with all joy and peace in believing.—ROM. 15: 13

Anon., 1858 PRINCE OF PEACE C. M. WILLIAM D. MACLAGAN

1. We bless Thee for Thy peace, O God, Deep as the sound - less sea,
2. We ask not, Fa - ther, for re - pose Which comes from out - ward rest,
3. That peace which suf - fers and is strong, Trusts where it can - not see,
4. That peace which flows se - rene and deep, A riv - er in the soul,
5. O Fa - ther, give our hearts this peace, What-e'er the out - ward be,

Which falls like sun - shine on the road Of those who trust in Thee.
If we may have thro' all life's woes Thy peace with - in our breast:
Deems not the tri - al - way too long, But leaves the end with Thee:
Whose banks a liv - ing ver - dure keep, God's sun-shine o'er the whole.
Till all life's dis - ci - pline shall cease, And we go home to Thee.

457 Yield Not to Temptation

God . . . will with the temptation also make a way to escape.—I COR. 10: 13

H. R. PALMER   6. 5. 6. 5. D. Ref.   H. R. PALMER, 1868

1. Yield not to temp-ta-tion, For yield-ing is sin; Each vic-t'ry will
2. Shun e-vil com-pan-ions, Bad lan-guage dis-dain, God's name hold in
3. To him that o'er-com-eth, God giv-eth a crown; Thro' faith we shall

help you Some oth-er to win; Fight man-ful-ly on-ward,
rev-'rence Nor take it in vain; Be thought-ful and ear-nest,
con-quer, Tho' oft-en cast down; He who is our Sav-iour,

Dark pas-sions sub-due, Look ev-er to Je-sus, He'll car-ry you through.
Kind-heart-ed and true, Look ev-er to Je-sus, He'll car-ry you through.
Our strength will re-new, Look ev-er to Je-sus, He'll car-ry you through.

CHORUS

Ask the Sav-iour to help you, Com-fort, strengthen and keep you;

He is will-ing to aid you, He will car-ry you through.

Faith of Our Fathers

458

Earnestly contend for the faith which was once delivered unto the saints.—JUDE 3

FREDERICK W. FABER, 1849   **ST. CATHARINE L. M. 6 l.**   Adapted by J. G. WALTON

1. Faith of our fa - thers! liv - ing still In spite of dun - geon,
2. Our fa - thers, chained in pris - ons dark, Were still in heart and
3. Faith of our fa - thers! we will love Both friend and foe in

fire, and sword; O how our hearts beat high with joy
con - science free: How sweet would be their chil - dren's fate,
all our strife; And preach thee, too, as love knows how,

When-e'er we hear that glo - rious word! Faith of our fa - thers!
If they, like them, could die for thee! Faith of our fa - thers!
By kind - ly words and vir - tuous life: Faith of our fa - thers!

ho - ly faith! We will be true to thee till death!
ho - ly faith! We will be true to thee till death!
ho - ly faith! We will be true to thee till death!

459   Would Men Know?

E. O. S.

E. O. SELLERS

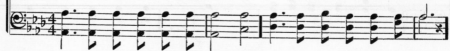

1. Would men know you've been with Je - sus, Can they feel His pres-ence near?
2. Would men know by word and ac - tion, In the small things of this life,
3. "In - as - much as un - to oth - ers Ye have done these things," said He,
4. Not by word of lip, full oft - en, Is the world con-vinced of truth,

As with them you joy and la - bor, As with them you jour - ney here?
In the dai - ly round of du - ty, In the midst of toil and strife?
"Un - to Me" ye did the serv - ice, Wit - ness that all men may see.
But the deed of lov - ing serv - ice, From the heart, brings fullest proof.

CHORUS

Can men tell that you love Je - sus, Can they by your life and mine,

See in dai - ly walk and ac - tion, That we have His life di - vine?

di - vine?

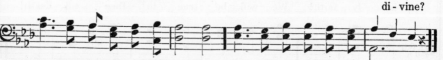

I Would Be True

Be thou an example of the believers.—I TIM. 4: 12

HOWARD ARNOLD WALTER 11. 10. 11. 10. 10. JOSEPH YATES PEEK

1. I would be true, for there are those who trust me; I would be
2. I would be friend of all—the foe, the friend-less; I would be

pure, for there are those who care; I would be strong, for
giv - ing, and for - get the gift; I would be hum - ble,

there is much to suf - fer; I would be brave, for there is
for I know my weak - ness; I would look up, and live, and

much to dare, I would be brave, for there is much to dare.
love, and lift, I would look up, and live, and love, and lift.

461 O For a Faith That Will Not Shrink

Beholding the steadfastness of your faith in Christ.—COL. 2: 5

EVAN C. M.

WILLIAM H. BATHURST, 1831

LOWELL MASON
Arr. from WILLIAM H. HAVERGAL

1. O for a faith that will not shrink Tho' pressed by many a foe,
2. That will not mur-mur nor com-plain Be-neath the chas-t'ning rod,
3. A faith that keeps the nar-row way Till life's last spark is fled,
4. Lord, give me such a faith as this, And then, what-e'er may come,

That will not trem-ble on the brink Of an-y earth-ly woe;
But in the hour of grief or pain Can lean up-on its God;
And with a pure and heav'n-ly ray Lights up a dy-ing bed.
I'll taste e'en here the hal-lowed bliss Of an e-ter-nal home.

462 How Sweet, How Heavenly

Increase and abound in love one toward another.— I THESS. 3: 12

JOSEPH SWAIN, 1792

BROWN C. M.

WILLIAM B. BRADBURY, 1844

1. How sweet, how heav'n-ly is the sight, When those who love the Lord
2. When each can feel His broth-er's sigh, And with Him bear a part;
3. When, free from en-vy, scorn, and pride, Our wish-es all a-bove,
4. Let love, in one de-light-ful stream, Thro' ev-'ry bos-om flow,
5. Love is the gold-en chain that binds The hap-py souls a-bove;

In one an-oth-er's peace de-light, And so ful-fill His Word.
When sor-row flows from eye to eye, And joy from heart to heart.
Each can his broth-er's fail-ings hide, And show a broth-er's love.
And un-ion sweet, and dear es-teem, In ev-'ry ac-tion glow.
And he's an heir of heav'n that finds His bos-om glow with love.

Whiter Than Snow

Wash me, and I shall be whiter than snow.—Ps. 51: 7

James Nicholson, 1872   11. 11. 11. 11.   Ref.   William G. Fischer, 1872

1. Lord Je - sus, I long to be per - fect - ly whole; I
2. Lord Je - sus, look down from Thy throne in the skies, And
3. Lord Je - sus, for this I most hum - bly en - treat; I
4. Lord Je - sus, Thou se - est I pa - tient - ly wait; Come

want Thee for - ev - er to live in my soul; Break down ev - 'ry
help me to make a com - plete sac - ri - fice; I give up my-
wait, bless - ed Lord, at Thy cru - ci - fied feet; By faith, for my
now, and with - in me a new heart cre - ate; To those who have

i - dol, cast out ev - 'ry foe; Now wash me, and I shall be
self, and what - ev - er I know—Now wash me, and I shall be
cleansing, I see Thy blood flow— Now wash me, and I shall be
sought Thee, Thou nev-er saidst No— Now wash me, and I shall be

REFRAIN

whit - er than snow. Whit - er than snow, yes, whit - er than

snow; Now wash me, and I shall be whit - er than snow.

12

464

Purer in Heart

Blessed are the pure in heart, for they shall see God.—MATT. 5: 8

Mrs. A. L. DAVISON   6. 4. 6. 4. 6. 6. 4. 4.   J. H. FILLMORE

1. Pur - er in heart, O God, Help me to be; May I de-
2. Pur - er in heart, O God, Help me to be; Teach me to
3. Pur - er in heart, O God, Help me to be; That I Thy

vote my life Whol - ly to Thee. Watch Thou my way-ward feet,
do Thy will Most lov - ing - ly. Be Thou my Friend and Guide,
ho - ly face One day may see. Keep me from se - cret sin,

Guide me with coun - sel sweet; Pur - er in heart, Help me to be.
Let me with Thee a - bide; Pur - er in heart, Help me to be.
Reign Thou my soul with - in; Pur - er in heart, Help me to be.

465

O Thou That Hear'st When Sinners Cry

A broken and a contrite heart, O God, Thou wilt not despise.—Ps. 51: 17

ISAAC WATTS, 1719   PENITENCE L. M.   ST. ALBAN'S Tune Book

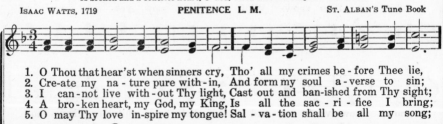

1. O Thou that hear'st when sinners cry, Tho' all my crimes be - fore Thee lie,
2. Cre-ate my na - ture pure with-in, And form my soul a - verse to sin;
3. I can-not live with-out Thy light, Cast out and ban-ished from Thy sight;
4. A bro-ken heart, my God, my King, Is all the sac - ri - fice I bring;
5. O may Thy love in-spire my tongue! Sal - va - tion shall be all my song;

O Thou That Hear'st When Sinners Cry—Concluded

Be-hold them not with an - gry look, But blot their mem-'ry from Thy book.
Let Thy good Spir-it ne'er de-part, Nor hide Thy pres-ence from my heart.
Thy ho - ly joys, my God, re-store, And guard me that I fall no more.
The God of grace will ne'er de-spise A bro-ken heart for sac - ri - fice.
And all my pow'rs shall join to bless The Lord, my strength and righteousness.

Keep Thyself Pure

466

Having on the breastplate of righteousness.—EPH. 6: 14

ADELAIDE M. PLUMTRE, 1908   PENTECOST L. M.   WILLIAM BOYD, 1868

1. Keep thy - self pure! Christ's sol - dier, hear, Thro' life's loud
2. Keep thy - self pure! thrice bless - ed he Whose heart from
3. Keep thy - self pure! for He who died, Him - self for
4. O Ho - ly Spir - it, keep us pure, Grant us Thy

strife, the call rings clear. Thy Cap - tain speaks: His
taint of sin is free; His feet shall stand where
thy sake sanc - ti - fied; Then hear Him speak - ing
strength when sins al - lure; Our bod - ies are Thy

word o - bey; So shall thy strength be as thy day.
saints have trod, He with rapt eyes shall see his God.
from the skies, And vic - tor o'er temp - ta - tion rise.
tem - ple, Lord; Be Thou in thought and act a - dored.

467 Open the Wells of Salvation

Spring up, O well.—NUM. 21: 17

10. 9. 10. 9. D.

E. A. HOFFMAN

CHAS. EDW. POLLOCK

Earnestly

1. Lord, I am fond - ly, ear - nest - ly long - ing In - to Thy
2. Dead to the world would I be, O Fa - ther! Dead un - to
3. I would be Thine, and serve Thee for - ev - er, Filled with Thy

ho - ly like - ness to grow; Thirst-ing for more and deep - er com-
sin, a - live un - to Thee; Cru - ci - fy all the earth - ly with-
Spir - it, lost in Thy love; Come to my heart, Lord, come with a-

mun - ion, Yearn-ing Thy love more ful - ly to know.
in me, Emp - tied of sin and self may I be. O - pen the
noint-ing, Show - ers of grace send down from a - bove.

REFRAIN

wells of grace and sal - va - tion, Pour the rich
O - pen the wells of grace and sal - va - tion,

streams deep in - to my heart; Cleanse and re - fine my
Pour the rich streams deep in-to my heart; Cleanse and re - fine my

Open the Wells of Salvation—Concluded

tho't and af - fec - tion, Seal me and make me pure as Thou art.
tho't and af - fec - tion, Seal me and make me pure as Thou art.

Lord, For To-morrow and Its Needs

468

E. R. WILBERFORCE

H. R. PALMER, 1887

1. Lord, for to-mor-row and its needs I do not pray; Keep me, my God, from
2. Let me both dil - i - gent-ly work, and du - ly pray; Let me be kind in
3. Let me be slow to do my will, prompt to o - bey; Help me to sac - ri -

stain of sin, just for to - day. Let me no wrong or i - dle word
word and deed, Fa - ther, to - day. Let me in sea - son, Lord, go forth,
fice my - self glad - ly to - day. So for to - mor - row and its needs

cres. *ff* *rall.*

un - think-ing say; Set Thou a seal up - on my lips, Fa - ther, to - day.
in sea - son stay; Let me be faith-ful to Thy grace, dear Lord, to - day.
I do not pray; Still keep me, guide me, love me, Lord, thro' each to - day.

469 More Holiness Give Me

P. P. Bliss

P. P. Bliss, 1873

1. More ho-li-ness give me, More striv-ings with-in;......
2. More grat-i-tude give me, More trust in the Lord,...
3. More pu-ri-ty give me, More strength to o'er-come;...

More pa-tience in suf-f'ring, More sor-row for sin;
More pride in His glo-ry, More hope in His Word;
More free-dom from earth-stains, More long-ings for home;

More faith in my Sav-iour, More sense of His care;
More tears for His sor-rows, More pain at His grief;
More fit for the king-dom, More used would I be;

More joy in His serv-ice, More pur-pose in prayer.
More meek-ness in tri-al, More praise for re-lief.
More bless-ed and ho-ly, More, Sav-iour, like Thee.

Who Are These in Bright Array

470

What are these which are arrayed in white robes?—REV. 7: 13, 14

JAMES MONTGOMERY, 1819   RAPTURE 7. 7. 7. 7. D.   HAYDN

1. Who are these in bright ar - ray, This in - nu - mer - a - ble throng,
2. These thro' fi - er - y tri - als trod; These from great af - flic - tion came;
3. Hun - ger, thirst, dis - ease un-known, On im - mor - tal fruits they feed;

Round the al - tar, night and day, Tun - ing their tri - um-phant song?
Now be - fore the throne of God, Sealed with His e - ter - nal name,
Them the Lamb a - midst the throne, Shall to liv - ing foun-tains lead:

"Wor - thy is the Lamb, once slain, Bless - ing, hon - or, glo - ry, pow'r,
Clad in rai - ment pure and white, Vic - tor palms in ev - 'ry hand,
Joy and glad-ness ban - ish sighs; Per - fect love dis - pels their fears;

Wis - dom, rich - es to ob - tain, New do - min - ion ev - 'ry hour."
Thro' their great Re - deem-er's might, More than con - quer-ors they stand.
And for - ev - er from their eyes God shall wipe a - way their tears.

471 Come, We That Love the Lord

We took sweet counsel together, and walked in the house of God in company.—Ps. 55: 14

WE'RE MARCHING TO ZION 6. 6. 8. 8. 6. 6. Ref.

ISAAC WATTS, 1709

ROBERT LOWRY, 1867

Spirited

1. Come, we that love the Lord, And let our joys be known; Join
2. Let those re - fuse to sing Who nev - er knew our God; But
3. The hill of Zi - on yields A thou - sand sa - cred sweets, Be -
4. Then let our songs a - bound, And ev - 'ry tear be dry; We're

in a song with sweet ac - cord, Join in a song with sweet ac - cord,
chil - dren of the heav'n-ly King, But chil - dren of the heav'n-ly King,
fore we reach the heav'n-ly fields, Be - fore we reach the heav'n-ly fields,
marching thro' Im-man-uel's ground, We're marching thro' Im-man-uel's ground,

And thus sur - round the throne, And thus sur - round the throne.
May speak their joys a - broad, May speak their joys a - broad.
Or walk the gold - en streets, Or walk the gold - en streets.
To fair - er worlds on high, To fair - er worlds on high.

1. And thus sur-round the throne, And thus sur - round the throne.

REFRAIN

We're march - ing to Zi - on, Beau - ti - ful, beau - ti - ful Zi - on; We're
We're march-ing on to Zi - on,

Come, We That Love the Lord—Concluded

march-ing up-ward to Zi - - on, The beau-ti-ful cit-y of God.
Zi - on, Zi - on,

So Let Our Lives and Lips Express 472

Adorn the doctrine of God our Saviour in all things.—TITUS 2: 10-14

ISAAC WATTS, 1709   UXBRIDGE L. M.   LOWELL MASON, 1830

1. So let our lives and lips ex - press The ho - ly
2. Thus shall we best pro - claim a - broad The hon - or
3. Our flesh and sense must be de - nied; Pas - sion and
4. Re - lig - ion bears our spir - its up, While we ex -
5. That sa - cred stream, Thy ho - ly Word, That all our

Gos - pel we pro - fess; So let our walks and
of our Sav - iour God; When the sal - va - tion
en - vy, lust and pride; While jus - tice, tem - p'rance,
pect that bless - ed hope, The bright ap - pear - ance
rag - ing fear con - trols: Sweet peace Thy prom - is -

vir - tues shine, To prove the doc - trine all di - vine.
reigns with - in, And grace sub - dues the pow'r of sin.
truth and love Our in - ward pi - e - ty ap - prove.
of the Lord, And faith stands lean - ing on His Word.
es af - ford, And give new strength to faint - ing souls.

473

Jesus Calls Us

They forsook all, and followed Him.—Lk. 5: 11

Mrs. Cecil F. Alexander, 1853   GALILEE 8. 7. 8. 7.   William H. Jude

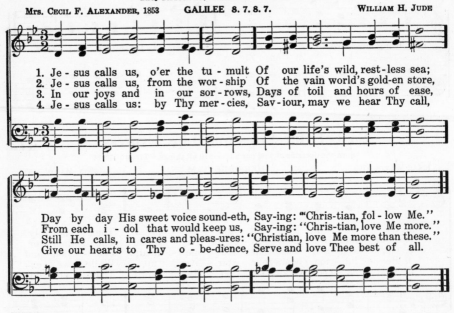

1. Je - sus calls us, o'er the tu - mult Of our life's wild, rest-less sea;
2. Je - sus calls us, from the wor - ship Of the vain world's gold-en store,
3. In our joys and in our sor - rows, Days of toil and hours of ease,
4. Je - sus calls us: by Thy mer - cies, Sav-iour, may we hear Thy call,

Day by day His sweet voice sound-eth, Say-ing: "Chris-tian, fol - low Me."
From each i - dol that would keep us, Say-ing: "Chris-tian, love Me more."
Still He calls, in cares and pleas-ures: "Christian, love Me more than these."
Give our hearts to Thy o - be-dience, Serve and love Thee best of all.

474

My Soul, Be On Thy Guard

Be sober, be vigilant.—I Pet. 5: 8

George Heath, d. 1822   LABAN S. M.   Lowell Mason, 1830

1. My soul, be on thy guard; Ten thou - sand foes a - rise;
2. O watch, and fight, and pray; The bat - tle ne'er give o'er;
3. Ne'er think the vic - t'ry won, Nor lay thine ar - mor down;
4. Fight on, my soul, till death Shall bring thee to thy God;

The hosts of sin are press-ing hard To draw thee from the skies.
Re - new it bold - ly ev - 'ry day, And help di - vine im - plore.
Thy ar - duous work will not be done, Till thou ob - tain thy crown.
He'll take thee, at thy part - ing breath, To His di - vine a - bode.

I'm Pressing On the Upward Way

The high calling of God in Christ Jesus.—PHIL. 3: 14

HIGHER GROUND L. M. D.

JOHNSON OATMAN, Jr.

CHARLES H. GABRIEL

1. I'm press-ing on the up-ward way, New heights I'm gain-ing ev-'ry day;
2. My heart has no de-sire to stay Where doubts a-rise and fears dis-may;
3. I want to live a-bove the world, Tho' Sa-tan's darts at me are hurled;
4. I want to scale the ut-most height, And catch a gleam of glo-ry bright;

Still pray-ing as I'm on-ward bound, "Lord, plant my feet on high-er ground."
Tho' some may dwell where these abound, My prayer, my aim is high-er ground.
For faith has caught the joy-ful sound, The song of saints on high-er ground.
But still I'll pray till heav'n I've found, "Lord, lead me on to high-er ground."

REFRAIN

Lord, lift me up and let me stand, By faith, on heav-en's ta-ble-land,

A high-er plane than I have found; Lord, plant my feet on high-er ground.

476

When Trials and Temptations

If we suffer, . . . we shall also reign with Him.—II TIM. 2: 12

ABRAM METZLER   BE NOT AFRAID 7. 6. 7. 6. D. Ref.   From Temple Star

1. When tri - als and temp-ta - tions A -round thee dark-ly flow, When storms and
2. When wa-ters of af - flic - tion May seem to o - ver-flow, Or through some
3. The soul that Je - sus lov - eth He'll chas-ten and re-fine, That like a
4. "Let not your heart be troub-led," Oh, hear the Saviour speak, God com-forts

griefs as - sail thee To bring thy cour - age low, Be not dis - cour-aged,
fi - ery tri - al You may be called to go, Keep up your faith and
gold - en lus - ter It may the bright - er shine; The dross a - lone will
you in sor - rows, When sad you feel and weak; He leads you through the

broth - er, But firm - ly stand and wait; The clouds a - gain will van - ish,
cour - age, The Lord will dis - si - pate The waves that dash a - gainst thee,
per - ish, The gold is bright-er made; Be not dis - cour-aged, broth - er,
riv - er Which sin-ners can - not wade, And death shall lose its ter - rors,

REFRAIN

Oh, be thou not a - fraid!
Fear not, be not a - fraid! There is sweet rest in heav'n, There is sweet rest in
Fear not, be not a - fraid!
Fear not, be not a - fraid!

When Trials and Temptations—Concluded

heav'n, There is sweet rest, there is sweet rest, There is sweet rest in heav'n.

Thou Thinkest, Lord, of Me

477

The Lord thinketh upon me.—Ps. 40: 17

E. D. MUND 8. 8. 8. 6. Ref. E. S. LORENZ

1. A - mid the tri - als which I meet, A - mid the thorns that pierce my feet,
2. The cares of life come thronging fast, Up - on my soul their shad-ow cast;
3. Let shadows come, let shad-ows go, Let life be bright or dark with woe,

FINE

One thought re - mains su - preme-ly sweet, Thou think - est, Lord, of me!
Their gloom re - minds my heart at last, Thou think - est, Lord, of me!
I am con - tent for this I know, Thou think - est, Lord, of me!

D.S.—*What need I fear since Thou art near, And think - est, Lord, of me!*

REFRAIN D.S.

Thou think-est, Lord, of me, Thou think-est, Lord, of me!
of me, of me!

478 The Righteous Marching Home

I therefore so run, not as uncertainly.—I Cor. 9: 24-26

W. P. Rivers   C. M. Ref.   Arr. by R. M. McIntosh

1. As Zi - on's pil - grims in ac - cord, The sol - diers of our King,
2. In fel - low - ship of joys and woes, We'll bear the com - mon strife,
3. With faith and prayer we'll urge the fray, Nor will we fear or fly;
4. Then while the Spir - it leads us on, Our march we'll still pur - sue,
5. Tho' worn with bat - tle-wounds and scars, Yet true to Christ in love,

In cov - 'nant bands we'll serve the Lord, And all His prais - es sing.
And on - ward press, thro' all our foes, And win e - ter - nal life.
For vic - t'ry waits us on the way, And crowns a - bove the sky.
Un - til the heav'n - ly goal is won, And we our King shall view.
We'll dwell with God be - yond the stars At home, in heav'n a - bove.

Refrain

See the right-eous march-ing on!.... And the an - gels bid them come;

D.S.—To.... wel - come trav - 'lers home,.. To.... wel - come trav - 'lers home;

D.S.

And the Sav - iour stands a - wait - ing To wel - come trav - 'lers home.
And the Sav - iour stands a - wait - ing To wel - come trav - 'lers home.

Give Me the Wings of Faith

479

They overcame him by the blood of the Lamb, and by the word of their testimony.—Rev. 12: 11

ISAAC WATTS, 1709   **WILTSHIRE C. M.**   GEORGE T. SMART

1. Give me the wings of faith to rise With-in the veil, and see
2. Once they were mourn-ing here be-low, And poured out cries and tears;
3. I ask them whence their vic-t'ry came; They, with u-nit-ed breath,
4. They marked the foot-steps that He trod, His zeal in-spired their breast;

The saints a-bove, how great their joys, How bright their glo-ries be.
They wres-tled hard, as we do now, With sins, and doubts, and fears.
As-cribe their con-quest to the Lamb, Their tri-umph to His death.
And, fol-l'wing their in-car-nate God, Pos-sess the prom-ised rest.

Oh, Happy is the Man

480

Her ways are ways of pleasantness.—Prov. 3: 17

MICHAEL BRUCE. Alt.   **MATTIE 8. 6. 8. 6. 6.**   L. C. EVERETT

Moderato

1. Oh, hap-py is the man who hears In-struc-tion's warning voice, And who ce-
2. For she hath treasures greater far Than east and west un-fold; And her re-
3. In her right hand is length of days For those who heed her voice; Her left hand
4. She guides the young with in-no-cence In pleasure's paths to tread; A crown of
5. Ac-cord-ing as her la-bors rise, So her re-wards increase; Her ways are

les-tial wisdom makes His ear-ly, on-ly choice, His ear-ly, on-ly choice.
wards more precious are Than all their stores of gold, Than all their stores of gold.
of-fers wealth and praise To make her sons re-joice, To make her sons re-joice.
glo-ry she be-stows Up-on the hoar-y head, Up-on the hoar-y head.
ways of pleas-ant-ness, And all her paths are peace, And all her paths are peace.

481

The Cross is Not Greater

Come, take up thy cross and follow me.—MARK. 10: 21

Com. BALLINGTON BOOTH

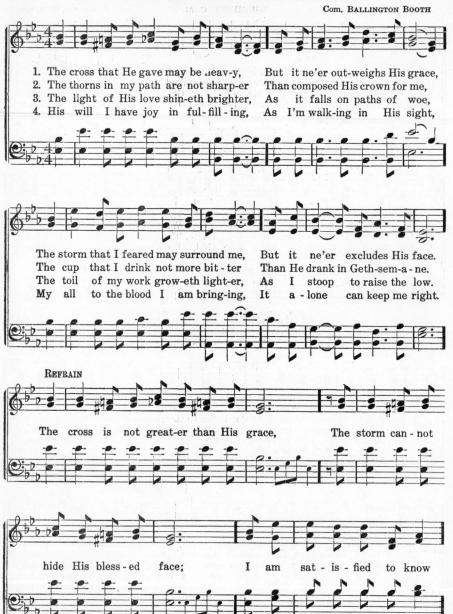

1. The cross that He gave may be heav-y,   But it ne'er out-weighs His grace,
2. The thorns in my path are not sharp-er   Than composed His crown for me,
3. The light of His love shin-eth brighter,   As it falls on paths of woe,
4. His will I have joy in ful-fill-ing,   As I'm walk-ing in His sight,

The storm that I feared may surround me,   But it ne'er excludes His face.
The cup that I drink not more bit-ter   Than He drank in Geth-sem-a-ne.
The toil of my work grow-eth light-er,   As I stoop to raise the low.
My all to the blood I am bring-ing,   It a-lone can keep me right.

REFRAIN

The cross is not great-er than His grace,   The storm can-not

hide His bless-ed face;   I am sat-is-fied to know

The Cross is Not Greater—Concluded

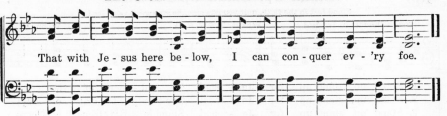

That with Je - sus here be - low, I can con - quer ev - 'ry foe.

Almighty God, Whose Only Son 482

Confess your faults one to another, and pray one for another.—JAS. 5: 16

HENRY W. BAKER   CANONBURY L. M.   R. SCHUMANN

1. Al - might - y God, whose on - ly Son O'er sin and
2. In His dear name to Thee we pray For all who
3. And some with - in Thy sa - cred fold, To ho - ly
4. And many a quick - ened soul with - in There lurks the
5. O give re - pent - ance true and deep To all Thy
6. That so from an - gel hosts a - bove May rise a

death the tri - umph won, And ev - er lives to
err and go a - stray, For sin - ners, where - so-
things are dead and cold, And waste the pre - cious
se - cret love of sin, A way - ward will, or
lost and wan - d'ring sheep! And kin - dle in their
sweet - er song of love, And we, with all the

in - ter - cede For souls who Thy sweet mer - cy need;
e'er they be, Who do not serve and hon - or Thee.
hours of life In self - ish ease, or toil, or strife;
anx - ious fears, Or lin - g'ring taint of by - gone years.
hearts the fire Of ho - ly love and pure de - sire:
blest, a - dore Thy name, O God, for - ev - er - more.

483 Stand Up, Stand Up For Jesus

Stand fast in the faith, quit you like men, be strong.—I Cor. 16: 13

GEORGE DUFFIELD, Jr., 1858   WEBB 7. 6. 7. 6. D.   GEORGE J. WEBB, 1837

1. Stand up, stand up for Je - sus! Ye sol - diers of the cross;
2. Stand up, stand up for Je - sus! The trump - et call o - bey;
3. Stand up, stand up for Je - sus! Stand in His strength a - lone;
4. Stand up, stand up for Je - sus! The strife will not be long;

Lift high His roy - al ban - ner, It must not suf - fer loss:
Forth to the might - y con - flict, In this His glo - rious day:
The arm of flesh will fail you; Ye dare not trust your own:
This day the noise of bat - tle, The next the vic - tor's song:

From vic - t'ry un - to vic - t'ry His ar - my shall He lead,
Ye that are men, now serve Him, A - gainst un - num-bered foes;
Put on the gos - pel ar - mor, And, watch-ing un - to prayer;
To him that o - ver - com - eth, A crown of life shall be;

Till ev - 'ry foe is van-quished And Christ is Lord in - deed.
Your cour - age rise with dan - ger, And strength to strength op - pose.
Where du - ty calls, or dan - ger, Be nev - er want - ing there.
He with the King of glo - ry Shall reign e - ter - nal - ly.

Beneath His Wings

PSALM 91

HENRY F. LYTE

IRA B. WILSON

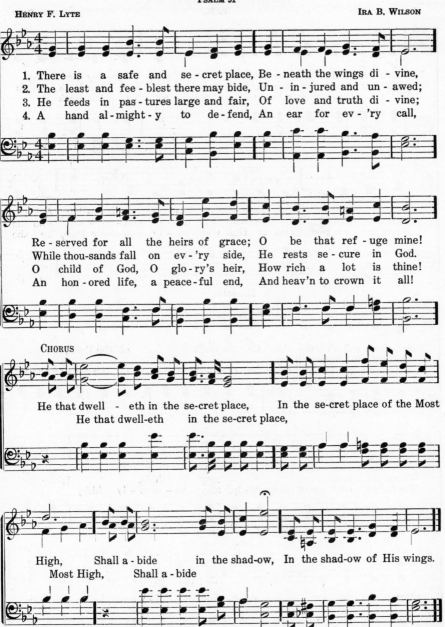

1. There is a safe and se - cret place, Be - neath the wings di - vine,
2. The least and fee - blest there may bide, Un - in - jured and un - awed;
3. He feeds in pas - tures large and fair, Of love and truth di - vine;
4. A hand al - might - y to de - fend, An ear for ev - 'ry call,

Re - served for all the heirs of grace; O be that ref - uge mine!
While thou-sands fall on ev - 'ry side, He rests se - cure in God.
O child of God, O glo - ry's heir, How rich a lot is thine!
An hon - ored life, a peace - ful end, And heav'n to crown it all!

CHORUS

He that dwell - eth in the se-cret place, In the se-cret place of the Most
He that dwell-eth in the se-cret place,

High, Shall a - bide in the shad-ow, In the shad-ow of His wings.
Most High, Shall a - bide

485 The Cleft of the Rock

Thou art my hiding place.—Ps. 32: 6, 7

S. E. Good, 1905

P. M.

S. E. Good

1. There's a cleft in the Rock of A - ges, Where my soul may
2. There is peace for the soul that hid - eth In the Rock that is
3. Oh, soul, thou who now art wea - ry, To the Rock do

safe - ly hide While the storms of life are rag - ing And the
high - er than I, For the soul that on - ly con - fid - eth And the
come for rest, Come to Him who on - ly can cheer thee, To the

REFRAIN

bil - lows roll o'er the tide. Oh, the cleft of the Rock,
cleft of the Rock will try.
dear lov-ing Saviour's breast. Oh, the cleft of the Rock, Oh, the cleft of the Rock,

Where my soul may hide, While the
Where my soul may se - cure - ly, may se - cure - ly hide,

storms of life are rag - ing, And the bil - lows roll o'er the tide.

Take the Name of Jesus With You

There is no other name under heaven given among men, whereby we must be saved.—ACTS. 4: 12

LYDIA BAXTER   8. 7. 8. 7. Ref.   W. H. DOANE, 1871

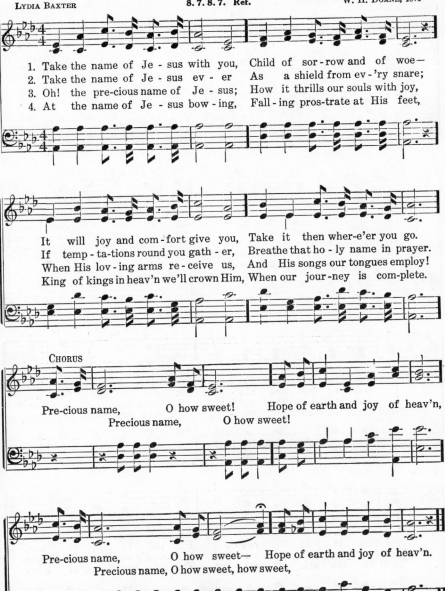

1. Take the name of Je - sus with you, Child of sor - row and of woe—
2. Take the name of Je - sus ev - er As a shield from ev - 'ry snare;
3. Oh! the pre-cious name of Je - sus; How it thrills our souls with joy,
4. At the name of Je - sus bow - ing, Fall - ing pros-trate at His feet,

It will joy and com - fort give you, Take it then wher-e'er you go.
If temp - ta-tions round you gath - er, Breathe that ho - ly name in prayer.
When His lov - ing arms re - ceive us, And His songs our tongues employ!
King of kings in heav'n we'll crown Him, When our jour - ney is com-plete.

CHORUS

Pre-cious name, O how sweet! Hope of earth and joy of heav'n,
Precious name, O how sweet!

Pre-cious name, O how sweet— Hope of earth and joy of heav'n.
Precious name, O how sweet, how sweet,

487 I Love to Tell the Story

I will speak of Thy wondrous works.—Ps. 145: 5

CATHARINE HANKEY, 1876

7. 6. 7. 6. D.

W. K. JACOBS, 1899

1. I love to tell the sto - ry Of un - seen things a - bove,
2. I love to tell the sto - ry! More won - der - ful it seems
3. I love to tell the sto - ry; 'Tis pleas - ant to re - peat
4. I love to tell the sto - ry! For those who know it best

Of Je - sus and His glo - ry, Of Je - sus and His love;
Than all the gold - en fan - cies Of all our gold - en dreams;
What seems, each time I tell it, More won - der - ful - ly sweet.
Seem hun - ger - ing and thirst - ing, To hear it, like the rest;

I love to tell the sto - ry, Be - cause I know it's true;
I love to tell the sto - ry! It did so much for me;
I love to tell the sto - ry, For some have nev - er heard
And when, in scenes of glo - ry, I sing the new, new song,

It sat - is - fies my long - ings, As noth - ing else would do.
And that is just the rea - son I tell it now to thee.
The mes - sage of sal - va - tion From God's own ho - ly Word.
'Twill be the old, old sto - ry That I have loved so long.

A Charge to Keep I Have

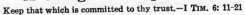

Keep that which is committed to thy trust.—I TIM. 6: 11-21

488

CHARLES WESLEY, 1762   **FERGUSON S. M.**   GEORGE KINGSLEY, 1843

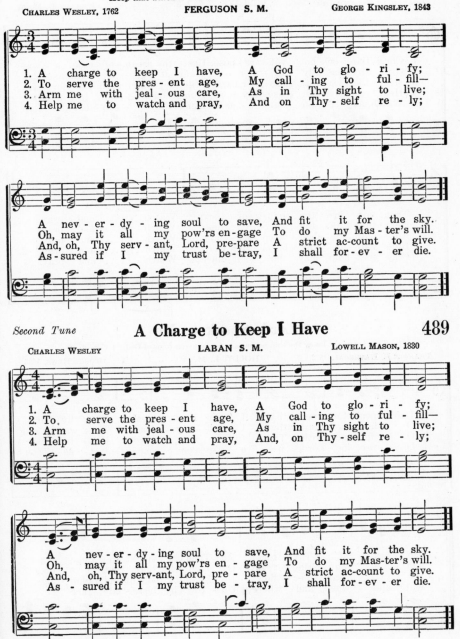

1. A charge to keep I have, A God to glo - ri - fy;
2. To serve the pres - ent age, My call - ing to ful - fill—
3. Arm me with jeal - ous care, As in Thy sight to live;
4. Help me to watch and pray, And on Thy - self re - ly;

A nev - er - dy - ing soul to save, And fit it for the sky.
Oh, may it all my pow'rs en - gage To do my Mas - ter's will.
And, oh, Thy serv - ant, Lord, pre - pare A strict ac - count to give.
As - sured if I my trust be - tray, I shall for - ev - er die.

Second Tune   # A Charge to Keep I Have   **489**

CHARLES WESLEY   **LABAN S. M.**   LOWELL MASON, 1830

1. A charge to keep I have, A God to glo - ri - fy;
2. To serve the pres - ent age, My call - ing to ful - fill—
3. Arm me with jeal - ous care, As in Thy sight to live;
4. Help me to watch and pray, And, on Thy - self re - ly;

A nev - er - dy - ing soul to save, And fit it for the sky.
Oh, may it all my pow'rs en - gage To do my Mas - ter's will.
And, oh, Thy serv - ant, Lord, pre - pare A strict ac - count to give.
As - sured if I my trust be - tray, I shall for - ev - er die.

490

Christian, Seek Not Yet Repose

Let us not sleep as do others, but let us watch and be sober.—I THESS. 5: 6

CHARLOTTE ELLIOTT, 1839   VIGILATE 7. 7. 7. 3.   WILLIAM H. MONK

1. Chris - tian, seek not yet re - pose, Cast thy dreams of ease a - way;
2. Gird thy heav'n-ly ar - mor on, Wear it ev - er night and day;
3. Hear the vic - tors who o'er-came; Still they watch each war-rior's way;
4. Hear, a - bove all these, thy Lord, Him thou lov - est to o - bey;
5. Watch, as if on that a - lone Hung the is - sue of the day;

Thou art in the midst of foes: Watch .... and pray.
Near thee lurks the e - vil one; Watch .... and pray.
All with one clear voice ex - claim, Watch .... and pray.
Hide with - in thy heart His word, "Watch .... and pray.'
Pray that help may be sent down; Watch .... and pray.

491

Lord, Speak to Me

That we might know the things that are freely given to us of God.—I COR. 2: 12

FRANCES R. HAVERGAL, 1872   HOLLY L. M.   GEORGE HEWS, 1835

1. Lord, speak to me that I may speak, In liv - ing
2. O lead me, Lord, that I may lead The wan - d'ring
3. O fill me with Thy full - ness, Lord, Un - til my
4. O use me, Lord, use e - - ven me, Just as Thou

ech - oes of Thy tone: As Thou hast sought, so let me
and the wav - 'ring feet; O feed me, Lord, that I may
ver - y heart o'er - flow In kin-dling thought and glow - ing
wilt, and when, and where; Un - til Thy bless - ed face I

Lord, Speak to Me—Concluded

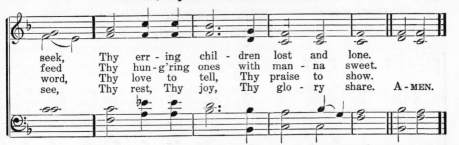

seek, Thy err - ing chil - dren lost and lone.
feed Thy hun-g'ring ones with man - na sweet.
word, Thy love to tell, Thy praise to show.
see, Thy rest, Thy joy, Thy glo - ry share. A-MEN.

Where Cross the Crowded Ways of Life 492

But to do good and to communicate forget not.—HEB. 13: 15, 16

F. MASON NORTH   GERMANY L. M.   LUDWIG VAN BEETHOVEN

1. Where cross the crowd - ed ways of life, Where sound the
2. In haunts of wretch - ed - ness and need, On shad-owed
3. The cup of wa - ter giv'n for Thee Still holds the
4. O Mas - ter, from the moun - tain side, Make haste to
5. Till sons of men shall learn Thy love And fol - low

cries of race.... and clan, A - bove the noise of
thresh-olds dark.... with fears, From paths which hide the
fresh - ness of...... Thy grace; Yet long these mul - ti -
heal these hearts.. of pain, A - mong these rest - less
where Thy feet.... have trod: Till glo - rious from Thy

self - ish strife, We hear Thy voice, O Son of man!
lures of greed, We catch the vi - sion of Thy tears.
tudes to see The sweet com - pas - sion of Thy face.
throngs a - bide, O tread the cit - y's streets a - gain,
heav'n a - bove Shall come the cit - y of our God.

493 Onward, Christian Soldiers

The weapons of our warfare are not carnal, but mighty through God to the pulling down of strongholds.—II Cor. 10: 4

Sabine Baring-Gould, 1864   ST. GERTRUDE 6. 5. 12 l.   Arthur S. Sullivan, 1871

1. On - ward, Chris-tian sol - diers, March-ing as to war, With the
2. Like a might-y ar - my Moves the Church of God; Broth-ers,
3. Crowns and thrones may per - ish, King-doms rise and wane, But the
4. On - ward then, ye peo - ple, Join our hap - py throng, Blend with

cross of Je - sus Go - ing on be - fore: Christ the Roy - al
we are tread - ing Where the saints have trod; We are not di -
Church of Je - sus Con - stant will re - main: Gates of hell can
ours your voi - ces In the tri - umph song; "Glo - ry, praise and

Mas - ter Leads a - gainst the foe; For - ward in - to bat - tle,
vid - ed, All one bod - y we, One in hope and doc - trine,
nev - er 'Gainst the Church pre-vail;" We have Christ's own prom - ise,
hon - or, Un - to Christ the King;" This thro' count-less a - ges

REFRAIN

See, His ban - ners go.
One in char - i - ty.
And that can - not fail.
Men and an - gels sing.

On - ward, Chris-tian sol - diers, March-ing

Onward, Christian Soldiers—Concluded

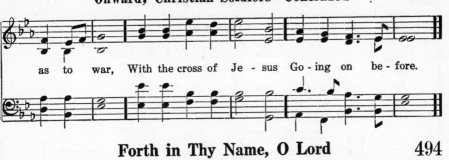

as to war, With the cross of Je - sus Go - ing on be - fore.

Forth in Thy Name, O Lord

494

Do all to the glory of God.—I COR. 10: 31

CHARLES WESLEY, 1749   INTERCESSION L. M.   "Easy Music," 1853

1. Forth in Thy name, O Lord, I go, My dai - ly la - bor to pur - sue, Thee, on - ly Thee, re - solved to know In all I think, or speak, or do.
2. The task Thy wis - dom hath as - signed O let me cheer - ful - ly ful - fill; In all my works Thy pres - ence find, And prove Thy good and per - fect will.
3. Pre - serve me from my call - ing's snare, And hide my sim - ple heart a - bove; A - bove the thorns of chok - ing care, The gild - ed baits of world - ly love.
4. Give me to bear Thy eas - y yoke, And ev - 'ry mo - ment watch and pray; And still to things e - ter - nal look, And has - ten to Thy glo - rious day:
5. For Thee de - light - ful - ly em - ploy, What-e'er Thy boun - teous grace hath giv'n, And run my course with e - - ven joy, And close - ly walk with Thee to heav'n.

495 Ye Servants of the Lord

Blessed are those servants, whom the Lord when He cometh shall find watching.—Lk. 12: 37

PHILIP DODDRIDGE, Publ. 1755   **LABAN S. M.**   LOWELL MASON, 1830

1. Ye serv-ants of the Lord, Each in his of-fice wait,
2. Let all your lamps be bright, And trim the gold-en flame;
3. Watch! 'tis your Lord's com-mand, And while we speak He's near;
4. O hap-py serv-ant he, In such a pos-ture found;

Ob-serv-ant of His heav'n-ly Word, And watch-ful at His gate.
Gird up your loins as in His sight, For aw-ful is His name.
Mark the first sig-nal of His hand, And read-y all ap-pear.
He shall His Lord with rap-ture see, And be with hon-or crowned.

496 Jesus, With Thy Church Abide

I will declare Thy name unto My brethren, in the midst of the Church will I sing praise unto Thee.—HEB. 2: 12

THOMAS B. POLLOCK, 1875. Alt.   **LITANY 7. 7. 7. 7.**   F. A. J. HERVEY

1. Je-sus, with Thy church a-bide, Be her Sav-iour, Lord and Guide,
2. May she guide the poor and blind, Seek the lost un-til she find,
3. May her lamp of truth be bright, Bid her bear a-loft its light,
4. May she soon all glo-rious be, Spot-less and from wrin-kle free,

While on earth her faith is tried: We be-seech Thee, hear us.
And the bro-ken-heart-ed bind: We be-seech Thee, hear us.
Bring all na-tions clear-er sight: We be-seech Thee, hear us.
Pure and bright and wor-thy Thee: We be-seech Thee, hear us.

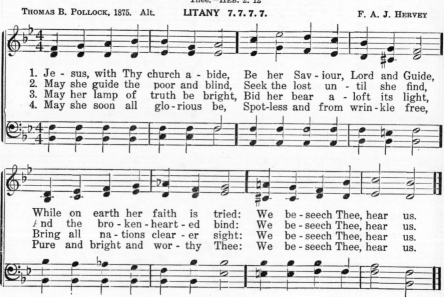

The Son of God Goes Forth to War

497

Thou therefore endure hardness as a good soldier of Jesus Christ.—II Tim. 2: 3

REGINALD HEBER, Publ. 1827   ALL SAINTS, NEW C. M. D.   HENRY S. CUTLER, 1872

1. The Son of God goes forth to war, A king-ly crown to gain;..
2. The mar-tyr first, whose ea-gle eye Could pierce be-yond the grave,..
3. A glo-rious band, the cho-sen few On whom the Spir-it came, ..
4. A no-ble ar-my, men and boys, The ma-tron and the maid,...

His blood-red ban-ner streams a-far: Who fol-lows in His train?
Who saw his Mas-ter in the sky, And called on Him to save:
Twelve val-iant saints, their hope they knew, And mocked the cross and flame:
A-round the Sav-iour's throne re-joice, In robes of light ar-rayed:

Who best can drink his cup of woe, Tri-um-phant o-ver pain,
Like Him, with par-don on his tongue In midst of mor-tal pain,
They met the ty-rant's brandished steel, The li-on's gor-y mane;
They climbed the steep as-cent of heav'n Thro' per-il, toil, and pain:

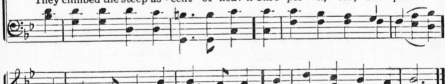

Who pa-tient bears his cross be-low, He fol-lows in His train.
He prayed for them that did the wrong: Who fol-lows in his train?
They bowed their necks the death to feel: Who fol-lows in their train?
O God, to us may grace be giv'n To fol-low in their train.

498 One More Day's Work For Jesus

I must work the works of Him that sent me, while it is day.—Jn. 9: 4

ANNA B. WARNER   P. M.   ROBERT LOWRY

1. One more day's work for Je - sus; One less of life for me!
2. One more day's work for Je - sus; How sweet the work has been,
3. One more day's work for Je - sus— O yes, a wea - ry day;
4. O bless - ed work for Je - sus! O rest at Je - sus' feet!

But heav'n is near - er, And Christ is dear - er, Than yes-
To tell the sto - ry, To show the glo - ry, When Christ's
But heav'n shines clear - er, And rest comes near - er, At each
There toil seems pleas - ure, My wants are treas - ure, And pain

ter - day to me; His love and light Fill all my soul to - night.
flock en - ter in! How it did shine In this poor heart of mine!
step of the way; And Christ in all— Be - fore His face I fall.
for Him is sweet; Lord, if I may, I'll serve an - oth - er day.

REFRAIN

One more day's work for Je - sus, One more day's work for Je - sus.

Copyright property of Mary Runyon Lowry. Used by permission

One More Day's Work For Jesus—Concluded

One more day's work for Je - sus, One less of life for me.

Go, Labor On

Always abounding in the work of the Lord.—I Cor. 15: 58

WILLIAMS L. M.

HORATIUS BONAR, 1843　　　　　　GEORGE KINGSLEY, 1853

1. Go, la - bor on; spend and be spent, Thy joy to
2. Go, la - bor on; 'tis not for naught; Thy earth - ly
3. Go, la - bor on; e - nough while here If He shall
4. Toil on, faint not, keep watch and pray; Be wise the
5. Toil on, and in thy toil re - joice; For toil comes

do the Fa - ther's will; It is the way the Mas - ter
loss is heav'n - ly gain; Men heed thee, love thee, praise thee
praise thee, if He deign Thy will - ing heart to mark and
err - ing soul to win; Go forth in - to the world's high-
rest, for ex - ile home; Soon shalt thou hear the Bride-groom's

went; Should not the serv - ant tread it still?
not; The Mas - ter prais - es:— what are men?
cheer; No toil for Him shall be in vain.
way, Com - pel the wan - d'rer to come in.
voice, The mid - night peal, "Be - hold, I come."

375

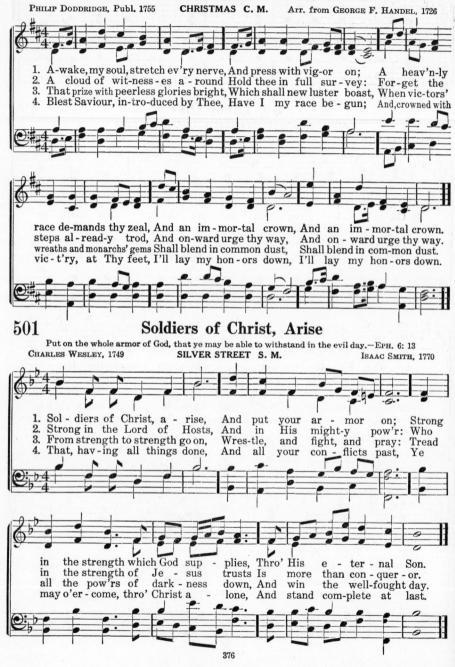

500

Awake, My Soul, Stretch Every Nerve

So run that ye may obtain.—I Cor. 9: 24

PHILIP DODDRIDGE, Publ. 1755   CHRISTMAS C. M.   Arr. from GEORGE F. HANDEL, 1726

1. A-wake, my soul, stretch ev'ry nerve, And press with vig-or on; A heav'n-ly
2. A cloud of wit-ness-es a-round Hold thee in full sur-vey: For-get the
3. That prize with peerless glories bright, Which shall new luster boast, When vic-tors'
4. Blest Saviour, in-tro-duced by Thee, Have I my race be-gun; And, crowned with

race de-mands thy zeal, And an im-mor-tal crown, And an im-mor-tal crown.
steps al-read-y trod, And on-ward urge thy way, And on-ward urge thy way.
wreaths and monarchs' gems Shall blend in common dust, Shall blend in com-mon dust.
vic-t'ry, at Thy feet, I'll lay my hon-ors down, I'll lay my hon-ors down.

501

Soldiers of Christ, Arise

Put on the whole armor of God, that ye may be able to withstand in the evil day.—EPH. 6: 13

CHARLES WESLEY, 1749   SILVER STREET S. M.   ISAAC SMITH, 1770

1. Sol-diers of Christ, a-rise, And put your ar-mor on; Strong
2. Strong in the Lord of Hosts, And in His might-y pow'r: Who
3. From strength to strength go on, Wres-tle, and fight, and pray: Tread
4. That, hav-ing all things done, And all your con-flicts past, Ye

in the strength which God sup-plies, Thro' His e-ter-nal Son.
in the strength of Je-sus trusts Is more than con-quer-or.
all the pow'rs of dark-ness down, And win the well-fought day.
may o'er-come, thro' Christ a-lone, And stand com-plete at last.

Work, For the Night is Coming

The night cometh, when no man can work.—JN. 9: 4

ANNA L. (WALKER) COGHILL, 1868   **7. 6. 7. 5. D.**   LOWELL MASON

1. Work, for the night is com - ing! Work thro' the morn - ing hours;
2. Work, for the night is com - ing! Work thro' the sun - ny noon;
3. Work, for the night is com - ing! Un - der the sun - set skies,

Work, while the dew is spar - kling; Work 'mid spring - ing flow'rs;
Fill bright-est hours with la - bor; Rest comes sure and soon.
While their bright tints are glow - ing, Work, for day - light flies;

Work while the day grows bright - er, Un - der the glow - ing sun;
Give ev - 'ry fly - ing min - ute Some-thing to keep in store;
Work till the last beam fad - eth, Fad - eth to shine no more;

Work, for the night is com - ing, When man's work is done.
Work, for the night is com - ing, When man works no more.
Work while the night is dark - 'ning, When man's work is o'er.

377

13

503 The Whole Wide World For Jesus

This Gospel of the kingdom shall be preached in all the world for a witness unto all nations.—MATT. 24: 14

J. DEMPSTER HAMMOND, 1880   7. 6. 7. 6. D. Ref.   JOHN H. MAUNDER, 1894

1. The whole wide world for Je-sus! This shall our watchword be; Up-on the
2. The whole wide world for Je-sus! In-spires us with the thought That all God's
3. The whole wide world for Je-sus! The march-ing or-der sound: Go ye and

high-est moun-tain, Down by the wid-est sea; The whole wide world for
wan-d'ring chil-dren Have by His love been sought. The whole wide world for
preach the Gos-pel Wher-ev-er man is found. The whole wide world for

Je - sus, To Him shall all men bow, In cit-y or in prai-rie—The
Je - sus, O faint not by the way! The cross shall sure-ly con-quer In
Je - sus, Ride forth, O conqu'ring King, Thro' all the might-y na-tions The

REFRAIN

world for Je-sus now!
this our glo-rious day. The whole wide world, The whole wide world—Proclaim the
world to glo - ry bring!

Gos-pel ti-dings thro' The whole wide world; Lift up the cross for Je-sus, His

378

The Whole Wide World For Jesus—Concluded

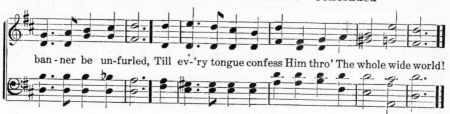

ban-ner be un-furled, Till ev-'ry tongue confess Him thro' The whole wide world!

Christ For the World We Sing

504

Christ Jesus came into the world to save sinners.—I TIM. 1: 15

SAMUEL WOLCOTT, 1869   **KIRBY BEDON 6. 6. 4. 6. 6. 6. 4.**   EDWARD BUNNETT, 1887

1. Christ for the world we sing; The world to Christ we bring
2. Christ for the world we sing; The world to Christ we bring
3. Christ for the world we sing; The world to Christ we bring
4. Christ for the world we sing; The world to Christ we bring

With lov-ing zeal; The poor and them that mourn, The faint and
With fer-vent prayer; The way-ward and the lost, By rest-less
With one ac-cord; With us the work to share, With us re-
With joy-ful song; The new-born souls whose days, Re-claimed from

o-ver-borne, Sin-sick and sor-row-worn, Whom Christ doth heal.
pas-sions tossed, Re-deemed at count-less cost, From dark de-spair.
proach to dare, With us the cross to bear, For Christ our Lord.
er-ror's ways, In-spired with hope and praise, To Christ be-long.

505 Christ's Everlasting Gospel

E. E. HEWITT

LOUIS LE SAINT

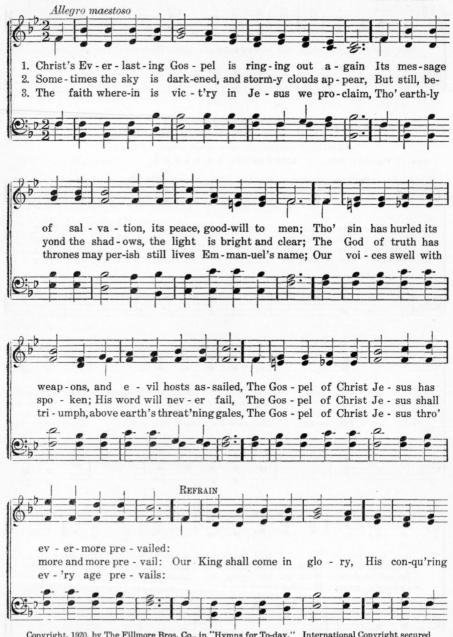

Allegro maestoso

1. Christ's Ev - er - last - ing Gos - pel is ring - ing out a - gain Its mes - sage
2. Some - times the sky is dark - ened, and storm - y clouds ap - pear, But still, be -
3. The faith where - in is vic - t'ry in Je - sus we pro - claim, Tho' earth - ly

of sal - va - tion, its peace, good - will to men; Tho' sin has hurled its
yond the shad - ows, the light is bright and clear; The God of truth has
thrones may per - ish still lives Em - man - uel's name; Our voi - ces swell with

weap - ons, and e - vil hosts as - sailed, The Gos - pel of Christ Je - sus has
spo - ken; His word will nev - er fail, The Gos - pel of Christ Je - sus shall
tri - umph, above earth's threat'ning gales, The Gos - pel of Christ Je - sus thro'

REFRAIN

ev - er - more pre - vailed:
more and more pre - vail: Our King shall come in glo - ry, His con - qu'ring
ev - 'ry age pre - vails:

Christ's Everlasting Gospel—Concluded

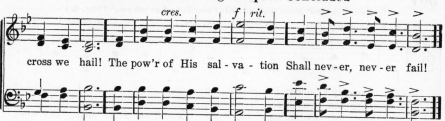

cross we hail! The pow'r of His sal-va-tion Shall nev-er, nev-er fail!

Arm of the Lord, Awake

506

Awake, awake, put on Thy strength, O arm of the Lord.—Isa. 51: 9

WILLIAM SCHRUBSOLE, 1795   STIASTNY L. M.   Arr. from JOHANN STIASTNY, 1700

1. Arm of the Lord, a - wake, a - wake! Put on Thy
2. Say to the hea - then, from Thy throne, "I am Je -
3. Let Zi - on's time of fa - vor come; O bring the
4. Al - might - y God, Thy grace pro - claim Thro' ev - 'ry

strength, the na - tions shake; Now let the world, a -
ho - vah, God a - lone:" Thy voice their i - dols
tribes of Is - rael home; And let our won - d'ring
clime, of ev - 'ry name; Let ad - verse pow'rs be -

dor - ing, see Tri - umphs of mer - cy wrought by Thee.
shall con - found, And cast their al - tars to the ground.
eyes be - hold Gen - tiles and Jews in Je - sus' fold.
fore Thee fall, And crown the Sav - iour Lord of all!

507 Our Country's Voice is Pleading

Possess the land which the Lord God of your fathers giveth you.—DEUT. 4: 1

Mrs. G. W. ANDERSON, 1849   CASKEY 7. 6. 7. 6. D.   THEODORE E. PERKINS

1. Our coun-try's voice is plead-ing; Ye men of God, a-rise!
2. Go where the waves are break-ing, On Cal-i-for-nia's shore,
3. The love of Christ un-fold-ing, Speed on from east to west,

His prov-i-dence is lead-ing, The land be-fore you lies;
Christ's pre-cious gos-pel tak-ing, More rich than gold-en ore;
Till all, His cross be-hold-ing, In Him are ful-ly blest.

Day-gleams are o'er it bright-'ning, And prom-ise clothes the soil;
On Al-le-ghe-ny's moun-tains, Thro' all the west-ern vale,
Great Au-thor of sal-va-tion, Haste, haste the glo-rious day,

Wide fields, for har-vest whit-'ning, In-vite the reap-er's toil.
Be-side Mis-sou-ri's foun-tains, Re-hearse the won-drous tale.
When we, a ran-somed na-tion, Thy scep-ter shall o-bey.

'Tis the Harvest Time

A. THOMAS

J. H. HALL

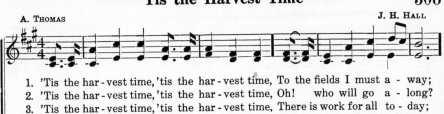

1. 'Tis the har - vest time, 'tis the har - vest time, To the fields I must a - way;
2. 'Tis the har - vest time, 'tis the har - vest time, Oh!   who will go a - long?
3. 'Tis the har - vest time, 'tis the har - vest time, There is work for all to - day;

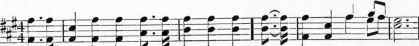

For   the Mas - ter now is   call - ing me, To   go and work to - day.
See,   the fields for har - vest now are white; I   hear the reap - er's song.
If   you can - not be   a   reap - er, You can   bear the sheaves a - way.

REFRAIN

Glean - ing on the hill - side,   Glean - ing on the plain,
Glean-ing on   the   hill-side, hill-side, Gleaning on   the   sun-ny plain,

Work - ing for the Mas - ter,   'Mong.........the golden grain.
Work-ing, work-ing   for the Master,'Mong the golden grain,   'Mong the golden grain.

509 From Greenland's Icy Mountains

Ye shall be witnesses unto me . . . unto the uttermost parts of the earth.—ACTS 1: 8

REGINALD HEBER, 1819   MISSIONARY HYMN 7. 6. 7. 6. D.   LOWELL MASON, 1823

1. From Green-land's i - cy moun-tains, From In - dia's cor - al strand,
2. What though the spi - cy breez - es Blow soft o'er Cey - lon's isle;
3. Can we, whose souls are light - ed With wis - dom from on high,
4. Waft, waft, ye winds, His sto - ry, And you, ye wa - ters, roll,

Where Af - ric's sun - ny foun - tains Roll down their gold - en sand,
Though ev - 'ry pros - pect pleas - es, And on - ly man is vile?
Can we to men be - night - ed The lamp of life de - ny?
Till like a sea of glo - ry It spreads from pole to pole;

From many an an - cient riv - er, From many a palm - y plain,
In vain with lav - ish kind - ness The gifts of God are strown;
Sal - va - tion! O Sal - va - tion! The joy - ful sound pro - claim,
Till o'er our ran-somed na - ture The Lamb for sin - ners slain,

They call us to de - liv - er Their land from er - ror's chain.
The hea - then in his blind - ness Bows down to wood and stone.
Till each re - mot - est na - tion Has learnt Mes - si - ah's name.
Re - deem - er, King, Cre - a - tor, In bliss re - turns to reign.

We Would See Jesus

JN. 12: 21

J. W. WAYLAND

5. 4. 12 l.

J. D. BRUNK, 1916

1. "We would see Je - sus!" Blest be the name That to the na - tions
2. "We would see Je - sus!" Blest are the men Come from the na - tions
3. "We would see Je - sus!" Blest be the name When all the na - tions

Bear - eth such fame. "We would see Je - sus!" I - dols of old,
Seek - ing a - gain. "We would see Je - sus!" Friend of the least,
Tru - ly shall say, "We would see Je - sus!" Glo - rious 'twill be,

Fall - en and bro - ken, Won - ders have told.
Je - sus is pres - ent Now at the feast. Seek - ing for Je - sus!
When as their Sav - iour Him they shall see.

Him would I see; Joy now, for Je - sus Seek - eth for me!

511 Rescue the Perishing

He which converteth the sinner from the error of his way shall save a soul from death.—JAS. 5: 20

FANNY J. CROSBY   11. 10. 11. 10.   W. H. DOANE, 1870

1. Res - cue the per - ish - ing, Care for the dy - ing, Snatch them in
2. Tho' they are slight-ing Him, Still He is wait-ing, Wait - ing the
3. Down in the hu - man heart, Crushed by the tempt - er, Feel - ings lie
4. Res - cue the per - ish - ing, Du - ty de-mands it; Strength for thy

pit - y from sin and the grave; Weep o'er the err - ing one,
pen - i - tent child to re - ceive; Plead with them ear - nest - ly,
bur - ied that grace can re - store; Touched by a lov - ing heart,
la - bor the Lord will pro - vide; Back to the nar - row way

Lift up the fall - en, Tell them of Je - sus the
Plead with them gen - tly; He will for - give if they
Wak - ened by kind - ness, Chords that are bro - ken will
Pa - tient - ly win them; Tell the poor wan - d'rer a

CHORUS

might - y to save.
on - ly be - lieve.   Res - cue the per - ish - ing, Care for the
vi - brate once more.
Sav - iour has died.

Rescue the Perishing—Concluded

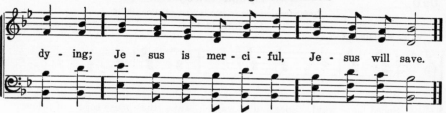

dy - ing; Je - sus is mer - ci - ful, Je - sus will save.

O God of Mercy! Hearken Now 512

Inasmuch as ye have done it unto the least of these my brethren, ye have done it unto me.—MATT. 25: 40

E. S. CLARK   HESPERUS L. M.   HENRY BAKER, 1866

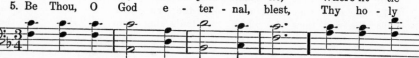

1. O God of mer - cy! heark - en now; Be - fore Thy
2. We seek Thee where Thou dwell'st on high, Be - yond the
3. Be ours the hearts and hands to bless The sor - r'wing
4. Where pov - er - ty in pain must lie, Where lit - tle
5. Be Thou, O God e - ter - nal, blest, Thy ho - ly

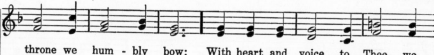

throne we hum - bly bow; With heart and voice to Thee we
glit - t'ring, star - ry sky: We find Thee where Thou dwell'st be-
sons of wretch - ed - ness; Send Thou the help we can - not
suf - f'ring chil - dren cry, Bid us haste forth as called by
name on earth con - fest! Ech - o Thy praise from ev - 'ry

cry, For all on earth who suf - f'ring lie.
low Be - side the beds of want and woe.
give; Bid dy - ing souls a - rise and live.
Thee, And in Thy poor, Thy - self to see.
shore For - ev - er and for - ev - er - more. A - MEN.

513 Speed Away

Preach the Gospel in regions beyond.—II Cor. 10: 16

12. 12. 12. 12. 12. 9.

W. E. M. Hackleman

From Woodbury
Har. by W. E. M. H.

1. Speed a - way! Speed a - way! Take the Gos - pel of light
2. Speed a - way! Speed a - way! Take the mes - sage of love
3. Speed a - way! Speed a - way! Take the Word that gives life

To the lands that are wrapped in the dark - ness of night. "Go ye
To the souls that know not of the Fa - ther a - bove, Who so
To the na - tions in which Sa - tan's king - dom is rife; For the

in - to the world," is the Sav-iour's com-mand, That the light of the
loved this dark world that He gave His own Son, Thro' whose blood on Cal-
Word if be - lieved and o - beyed will give peace, To the cap-tives of

Gos - pel shine o'er ev - 'ry land, Go ye forth in His name and the
va - ry re - demp-tion was won. Let us haste while 'tis day, not a
Sa - tan it will bring re - lease; To the res - cue make haste, there is

Speed Away—Concluded

Gos - pel pro - claim, Speed a - way! Speed a - way! Speed a - way!
mo - ment's de - lay, Speed a - way! Speed a - way! Speed a - way!
no time to waste, Speed a - way! Speed a - way! Speed a - way!

Thou, Whose Almighty Word   514

And God said, Let their be light: and there was light.—GEN. 1: 3

JOHN MARRIOTT, 1813   RIGHINI 6. 6. 4. 6. 6. 4.   VINCENZO RIGHINI

1. Thou, whose al - might - y word   Cha - os and   dark - ness heard,
2. Thou who didst come to bring   On Thy re - deem - ing wing,
3. Spir - it of truth and love,   Life - giv - ing, ho - ly Dove,
4. Ho - ly and bless - ed Three,   Glo - ri - ous Trin - i - ty,

And took their flight; Hear us, we hum - bly pray, And where the
Heal - ing and sight, Health to the sick in mind, Sight to the
Speed forth Thy flight; Move o'er the wa - ters' face Bear - ing the
Wis - dom, Love, Might; Bound-less as o - cean's tide Roll - ing in

gos - pel day Sheds not its glo - rious ray, Let there be light!
in - ly blind; O now, to all man-kind, Let there be light!
lamp of grace; And in earth's dark - est place, Let there be light!
full - est pride, Through the world far and wide, Let there be light!

389

515 Let the Lower Lights Be Burning

Let your light so shine before men, that they may see your good works, and glorify your Father
which is in heaven.—MATT. 5: 16

P. P. BLISS

8. 7. 8. 7. D.

P. P. BLISS

1. Bright-ly beams our Fa-ther's mer-cy From His light-house ev - er - more,
2. Dark the night of sin has set-tled, Loud the an - gry bil-lows roar;
3. Trim your fee - ble lamp, my broth-er: Some poor sail - or tem-pest-tossed,

But to us He gives the keep-ing Of the lights a - long the shore.
Ea - ger eyes are watch-ing, long-ing, For the lights a - long the shore.
Try - ing now to make the har - bor, In the dark-ness may be lost.

REFRAIN

Let the low - er lights be burn-ing! Send a gleam a - cross the wave!

Some poor faint - ing struggling sea-man You may res-cue, you may save.

Who is On the Lord's Side

Ex. 32: 26

FRANCES R. HAVERGAL, 1877   **ARMAGEDDON 6. 5. 12 l.**   Arr. by JOHN GOSS, 1871

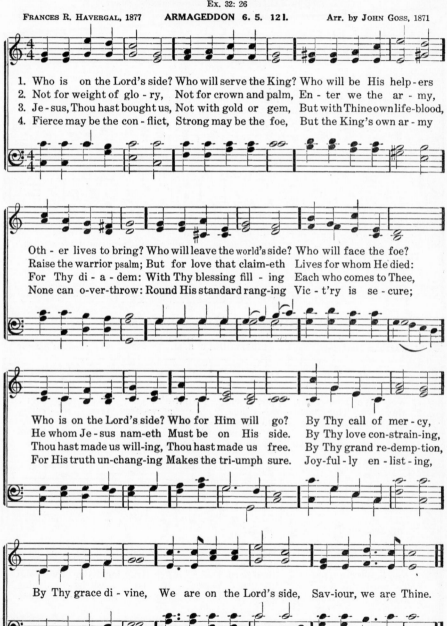

1. Who is on the Lord's side? Who will serve the King? Who will be His help - ers
2. Not for weight of glo - ry, Not for crown and palm, En - ter we the ar - my,
3. Je - sus, Thou hast bought us, Not with gold or gem, But with Thine own life-blood,
4. Fierce may be the con - flict, Strong may be the foe, But the King's own ar - my

Oth - er lives to bring? Who will leave the world's side? Who will face the foe?
Raise the warrior psalm; But for love that claim-eth Lives for whom He died:
For Thy di - a - dem: With Thy blessing fill - ing Each who comes to Thee,
None can o - ver-throw: Round His standard rang-ing Vic - t'ry is se - cure;

Who is on the Lord's side? Who for Him will go? By Thy call of mer - cy,
He whom Je - sus nam-eth Must be on His side. By Thy love con-strain-ing,
Thou hast made us will-ing, Thou hast made us free. By Thy grand re-demp-tion,
For His truth un-chang-ing Makes the tri-umph sure. Joy-ful - ly en - list - ing,

By Thy grace di - vine, We are on the Lord's side, Sav-iour, we are Thine.

517   O Still in Accents Sweet

The harvest truly is plenteous, but the laborers are few.—MATT. 9: 37

SAMUEL LONGFELLOW, 1864   **BELMONT C. M.**   Arr. from WILLIAM GARDINER, 1812

1. O still in ac-cents sweet and strong Sounds forth the an-cient word,
2. We hear the call; in dreams no more In self-ish ease we lie,
3. Where prophets' word, and mar-tyrs' blood, And prayers of saints were sown,
4. O Thou whose call our hearts has stirred, To do Thy will we come;

"More reap-ers for white har-vest fields, More la-b'rers for the Lord."
But, gird-ed for our Fa-ther's work, Go forth be-neath His sky.
We, to their la-bors en-t'ring in, Would reap where they have strown.
Thrust in our sick-les at Thy word, And bear our har-vest home.

518   We Give Thee But Thine Own

Of Thine own have we given Thee.—I CHRON. 29: 14

W. WALSHAM HOW, 1858   **CHISELHURST S. M.**   JOSEPH BARNBY

1. We give Thee but Thine own, What-e'er the gift may be;
2. May we Thy boun-ties thus As stew-ards true re-ceive,
3. O, hearts are bruised and dead, And homes are bare and cold,
4. The cap-tive to re-lease, To God the lost to bring,
5. And we be-lieve Thy Word, Though dim our faith may be,

All that we have is Thine a-lone, A trust, O Lord, from Thee.
And glad-ly, as Thou bless-est us, To Thee our first fruits give.
And lambs for whom the Shep-herd bled Are stray-ing from the fold!
To teach the way of life and peace,— It is a Christ-like thing.
What-e'er for Thine we do, O Lord, We do it un-to Thee.

O Zion, Haste

O Jerusalem, that bringest good tidings, lift up thy voice with strength.—Isa. 40: 9

MARY A. THOMSON, 1834   TIDINGS 11. 10. 11. 10. 9. 11.   JAMES WALCH, 1875

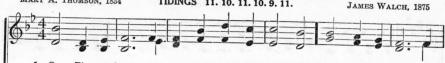

1. O   Zi - on, haste, thy mis-sion high ful - fill - ing, To   tell   to   all   the
2. Pro-claim to   ev - 'ry peo - ple, tongue, and na - tion That God, in whom they
3. Give of thy sons   to   bear the mes-sage glo - rious; Give of thy wealth to
4. He comes a - gain, — O   Zi - on, ere Thou meet Him, Make known to ev - 'ry

world that God   is Light; That He who made all   na - tions is   not will - ing
live   and move, is Love: Tell how He stooped to save His lost cre - a - tion,
speed them on their way; Pour out thy soul   for them in prayer vic - to - rious;
heart His sav - ing grace: Let none whom He hath ran-somed fail to greet Him,

REFRAIN

One soul should per - ish,   lost in shades of night.
And   died on earth that   man might live a - bove. Pub - lish glad ti - dings,
And   all thou spend - est   Je - sus will   re - pay.
Thro' thy neg - lect,   un - fit   to see His face.

ti - dings of peace;   Ti - dings of Je - sus, re-demp-tion and   re - lease.

520 Sowing the Seed of Truth

In the morning sow thy seed, and in the evening withold not thine hand.—Eccl. 11: 6

E. R. LATTA   6s. 8 l. Ref.   WM. J. KIRKPATRICK

1. Sow-ing the seed of truth,   Pa-tient-ly on we go,   Sow-ing it here and
2. Sow-ing at ear-ly dawn,   Sow-ing in noontide ray,   Scat-ter-ing still at
3. Sow-ing from year to year,   Ev-er till life is past;   Know-ing that we shall

there, Knowing not which will grow;   Je-sus be-holds it fall,   He will the
eve, Aft-er the bus-y day;   Sowing the Word of life   In the im-
reap Glo-ri-ous fruit at last;   Je-sus be-holds it fall,   He will our

work re-cord;   Pa-tient-ly sow the seed,   Leav-ing it with the Lord.
mor-tal soul;   Whol-ly by sin un-done,   Free-ly by grace made whole.
work re-ward;   Pa-tient-ly sow the seed,   Leav-ing it with the Lord.

CHORUS

Sow - - - ing the pre-cious seed, Pa - - - - tient-ly   on we go,
Sowing and watching the pre-cious seed, Pa-tient-ly, lov-ing-ly   on we go,

Sowing the Seed of Truth—Concluded

Sow-ing it here, sow-ing it there, Know-ing not which will grow.

Thou, Lord of Life 521

Establish Thou the works of our hands upon us.—Ps. 90: 17

SAMUEL LONGFELLOW, 1886   QUEBEC L. M.   HENRY BAKER, 1862

1. Thou, Lord of Life, our sav - ing health, Who mak'st Thy
2. As on the riv - er's ris - ing tide Flow strength and
3. To heal the wound, to still the pain, And strength to
4. Bless Thou the gifts our hands have brought! Bless Thou the

suf - f'ring ones our care, Our gifts are still our tru - est
cool - ness from the sea, So through the ways our hands pro-
fail - ing puls - es bring, Till the lame feet shall leap a-
work our hearts have planned, Ours is the faith, the will, the

wealth, To serve Thee our sin - cer - est prayer.
vide, May quick-'ning life flow in from Thee;—
gain, And the parched lips with glad - ness sing.
thought— The rest, O God, is in Thy hand. A - MEN.

522 The Morning Light is Breaking

Then shall thy light break forth as the morning.—ISA. 58: 8

SAMUEL F. SMITH   WEBB 7. 6. 7. 6. D.   GEORGE J. WEBB, 1837

1. The morn - ing light is break - ing, The dark - ness dis - ap - pears;
2. Rich dews of grace come o'er us, In many a gen - tle show'r,
3. See hea - then na - tions bend - ing Be - fore the God we love,
4. Blest riv - er of sal - va - tion, Pur - sue thine on - ward way;

The sons of earth are wak - ing To pen - i - ten - tial tears:
And bright - er scenes be - fore us Are ope - ning ev - 'ry hour:
And thou - sand hearts as - cend - ing In grat - i - tude a - bove;
Flow thou to ev - 'ry na - tion, Nor in thy rich - ness stay;

Each breeze that sweeps the o - cean Brings ti - dings from a - far,
Each cry to heav - en go - ing, A - bun - dant an - swer brings,
While sin - ners, now con - fess - ing, The Gos - pel call o - bey,
Stay not till all the low - ly Tri - um - phant reach their home:

Of na - tions in com - mo - tion, Pre - pared for Zi - on's war.
And heav'n - ly gales are blow - ing With peace up - on their wings.
And seek the Sav - iour's bless - ing, A na - tion in a day.
Stay not till all the ho - ly Pro - claim, "The Lord is come!"

The Call For Reapers

Look on the fields; for they are white already to harvest.—Jn. 4: 35

J. O. THOMPSON

8. 7. 8. 7. D.

J. B. O. CLEMM

Spirited

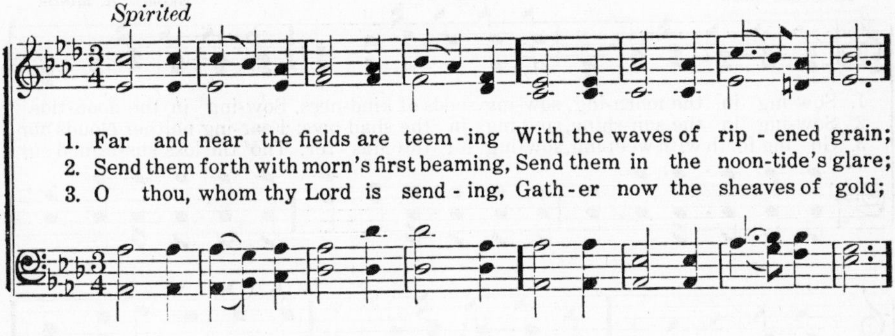

1. Far and near the fields are teem-ing With the waves of rip-ened grain;
2. Send them forth with morn's first beaming, Send them in the noon-tide's glare;
3. O thou, whom thy Lord is send-ing, Gath-er now the sheaves of gold;

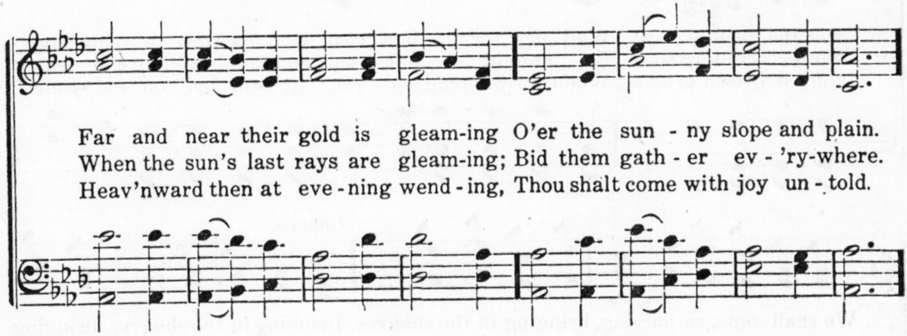

Far and near their gold is gleam-ing O'er the sun-ny slope and plain.
When the sun's last rays are gleam-ing; Bid them gath-er ev-'ry-where.
Heav'nward then at eve-ning wend-ing, Thou shalt come with joy un-told.

REFRAIN

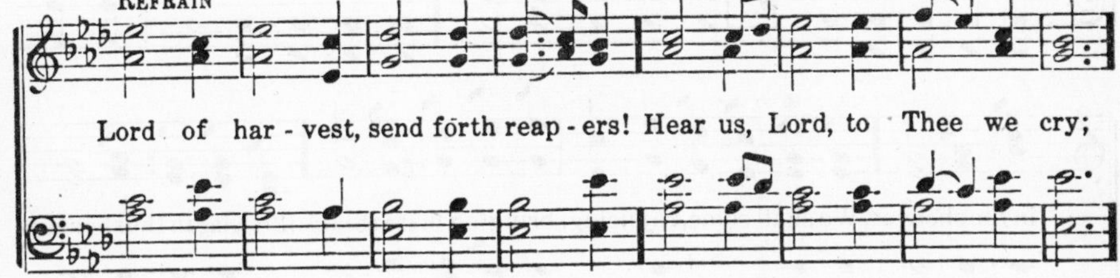

Lord of har-vest, send forth reap-ers! Hear us, Lord, to Thee we cry;

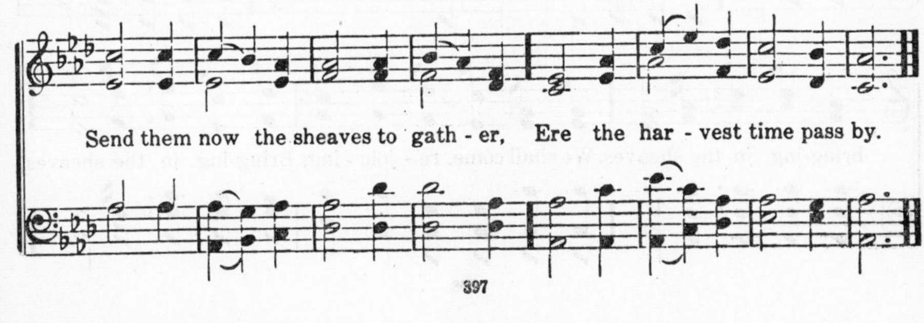

Send them now the sheaves to gath-er, Ere the har-vest time pass by.

524 Sowing in the Morning

Bringing his sheaves with him.—Ps. 126: 6

BRINGING IN THE SHEAVES 12. 11. 12. 11. Ref.

Knowles Shaw

George A. Minor

1. Sow-ing in the morn-ing, sow-ing seeds of kind-ness, Sow-ing in the noon-tide
2. Sow-ing in the sun-shine, sow-ing in the shad-ows, Fear-ing neither clouds nor
3. Go-ing forth with weeping, sow-ing for the Mas-ter, Tho' the loss sus-tained our

and the dew-y eve; Wait-ing for the har-vest, and the time of reap-ing,
winter's chilling breeze; By and by the har-vest, and the la-bor end-ed,
spir-it oft-en grieves; When our weeping's o-ver, He will bid us wel-come,

Chorus

We shall come, re-joic-ing, bringing in the sheaves. Bringing in the sheaves, bringing

in the sheaves, We shall come, rejoicing, bringing in the sheaves; Bringing in the sheaves,

bring-ing in the sheaves, We shall come, re-joic-ing, Bring-ing in the sheaves.

In the Harvest Field

525

She gleaned in the field until even.—RUTH 2: 17

C. R. BLACKALL · LABOR ON 10. 10. 10. 8. Ref. · W. H. DOANE, 1870

1. In the har-vest field there is work to do, For the grain is ripe,
2. Crowd the gar-ner well, with its sheaves all bright, Let the song be glad,
3. In the glean-ers' path may be rich re-ward, Tho' the time seems long,
4. Lo! the Har-vest Home in the realms a-bove Shall be gained by each

and the reap-ers few; And the Mas-ter's voice bids the work-ers true
and the heart be light; Fill the pre-cious hours, ere the shades of night
and the la-bor hard; For the Mas-ter's joy, with His cho-sen shared,
who has toiled and strove, When the Mas-ter's voice, in its tones of love,

CHORUS

Heed the call that He gives to-day.
Take the place of the gold-en day. La-bor on! la-bor
Drives the gloom from the dark-est day.
Calls a-way to e-ter-nal day. La-bor on!

on! la-bor on! Keep the bright re-ward in view; For the Mas-ter has

said He will strength re-new; La-bor on till the close of day!

526 Eternal Father, Strong to Save

He maketh the storm a calm; so that the waves thereof are still.— Ps. 107: 29

WILLIAM WHITING, 1860   MELITA 8s. 6 l.   JOHN B. DYKES, 1861

1. E - ter - nal Fa - ther, strong to save, Whose arm doth
2. O Sav - iour, whose al - might - y word The winds and
3. O Sa - cred Spir - it, who didst brood Up - on the
4. O Trin - i - ty of love and pow'r, Our breth - ren

bind the rest - less wave, Who bid'st the might - y o - cean deep
waves sub - mis - sive heard, Who walk - edst on the foam - ing deep
cha - os dark and rude, Who bad'st its an - gry tu - mult cease,
shield in dan - ger's hour; From rock and tem - pest, fire and foe,

Its own ap - point - ed lim - its keep: O hear us when we
And calm a - mid its rage didst sleep: O hear us when we
And gav - est light and life and peace: O hear us when we
Pro - tect them where - so - e'er they go; And ev - er let there

cry to Thee For those in per - il on the sea.
cry to Thee For those in per - il on the sea.
cry to Thee For those in per - il on the sea.
rise to Thee Glad hymns of praise from land and sea.   A - MEN.

400

Revive Thy Work, O Lord

527

O Lord, revive Thy work. —HAB. 3: 2

ALBERT MIDLANE, 1858

VIGIL S. M. Arr. from ST. ALBAN'S Tune Book, 1865

1. Re - vive Thy work, O Lord, Thy might - y arm make bare;
2. Re - vive Thy work, O Lord, Dis - turb this sleep of death;
3. Re - vive Thy work, O Lord, Cre - ate soul thirst for Thee;
4. Re - vive Thy work, O Lord, Ex - alt Thy pre - cious name;
5. Re - vive Thy work, O Lord, And give re - fresh - ing show'rs;

Speak with the voice that wakes the dead, And make Thy peo - ple hear.
Quick - en the smould'ring em - bers now By Thine al - might - y breath.
And hun - g'ring for the Bread of life, O may our spir - its be!
And, by the Ho - ly Ghost, our love For Thee and Thine in - flame.
The glo - ry shall be all Thine own, The bless - ing, Lord, be ours. A - MEN.

Spirit of Holiness, Descend

528

He will reprove the world of sin, and of righteousness, and of judgment. —JN. 16: 8

NAOMI C. M.

JOHANN G. NAEGELI, 1826
Arr. by LOWELL MASON, 1836

SAMUEL F. SMITH, 1832

1. Spir - it of ho - li - ness, de - scend; Thy peo - ple wait for Thee;
2. Thy light that on our souls hath shone, Leads us in hope to Thee;
3. O bring our dear - est friends to God; Re - mem - ber those we love;
4. Spir - it of ho - li - ness, 'tis Thine To hear our fee - ble prayer;

Thine ear in kind com - pas - sion lend; Let us Thy mer - cy see.
Let us not feel its rays a - lone, —A - lone Thy peo - ple be.
Fit them on earth for Thine a - bode, Fit them for joys a - bove.
Come, —for we wait Thy pow'r di - vine, —Let us Thy mer - cy share.

529 I Was a Wandering Sheep

I have found my sheep that was lost.—Lk. 15: 6

HORATIUS BONAR, 1843   **LEBANON S. M. D.**   JOHN ZUNDEL, 1855

1. I was a wan-d'ring sheep, I did not love the fold;
2. The Shep-herd sought His sheep, The Fa-ther sought His child;
3. Je-sus my Shep-herd is; 'Twas He that loved my soul,
4. I was a wan-d'ring sheep, I would not be con-trolled;

I did not love my Shep-herd's voice, I would not be con-trolled.
They fol-lowed me o'er vale and hill, O'er des-erts waste and wild:
'Twas He that washed me in His blood, 'Twas He that made me whole;
But now I love my Shep-herd's voice, I love, I love the fold.

I was a way-ward child, I did not love my home;
They found me nigh to death, Fam-ished and faint and lone;
'Twas He that sought the lost, That found the wan-d'ring sheep,
I was a way-ward child, I once pre-ferred to roam;

I did not love my Fa-ther's voice, I loved a-far to roam.
They bound me with the bands of love, They saved the wan-d'ring one.
'Twas He that brought me to the fold, 'Tis He that still doth keep.
But now I love my Fa-ther's voice, I love, I love His home.

The Haven of Rest

He bringeth them to their desired haven.—Ps. 107: 30

11. 8. 11. 8. Ref.

H. L. Gilmour

Geo. D. Moore

1. My soul in sad ex-ile was out on life's sea, So bur-dened with sin and dis-trest, Till I heard a sweet voice say-ing, "Make me your choice;" And I en-tered the ha-ven of rest.
2. I yield-ed my-self to His ten-der em-brace, And faith tak-ing hold of the Word, My fet-ters fell off, and I an-chored my soul; The ha-ven of rest is my Lord.
3. The song of my soul since the Lord made me whole Has been the old sto-ry so blest, Of Je-sus, who'll save who-so-ev-er will have A home in the ha-ven of rest.
4. Oh, come to the Sav-iour, He pa-tient-ly waits, To save by His pow-er di-vine; Come, an-chor your soul in the ha-ven of rest, And say, "My Be-lov-ed is mine."

D. S.—The tem-pest may sweep o'er the wild, storm-y deep, In.... Je-sus I'm safe ev-er-more.

FINE

REFRAIN

D. S.

I've anchored my soul in the ha-ven of rest, I'll sail the wide seas no more;

403

531 Tell Me the Old, Old Story

For God so loved the world, that He gave His only begotten Son.—Jn. 3: 16

KATHARINE HANKEY, 1866   EVANGEL 7. 6. 7. 6. Ref.   W. H. DOANE, 1868

1. Tell me the Old, Old Sto - ry, Of un-seen things a - bove, Of Je - sus and His glo - ry, Of Je - sus and His love; Tell me the sto - ry sim - ply, As to a lit - tle child, For I am weak and wea - ry, And help - less and de - filed.

2. Tell me the sto - ry slow - ly, That I may take it in— That won-der-ful re - demp-tion, God's rem-e - dy for sin; Tell me the sto - ry oft - en, For I for - get so soon, The "ear-ly dew" of morn-ing Has passed a - way at noon.

3. Tell me the sto - ry soft - ly, With ear-nest tones and grave; Re - mem - ber! I'm the sin - ner Whom Je - sus came to save; Tell me the sto - ry al - ways, If you would real-ly be, In an - y time of troub-le, A com - fort - er to me.

4. Tell me the same old sto - ry, When you have cause to fear That this world's emp-ty glo - ry Is cost - ing me too dear; Yes, and when that world's glo - ry Is dawn-ing on my soul, Tell me the Old, Old Sto - ry: "Christ Je - sus makes thee whole."

REFRAIN

Tell me the Old, Old Sto - ry, Tell me the Old, Old

404

Tell Me the Old, Old Story—Concluded

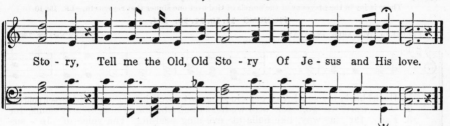

Sto - ry, Tell me the Old, Old Sto - ry Of Je - sus and His love.

Lord, I Hear of Showers of Blessing 532

The parched ground shall become a pool, and the thirsty land a spring of water.—ISA. 35: 7

ELIZABETH CODNER, 1858. Alt. EVEN ME 8. 7. 8. 7. 6. 7. WILLIAM B. BRADBURY

1. Lord, I hear of show'rs of bless - ing Thou art scat-t'ring full and free;
2. Pass me not, O gra - cious Fa - ther! Sin - ful though my heart may be;
3. Pass me not, O ten - der Sav - iour! Let me live and cling to Thee;
4. Pass me not, O might - y Spir - it! Thou canst make the blind to see;
5. Love of God, so pure and change-less, Blood of Christ, so rich and free,

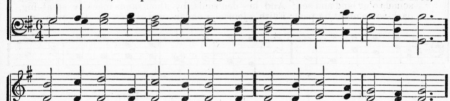

Show'rs, the thirst-y land re - fresh - ing; Let some drops now fall on me,
Thou might'st leave me, but the rath - er Let Thy mer - cy light on me,
I am long - ing for Thy fa - vor, Whilst Thou'rt calling, oh, call me,
Wit - ness - er of Je - sus' mer - it, Speak the word of pow'r to me,
Grace of God, so strong and bound - less, Mag - ni - fy them all in me,

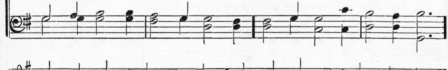

E - ven me, e - ven me, Let some drops now fall on me.
E - ven me, e - ven me, Let Thy mer - cy light on me.
E - ven me, e - ven me, Whilst Thou'rt calling, oh, call me.
E - ven me, e - ven me, Speak the word of pow'r to me.
E - ven me, e - ven me, Mag - ni - fy them all in me.

405

533
Hark! Hark, My Soul

There is joy in the presence of the angels of God over one sinner that repenteth.—LK. 15: 10

PILGRIMS 11. 10. 11. 10. Ref.

FREDERICK W. FABER, 1854. Alt.

HENRY SMART, 1868

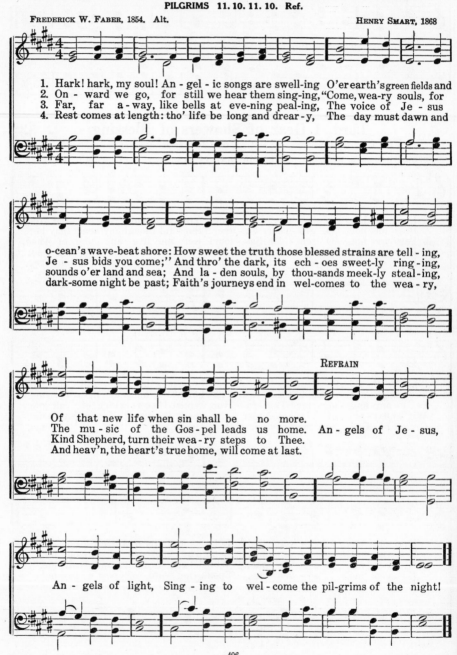

1. Hark! hark, my soul! An - gel - ic songs are swell-ing O'er earth's green fields and
2. On - ward we go, for still we hear them sing-ing, "Come, wea-ry souls, for
3. Far, far a - way, like bells at eve-ning peal-ing, The voice of Je - sus
4. Rest comes at length: tho' life be long and drear-y, The day must dawn and

o-cean's wave-beat shore: How sweet the truth those blessed strains are tell - ing,
Je - sus bids you come;" And thro' the dark, its ech - oes sweet-ly ring-ing,
sounds o'er land and sea; And la - den souls, by thou-sands meek-ly steal-ing,
dark-some night be past; Faith's journeys end in wel-comes to the wea - ry,

REFRAIN

Of that new life when sin shall be no more.
The mu - sic of the Gos - pel leads us home. An - gels of Je - sus,
Kind Shepherd, turn their wea - ry steps to Thee.
And heav'n, the heart's true home, will come at last.

An - gels of light, Sing - ing to wel - come the pil-grims of the night!

406

The Light of the World is Jesus

P. P. BLISS

P. P. BLISS

1. The whole world was lost in the dark-ness of sin; The Light of the
2. No dark-ness have we who in Je - sus a - bide, The Light of the
3. Ye dwell-ers in dark-ness, with sin-blind-ed eyes, The Light of the
4. No need of the sun-light in heav-en, we're told, The Light of the

world is Je - sus; Like sun-shine at noon-day, His glo - ry shone in,
world is Je - sus; We walk in the light when we fol-low our Guide,
world is Je - sus; Go, wash at His bid-ding, and light will a - rise,
world is Je - sus; The Lamb is the light in the cit - y of gold,

CHORUS

The Light of the world is Je - sus. Come to the Light, 'tis

shin-ing for thee; Sweet-ly the Light has dawned up-on me, Once I was

blind, but now I can see: The Light of the world is Je - sus.

535

He Seeks His Wandering Sheep

And goeth after that which was lost until He find it.—Lk. 15: 4

MARTHA MILLS NEWTON   7. 6. 8. 6. 8. 6. 8. 6. Ref.   J. HENRY SHOWALTER

1. The Shepherd's heart is saddened, His sheep have gone astray; Thro' summer's heat, and
2. Thro' briers, thorns, and brambles, He seeks with anxious heart; O'er mountain, vale, or
3. He's call-ing for thee, lost one, Can you not hear His voice? Then an-swer to His

win-ter's cold, He seeks His sheep al-way. Some wand'ring sheep He's seeking now, Say
for - est wild, Or in the crowded mart, O'er o-cean's main, o'er desert sands, He
lov - ing call, Go meet Him and re-joice. Are you not wea-ry wan-der-ing Out

broth-er, is it you? Are you safe sheltered in the fold, Or are you wand'ring too?
seeks the wide world o'er; In gild-ed pal-ace of the rich; In cot-tage of the poor.
in the storm and cold? A-rise, and seek your Shepherd's face, Re-turn un-to the fold.

REFRAIN

He seeks His wan-d'ring sheep,   Out in the storm and cold;
He seeks His wan-d'ring, wan-d'ring sheep to-day, Out in the storm and cold;

He Seeks His Wandering Sheep—Concluded

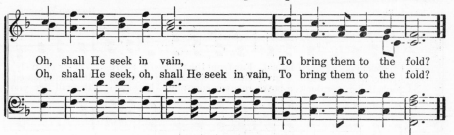

Oh, shall He seek in vain, To bring them to the fold?
Oh, shall He seek, oh, shall He seek in vain, To bring them to the fold?

Lift Your Glad Voices

536

Whosoever liveth and believeth in Me shall never die.—Jn. 11: 26

HENRY WARE   RESURRECTION 12. 11. 11. 11.   JOHN E. GOULD

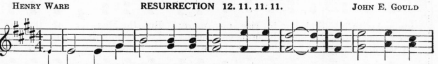

1. Lift your glad voi - ces in tri - umph on high, For Je - sus hath
2. He burst from the fet - ters of darkness that bound Him, Re-splen-dent in
3. Glo - ry to God, in full an - thems of joy; The be - ing He
4. But Je - sus hath cheered the dark val - ley of sor - row, And bade us, im-

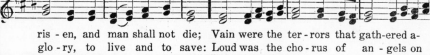

ris - en, and man shall not die; Vain were the ter - rors that gath-ered a-
glo - ry, to live and to save: Loud was the cho - rus of an - gels on
gave us death can - not de-stroy: Sad were the life we may part with to -
mor-tal, to heav - en as - cend: Lift then your voi - ces in tri - umph on

round Him, And short the do - min - ion of death and the grave.
high,— The Sav - iour hath ris - en, and man shall not die.
mor - row, If tears were our birth-right, and death were our end.
high, For Je - sus hath ris - en, and man shall not die.

409

14

537 Love Lifted Me

JAMES ROWE

HOWARD E. SMITH

1. I was sink-ing deep in sin, Far from the peace-ful shore, Ver - y deep - ly stained with-in, Sink-ing to rise no more; But the Mas - ter of the sea Heard my de-spair-ing cry, From the wa-ters lift - ed me, Now safe am I.

2. All my heart to Him I give, Ev - er to Him I'll cling, In His bless-ed pres - ence live, Ev - er His prais-es sing. Love so might-y and so true, Mer - its my soul's best songs; Faith-ful, lov-ing serv-ice, too, To Him be - longs.

3. Souls in dan-ger, look a-bove, Je - sus com-plete-ly saves; He will lift you by His love Out of the an-gry waves. He's the Mas - ter of the sea, Bil - lows His will o - bey; He your Sav-iour wants to be—Be saved to - day.

CHORUS

Love lift - ed me!....... Love lift - ed me!....... When noth-ing
e - ven me! e - ven me!
else could help, Love lift - ed me..... Love lift - ed me....

The Gate Ajar For Me

The gates of it shall not be shut at all by day; for there shall be no night there.—Rev. 21: 25

LYDIA BAXTER   8. 7. 8. 7. Ref.   S. J. VAIL

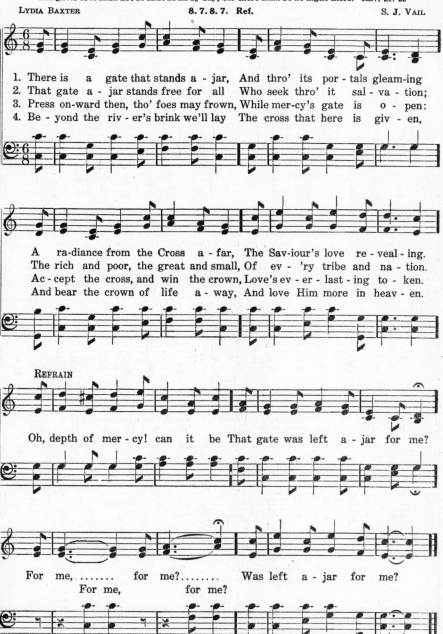

1. There is a gate that stands a-jar, And thro' its por-tals gleam-ing
2. That gate a-jar stands free for all Who seek thro' it sal-va-tion;
3. Press on-ward then, tho' foes may frown, While mer-cy's gate is o-pen:
4. Be-yond the riv-er's brink we'll lay The cross that here is giv-en,

A ra-diance from the Cross a-far, The Sav-iour's love re-veal-ing.
The rich and poor, the great and small, Of ev-'ry tribe and na-tion.
Ac-cept the cross, and win the crown, Love's ev-er-last-ing to-ken.
And bear the crown of life a-way, And love Him more in heav-en.

REFRAIN

Oh, depth of mer-cy! can it be That gate was left a-jar for me?

For me, ... for me? .... Was left a-jar for me?
For me,   for me?

539

Behold! A Stranger's At the Door

Behold, I stand at the door, and knock.—Rev. 3: 20

Joseph Grigg, 1765   **ZEPHYR L. M.**   William B. Bradbury, 1844

1. Be-hold! a Stran-ger's at the door; He gen-tly knocks, has knocked be-fore;
2. But will He prove a friend in-deed? He will, the ver-y friend you need;
3. O love-ly at-ti-tude! He stands With melting heart and la-den hands:
4. Ad-mit Him ere His an-ger burn; His feet, de-part-ed, ne'er re-turn:

Has wait-ed long, is wait-ing still: You treat no oth-er friend so ill.
The Man of Naz-a-reth, 'tis He, With garments dyed at Cal-va-ry.
O match-less kind-ness! and He shows This matchless kind-ness to His foes.
Ad-mit Him, or the hour's at hand When at His door de-nied you'll stand.

540

For Me

Anon.   I. H. Meredith

Slowly

1. Un-der an east-ern sky, A-mid a rab-ble's cry....
2. Thorn-crowned His bless-ed head, Blood-stained His ev-'ry tread;
3. Pierc-ed His hands and feet, Three hours o'er Him beat
4. Thus wert Thou made all mine; Lord, make me whol-ly Thine;
5. In thought and word and deed, Thy will to do, O lead

cres.   *p rall.*   *pp*

A Man went forth to die,...... For me, (for me,) for me.
Cross-la-den, on He sped..... For me, (for me,) for me.
Fierce rays of noon-tide heat,..... For me, (for me,) for me.
Grant grace and strength di-vine...... To me, (to me,) to me.
My soul, e'en though it bleed,.... To Thee, (to Thee,) to Thee.

"Some Day" May Be Too Late

JAMES ROWE

DE LOSS SMITH

1. "Some day," you say, while Je-sus pleads, "I'll come and fill my soul's deep need."
2. The pre-cious time is speed-ing fast;   Let all your wand'ring days be past;
3. You know that e - vil does not pay,   You know you need a friend to - day;
4. You do not wish to lose your soul;   Then, why let sin your life con-trol?
5. You can - not save yourself, my friend,   On God's great Son you must de-pend;

Come while the Spir - it   in - ter-cedes—"Some day"... may be too late.
On   Je - sus now your bur - den cast—"Some day"... may be too late.
Then, why from Je - sus turn a - way?—"Some day"... may be too late.
Come home, come home, be glad and whole;—"Some day"... may be too late.
Come now, while arms of love ex - tend;—"Some day"... may be too late.

CHORUS

1. "Some day" ..... may be too late,   For death may shut the vine-yard
2. "Some day" ...... may be too late,   For death may call; oh, do not
3. "Some day" ..... may be too late,   For death may close the gold-en
"Some day"

may be too late;

gate; The time is now, this ver - y hour, "Some day".. may be too late.
wait; The time is now, this ver - y hour, "Some day".. may be too late.
gate; The time is now, this ver - y hour, "Some day".. may be too late.

542 Jesus Pleads For Me

J. Sparrow Simpson

E. O. Sellers

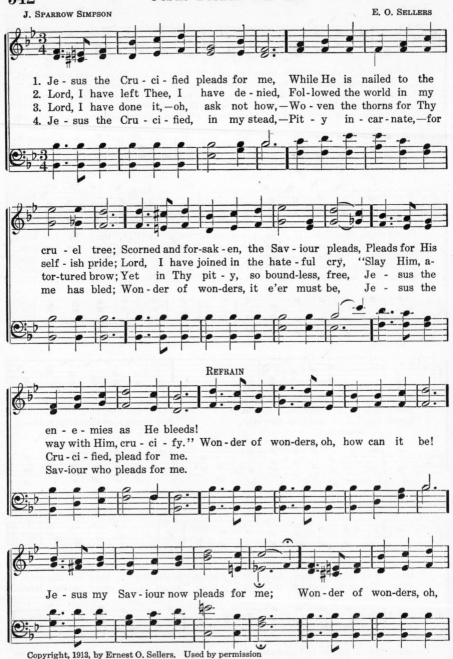

1. Je - sus the Cru - ci - fied pleads for me, While He is nailed to the
2. Lord, I have left Thee, I have de - nied, Fol - lowed the world in my
3. Lord, I have done it, — oh, ask not how, — Wo - ven the thorns for Thy
4. Je - sus the Cru - ci - fied, in my stead, — Pit - y in - car - nate, — for

cru - el tree; Scorned and for - sak - en, the Sav - iour pleads, Pleads for His
self - ish pride; Lord, I have joined in the hate - ful cry, "Slay Him, a-
tor - tured brow; Yet in Thy pit - y, so bound - less, free, Je - sus the
me has bled; Won - der of won - ders, it e'er must be, Je - sus the

REFRAIN

en - e - mies as He bleeds!
way with Him, cru - ci - fy." Won - der of won - ders, oh, how can it be!
Cru - ci - fied, plead for me.
Sav - iour who pleads for me.

Je - sus my Sav - iour now pleads for me; Won - der of won - ders, oh,

Jesus Pleads For Me—Concluded

how can it be! Je-sus the Cru-ci-fied pleads for me.

Lord, At Thy Mercy-Seat

543

Christ is all and in all.—COL. 3: 11

FANNY J. CROSBY   JESUS MY ALL 6. 4. 6. 4. 6. 6. 6. 4.   Anon.

rit.

1. Lord, at Thy mer-cy-seat Hum-bly I fall; Plead-ing Thy
2. Tears of re-pent-ant grief Si-lent-ly fall; Help Thou my
3. Still at Thy mer-cy-seat, Sav-iour, I fall; Trust-ing Thy

rit.

prom-ise sweet, Lord, hear my call; Now let Thy work be-gin,
un-be-lief, Hear Thou my call; Oh, how I pine for Thee!
prom-ise sweet, Heard is my call; Faith wings my soul to Thee;

rit.

Oh, make me pure with-in, Cleanse me from ev-'ry sin, Je-sus, my all.
'Tis all my hope and plea: Je-sus has died for me, Je-sus, my all.
This all my song shall be, Je-sus has died for me, Je-sus, my all.

544

Not Far From the Kingdom

Thou art not far from the kingdom of God.—Mk. 12: 34

E. R. LATTA

J. H. TENNEY

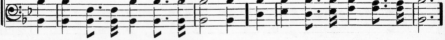

1. Not far from the king-dom of heav-en,—The king-dom of heav-en with men,
2. Not far from the king-dom of heav-en,—The king-dom of peace and of love,
3. Not far from the king-dom of heav-en, Yet will not on Je-sus be-lieve!

And yet in the bond-age of Sa-tan, And yet in the shad-ow of sin!
Yet out on the edge of the des-ert, The prod-i-gal's for-tune to prove!
O sin-ner, what ter-rors a-wait thee! The bless-ing of par-don re-ceive!

Not far from the path that is nar-row, And lead-eth to glo-ry on high;
Oh, rise, and re-turn to thy Fa-ther, And crave in His mer-cy a share!
The por-tal of mer-cy is o-pen, Poor prod-i-gal, do not de-lay!

Yet tread-ing the broad road to ru-in,— Oh, why is it, sin-ner? oh, why?
Far off He will see thee and know thee, And res-cue thy soul from de-spair!
A-rise, and re-turn to thy Fa-ther! Oh, en-ter the king-dom to-day!

416

Not Far From the Kingdom—Concluded

CHORUS

Not far, not far, Not far from the king-dom of heav'n!
Not far, not far, the kingdom of heav'n!

rit.

Still tread-ing the broad road to ru - in, Yet near to the king-dom of heav'n!

Child of Sin and Sorrow   545

Lord, it is done, and yet there is room.—Lk. 14: 22

THOMAS HASTINGS, 1832   AVA 6. 4. 6. 4. 4. 4. 6. 4.   THOMAS HASTINGS, 1832

1. Child of sin and sor - row, Filled with dis - may, Wait not
2. Child of sin and sor - row, Why wilt thou die? Come, while
3. Child of sin and sor - row, Thy mo - ments glide, Like the

for to - mor - row, Yield thee to - day: Heav'n bids thee come,
thou canst bor - row Help from on high: Grieve not that love
flit - ting ar - row, Or the rush - ing tide; Ere time is o'er,

While yet there's room. Child of sin and sor - row, Hear and o - bey.
Which from a - bove, Child of sin and sor - row, Would bring thee nigh.
Heav'n's grace implore, Child of sin and sor - row, In Christ con - fide.

417

546 Where He Leads I'll Follow

W. A. O.　　　　　　6. 4. 12. D. Ref.　　　　　W. A. OGDEN

1. Sweet are the prom-is-es, Kind is the word, Dear-er far than an - y mes-sage
2. Sweet is the ten-der love Je-sus hath shown, Sweeter far than an - y love that
3. List to His loving words, "Come un - to Me!" Wea-ry, heav-y - la-den, there is

man ev - er heard; Pure was the mind of Christ, Sin - less I see; He the great ex-
mortals have known; Kind to the err-ing one, Faith-ful is He; He the great ex-
sweet rest for thee; Trust in His prom-is-es, Faithful and sure; Lean up - on the

CHORUS

am - ple is, and pat - tern for me. Where..... .... He leads I'll
am - ple is, and pat - tern for me.
Sav-iour, and thy soul is se-cure. Where He leads I'll fol - low,

fol - - - low, Fol - - - low all the way;
Where He leads I'll fol-low, Fol-low all the way, yes, fol - low all the way;

Where........ He leads I'll fol - - low, Fol-low Je-sus ev - 'ry day.
Where He leads I'll follow, Where He leads I'll follow,

No Hope in Jesus

Having no hope and without God in the world.—EPH. 2: 12

W. O. CUSHING

ROBERT LOWRY

1. Oh, to have no Christ, no Sav-iour! No Rock, no Ref-uge nigh!
2. Oh, to have no Christ, no Sav-iour! How lone-ly life must be!
3. Oh, to have no Christ, no Sav-iour! No hand to clasp thine own!
4. Now, we pray thee, come to Je-sus; His par-d'ning love re-ceive;

When the dark days round thee gath-er, When the storms sweep o'er the sky!
Like a sail-or, lost and driv-en On a wide and shore-less sea.
Thro' the dark, dark vale of shad-ows Thou must press thy way a-lone.
For the Sav-iour now is call-ing, And He bids thee turn and live.

REFRAIN

1-3. Oh, to have no hope in Je-sus! No friend, no light in Je-sus!
4. Come to Je-sus, He will save you; He is the friend of sin-ners;

Oh, to have no hope in Je-sus! How dark this world must be!
Then, when thou hast found the Sav-iour, How bright this world will be!

548 # Is My Name Written There?

Rejoice, because your names are written in heaven.—Lk. 10: 20

MARY A. KIDDER   7. 6. 7. 6. D. Ref.   FRANK M. DAVIS

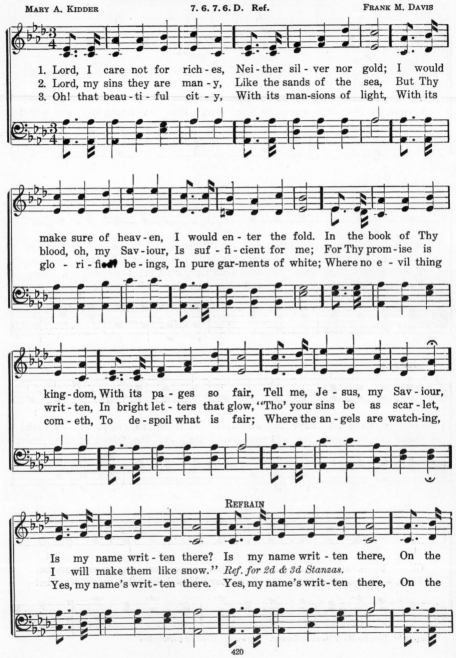

1. Lord, I care not for rich-es, Nei-ther sil-ver nor gold; I would
2. Lord, my sins they are man-y, Like the sands of the sea, But Thy
3. Oh! that beau-ti-ful cit-y, With its man-sions of light, With its

make sure of heav-en, I would en-ter the fold. In the book of Thy
blood, oh, my Sav-iour, Is suf-fi-cient for me; For Thy prom-ise is
glo-ri-fied be-ings, In pure gar-ments of white; Where no e-vil thing

king-dom, With its pa-ges so fair, Tell me, Je-sus, my Sav-iour,
writ-ten, In bright let-ters that glow, "Tho' your sins be as scar-let,
com-eth, To de-spoil what is fair; Where the an-gels are watch-ing,

REFRAIN

Is my name writ-ten there? Is my name writ-ten there, On the
I will make them like snow." *Ref. for 2d & 3d Stanzas.*
Yes, my name's writ-ten there. Yes, my name's writ-ten there, On the

Is My Name Written There?—Concluded

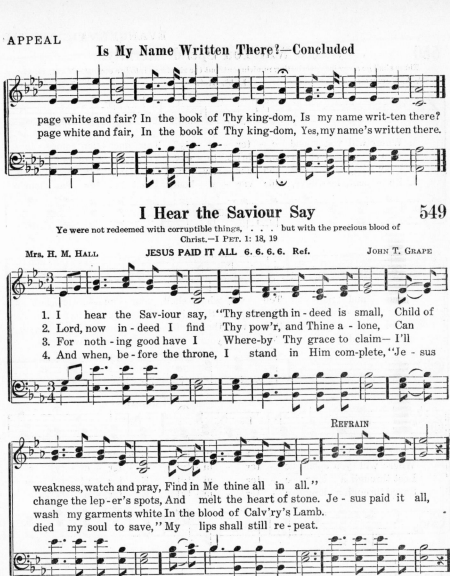

page white and fair? In the book of Thy king-dom, Is my name writ-ten there?
page white and fair, In the book of Thy king-dom, Yes, my name's written there.

I Hear the Saviour Say 549

Ye were not redeemed with corruptible things, . . . but with the precious blood of
Christ.—I Pet. 1: 18, 19

Mrs. H. M. Hall   JESUS PAID IT ALL 6. 6. 6. 6. Ref.   John T. Grape

1. I   hear the Sav-iour say, "Thy strength in - deed is small, Child of
2. Lord, now in - deed I   find   Thy pow'r, and Thine a - lone, Can
3. For noth - ing good have I   Where-by Thy grace to claim— I'll
4. And when, be - fore the throne, I   stand in Him com-plete, "Je - sus

REFRAIN

weakness, watch and pray, Find in Me thine all in all."
change the lep - er's spots, And   melt the heart of stone. Je - sus paid it all,
wash my garments white In the blood of Calv'ry's Lamb.
died   my soul to save," My   lips shall still re - peat.

All to Him I owe; Sin had left a crim-son stain, He washed it white as snow.

550 Where Will You Spend Eternity?

These shall go away into everlasting punishment, but the righteous into life eternal.—MATT. 25: 46

E. A. HOFFMAN   L. M. Ref.   J. H. TENNEY

1. Where will you spend e - ter - ni - ty? This ques - tion comes to
2. Man - y are choos - ing Christ to - day, Turn - ing from all their
3. Leav - ing the strait and nar - row way, Go - ing the down - ward
4. Re - pent, be - lieve, this ver - y hour, Trust in the Sav - iour's

you and me! Tell me, what shall your an - swer be?
sins a - way; Heav'n shall their hap - py por - tion be;
road to - day, Sad will their fi - nal end - ing be,—
grace and pow'r; Then will your joy - ous an - swer be,

REFRAIN

Where will you spend e - ter - ni - ty? E - ter - ni - ty! e-
Where will you spend e - ter - ni - ty! E - ter - ni - ty! e-
Lost through a long e - ter - ni - ty! E - ter - ni - ty! e-
Saved through a long e - ter - ni - ty! E - ter - ni - ty! e-

ter - ni - ty! Where will you spend e - ter - ni - ty?
ter - ni - ty! Where will you spend e - ter - ni - ty?
ter - ni - ty! Lost through a long e - ter - ni - ty!
ter - ni - ty! Saved through a long e - ter - ni - ty!

I Am Coming to the Cross

Having made peace through the blood of the cross.—COL. 1: 20

WM. McDONALD, 1872   **7. 7. 7. 7. D.**   WILLIAM G. FISCHER, 1869

1. I am com - ing to the cross: I am poor and weak and blind;
2. Long my heart has sighed for Thee; Long has e - vil reigned with-in;
3. Here I give my all to Thee— Friends and time and earth - ly store;
4. Je - sus comes! He fills my soul! Per - fect - ed in Him I am;

I am count - ing all but dross; I shall full sal - va - tion find.
Je - sus sweet - ly speaks to me: "I will cleanse you from all sin."
Soul and bod - y Thine to be— Whol-ly Thine—for - ev - er - more.
I am ev - 'ry whit made whole; Glo - ry, glo - ry to the Lamb.

REFRAIN

I am trust - ing, Lord, in Thee, Bless - ed Lamb of Cal - va - ry;

Hum - bly at Thy cross I bow; Save me, Je - sus, save me now.

552 Jesus, and Shall It Ever Be

Whosoever shall be ashamed of me, . . . of him shall the Son of man be ashamed.—Lk. 9: 26

JOSEPH GRIGG, 1765. Alt. FEDERAL STREET L. M. HENRY K. OLIVER

1. Je-sus, and shall it ev-er be, A mor-tal man, a-shamed of Thee? A-shamed of Thee, whom an-gels praise, Whose glo-ries shine through end-less days!
2. A-shamed of Je-sus! soon-er far Let eve-ning blush to own a star; He sheds the beams of light di-vine O'er this be-night-ed soul of mine.
3. A-shamed of Je-sus! just as soon Let mid-night be a-shamed of noon; 'Tis mid-night with my soul till He, Bright Morn-ing-Star, bid dark-ness flee.
4. A-shamed of Je-sus! that dear Friend On whom my hopes of heav'n de-pend! No; when I blush, be this my shame, That I no more re-vere His name.
5. A-shamed of Je-sus! yes, I may, When I've no guilt to wash a-way; No tear to wipe, no good to crave, No fears to quell, no soul to save.
6. Till then, nor is my boast-ing vain, Till then I boast a Sav-iour slain; And O, may this my glo-ry be, That Christ is not a-shamed of me!

553 Approach, My Soul, the Mercy-Seat

Cast thy burden upon the Lord.—Ps. 55: 22

JOHN NEWTON, 1779 BYEFIELD C. M. THOMAS HASTINGS, 1840

1. Ap-proach, my soul, the mer-cy-seat, Where Je-sus an-swers prayer;
2. Thy prom-ise is my on-ly plea, With this I ven-ture nigh;
3. Bowed down be-neath a load of sin, By Sa-tan sore-ly pressed,
4. O won-drous love! to bleed and die, To bear the cross and shame,

Approach, My Soul, the Mercy-Seat—Concluded

There hum-bly fall be-fore His feet, For none can per-ish there.
Thou call-est burdened souls to Thee, And such, O Lord, am I.
By wars without, and fears with-in, I come to Thee for rest.
That guilt-y sin-ners, such as I, Might plead Thy gra-cious name! A-MEN.

Coming Now, O Lord, to Thee

Being justified freely by His grace.—ROM. 3: 24

GEORGE P. HOTT   6. 4. 6. 4. 6. 4. 6. 5.   ALDINE S. KIEFFER

554

1. Sav-iour, to Thee I come, Bur-dened with sin; O-pen the
2. Plead-ing Thy grace a-lone, Hum-bly I bow; No oth-er
3. Trust-ing Thy mer-cy, Lord, Night turns to day; Rest-ing up-

cres. — — — —

door, I pray; Oh, let me in! How can I lon-ger stay,
help I know, Save me just now. Heal Thou my bro-ken heart,
on Thy Word, Doubts flee a-way. Ev-er my path shall be

p

My God, from Thee? Thou art the Life, the Way, All in all to me.
Sav-iour di-vine; On me Thy love be-stow, Make me whol-ly Thine.
Where Thou hast trod; I come, O Christ, to Thee, Bless-ed Lamb of God.

555 I Am Coming, Lord

Whosoever will, let him take the water of life freely—Rev. 22: 17

L. Hartsough, c. 1873   S. M. Ref.   L. Hartsough

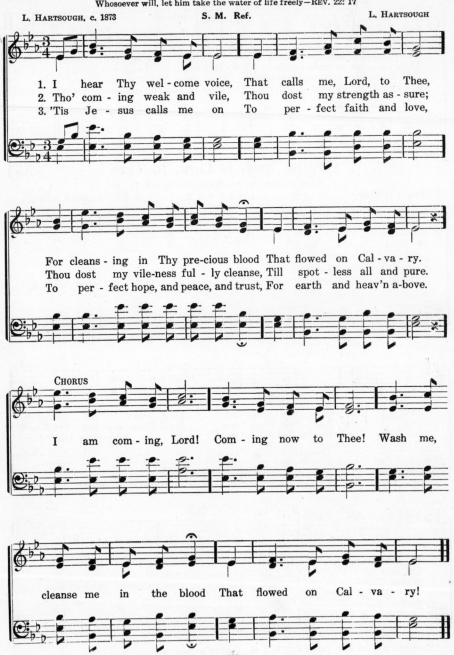

1. I hear Thy wel-come voice, That calls me, Lord, to Thee,
2. Tho' com-ing weak and vile, Thou dost my strength as-sure;
3. 'Tis Je-sus calls me on To per-fect faith and love,

For cleans-ing in Thy pre-cious blood That flowed on Cal-va-ry.
Thou dost my vile-ness ful-ly cleanse, Till spot-less all and pure.
To per-fect hope, and peace, and trust, For earth and heav'n a-bove.

CHORUS

I am com-ing, Lord! Com-ing now to Thee! Wash me,

cleanse me in the blood That flowed on Cal-va-ry!

426

There's a Stranger At the Door

If any man hear my voice, and open the door, I will come in.—Rev. 3: 20

J. B. Atchinson

E. O. Excell

1. There's a Stran-ger at the door, Let Him in;
2. O - pen now to Him your heart, Let Him in;
3. Hear you now His lov - ing voice? Let Him in;
4. Now ad - mit the heav'n-ly Guest, Let Him in;

Let the Saviour in, Let the Saviour in;

He has been there oft be - fore, Let Him in;
If you wait He will de - part, Let Him in;
Now, oh, now make Him your choice, Let Him in;
He will make for you a feast, Let Him in;

Let the Saviour in, Let the Saviour in;

Let Him in, ere He is gone, Let Him in, the Ho - ly One,
Let Him in, He is your Friend, And your soul He will de - fend,
He is stand-ing at your door, Joy to you He will re - store,
He will speak your sins for - giv'n, And when earth-ties all are riv'n,

Je - sus Christ, the Fa-ther's Son, Let Him in.
He will keep you to the end, Let Him in.
And His name you will a - dore, Let Him in.
He will take you home to heav'n, Let Him in.

Let the Saviour in, Let the Saviour in.

557 **Why Do You Wait?**

Arise, He calleth thee.—MK. 10: 49

G. F. R.   7. 8. 9. 8. Ref.   GEO. F. ROOT

1. Why do you wait, dear broth-er,...... Oh, why do you tar-ry so long? Your Sav-iour is wait-ing to give you...... A place in His sanc-ti-fied throng.
2. What do you hope, dear broth-er,...... To gain by a fur-ther de-lay? There's no one to save you but Je-sus,...... There's no oth-er way but His way.
3. Do you not feel, dear broth-er,...... His Spir-it now striv-ing with-in? Oh, why not ac-cept His sal-va-tion,..... And throw off thy bur-den of sin.
4. Why do you wait, dear broth-er?...... The har-vest is pass-ing a-way, Your Sav-iour is long-ing to bless you, ... There's dan-ger and death in de-lay.

CHORUS

Why not? why not? Why not come to Him now?....

428

Why Do You Wait?—Concluded

Why not? why not? Why not come to Him now?

Almost Persuaded 558

Almost thou persuadest me to be a Christian.—ACTS. 26: 28

P. P. BLISS

9. 9. 6. 6. 6. 4.

P. P. BLISS

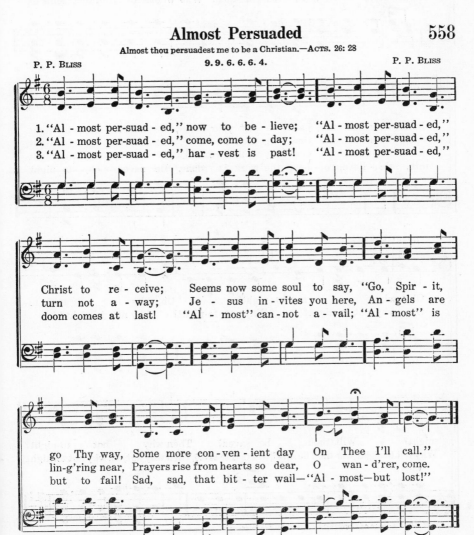

1. "Al - most per-suad - ed," now to be - lieve; "Al - most per-suad - ed,"
2. "Al - most per-suad - ed," come, come to - day; "Al - most per-suad - ed,"
3. "Al - most per-suad - ed," har - vest is past! "Al - most per-suad - ed,"

Christ to re - ceive; Seems now some soul to say, "Go, Spir - it,
turn not a - way; Je - sus in - vites you here, An - gels are
doom comes at last! "Al - most" can - not a - vail; "Al - most" is

go Thy way, Some more con - ven - ient day On Thee I'll call."
lin-g'ring near, Prayers rise from hearts so dear, O wan - d'rer, come.
but to fail! Sad, sad, that bit - ter wail—"Al - most—but lost!"

559 ## Oh, Why Not To-night?

Now is the accepted time; Behold, now is the day of salvation.—II Cor. 6: 2

HORATIUS BONAR   8. 8. 8. 5. Ref.   J. CALVIN BUSHEY

1. Oh, do not let the Word de-part, And close thine eyes a-gainst the
2. To-mor-row's sun may nev-er rise To bless thy long de-lud-ed
3. Our Lord in pit-y lin-gers still: And wilt thou thus His love re-
4. Our bless-ed Lord re-fus-es none Who would to Him their souls u-

light; Poor sin-ner, hard-en not your heart, Be saved, oh, to-night.
sight; This is the time, oh, then be wise, Be saved, oh, to-night.
quite? Re-nounce at once thy stub-born will, Be saved, oh, to-night.
nite. Be-lieve, o-bey, the work is done, Be saved, oh, to-night.

REFRAIN

Oh, why not to-night? Oh, why not to-
Oh, why not to-night? Why not to-night? Why not to-night?

night? Wilt thou be saved? Then why not to-night?
Why not to-night? Wilt thou be saved, wilt thou be saved, Then why not, oh, why not to-night?

Softly and Tenderly

Come unto me, all ye that labor and are heavy laden.—MATT. 11: 28

W. L. T.   11. 7. 11. 7. Ref.   WILL L. THOMPSON

1. Soft-ly and ten-der-ly Je-sus is call-ing, Call-ing for you and for me;
2. Why should we tarry when Jesus is pleading, Plead-ing for you and for me;
3. Time is now fleeting, the moments are passing, Passing for you and for me;
4. Oh! for the won-der-ful love He has promised, Promised for you and for me;

See, on the por-tals He's watching and waiting, Watch-ing for you and for me.
Why should we lin-ger and heed not His mer-cies, Mer-cies for you and for me.
Shad-ows are gath-er-ing, death beds are com-ing, Com-ing for you and for me.
Tho' we have sinned, He has mer-cy and par-don, Par-don for you and for me.

REFRAIN

Come home,.... come home,.... Ye who are wea-ry, come home!....
Come home, come home,

Ear-nest-ly, ten-der-ly, Je-sus is call-ing, Call-ing, O sin-ner, come home!

rit.

561 O Weary Wanderer

I will arise and go to my father.—Lk. 15: 18

JOHN S. COFFMAN, 1883   REMEMBER ME C. M.   ASA HALL

1. O wea-ry wan-der-er, come home, Thy Sav-iour bids thee come;
2. Think of thy Fa-ther's house to-day, So blest with plen-teous store.
3. Poor prod-i-gal, come home and rest, Come and be rec-on-ciled;

REF.—*Help me, dear Sav-iour, Thee to own, And ev-er faith-ful be;*

Thou long in sin didst love to roam, Yet still He calls thee, come.
Think of thy sin-ful, wan-d'ring way, Then come, and roam no more.
Here lean up-on thy Fa-ther's breast, He loves His wan-d'ring child.
And when Thou sit-test on Thy throne, O Lord, re-mem-ber me.

562 Come, Ye Sinners, Poor and Needy

Ho, every one that thirsteth, come ye to the waters.—Isa. 55: 1

JOSEPH HART, 1859   GREENVILLE 8. 7. 8. 7. 8. 7.   JEAN J. ROUSSEAU, 1750

1. Come, ye sin-ners, poor and need-y, Weak and wound-ed, sick and sore;
2. Now, ye need-y, come and wel-come; God's free boun-ty glo-ri-fy;
3. Let not con-science make you lin-ger, Nor of fit-ness fond-ly dream;
4. Come, ye wea-ry, heav-y-la-den, Bruised and man-gled by the fall;

Je-sus read-y stands to save you, Full of pit-y, love, and pow'r;
True be-lief and true re-pent-ance, Ev-'ry grace that brings you nigh,
All the fit-ness He re-quir-eth Is to feel your need of Him:
If you tar-ry till you're bet-ter, You will nev-er come at all;

Come, Ye Sinners, Poor and Needy—Concluded

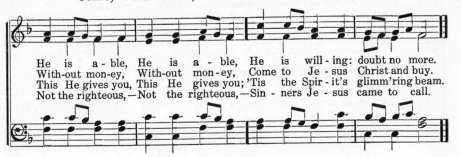

He is a - ble, He is a - ble, He is will - ing: doubt no more.
With-out mon-ey, With-out mon-ey, Come to Je - sus Christ and buy.
This He gives you, This He gives you; 'Tis the Spir - it's glimm'ring beam.
Not the righteous,—Not the righteous,—Sin - ners Je - sus came to call.

Come, Every Soul By Sin Oppressed   563

Let him return unto the Lord, and He will have mercy upon him.—ISA. 55: 7

J. H. S. Alt.   ONLY TRUST HIM C. M. Ref.   J. H. STOCKTON

1. Come, ev - 'ry soul by sin op-pressed, There's mer-cy with the Lord,
2. For Je - sus shed His pre-cious blood, Rich bless-ings to be - stow;
3. Yes, Je - sus is the Truth, the Way, That leads you in - to rest;
4. Come, then, and join this ho - ly band, And on to glo-ry go,

And He will sure - ly give you rest By trust - ing in His Word.
Come now un - to that fount which flowed, That wash-es white as snow.
Be - lieve in Him with - out de - lay, And you are ful - ly blest.
To dwell in that ce - les - tial land, Where joys im - mor - tal flow.

CHORUS

On - ly trust Him, on - ly trust Him, On - ly trust Him now;
He will save you, He will save you, He will (*Omit* . . . .) save you now.

564   To-day the Saviour Calls

To-day if ye will hear His voice, harden not your hearts.—HEB. 3: 7

SAMUEL F. SMITH   **TO-DAY 6. 4. 6. 4.**   LOWELL MASON, 1831

1. To - day the Sav - iour calls: Ye wan - d'rers, come;
2. To - day the Sav - iour calls: Oh, hear Him now;
3. To - day the Sav - iour calls: For ref - uge fly;
4. The Spir - it calls to - day: Yield to His pow'r;

O ye be - night - ed souls, Why lon - ger roam?
With - in these sa - cred walls To Je - sus bow.
The storm of jus - tice falls, And death is nigh.
Oh, grieve Him not a - way, 'Tis mer - cy's hour.

565   Come, Just As You Are

I am not come to call the righteous, but sinners to repentance.—MATT. 9: 13

E. A. HOFFMAN

J. HENRY SHOWALTER

1. Shall I come just as I am, Come with all my guilt and sin? If I
2. Shall I come vile as I am, And bend low at Je - sus' feet? Shall I
3. Shall I come with all my fear, Lest my sins have been too great? Shall I
4. Shall I come, tho' far a - way From the lov - ing Shepherd's fold? Will He

REFRAIN

o - pen wide my heart, Will He en - ter in?
plead His pard'ning grace, And His love en - treat? As you are, just as you are
break thro' all my doubts, To sweet mer - cy's gate?
bless me if I firm To His prom - ise hold?

Copyright, 1899, by J. Henry Showalter. Used by permission

Come, Just As You Are—Concluded

Come to Je-sus, come to-day; He will kind-ly welcome you, Take your sins a-way.

Just As I Am

Behold the Lamb of God.—Jn. 1: 29

566

CHARLOTTE ELLIOTT

WOODWORTH L. M.

WILLIAM B. BRADBURY

1. Just as I am, with-out one plea, But that Thy
2. Just as I am, and wait-ing not To rid my
3. Just as I am, though tossed a-bout With many a
4. Just as I am, poor, wretch-ed, blind; Sight, rich-es,
5. Just as I am, Thou wilt re-ceive, Wilt wel-come,
6. Just as I am, Thy love un-known Hath bro-ken

blood was shed for me, And that Thou bid'st me
soul of one dark blot, To Thee whose blood can
con-flict, many a doubt, Fight-ings and fears with-
heal-ing of the mind, Yea, all I need in
par-don, cleanse, re-lieve; Be-cause Thy prom-ise
ev-'ry bar-rier down; Now, to be Thine, yea,

come to Thee, O Lamb of God, I come, I come!
cleanse each spot, O Lamb of God, I come, I come!
in, with-out, O Lamb of God, I come, I come!
Thee to find, O Lamb of God, I come, I come!
I be-lieve, O Lamb of God, I come, I come!
Thine a-lone, O Lamb of God, I come, I come!

435

567 Come, Lost One

Come, for all things are now ready.—Lk. 14: 17

9. 8. 9. 8. D.

Words and melody by
J. S. Shoemaker, 1901

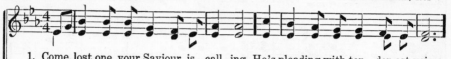

1. Come, lost one, your Saviour is call-ing, He's pleading with ten - der-est voice;
2. Come with all thy guilt and pol - lu - tion, And call on the name of the Lord;
3. Thy sins tho' they be red like crim-son, Yea, tho' they be man - y and great,
4. The Lord has pro - vid - ed a - bun-dance, Yea, all that ye need is in store;

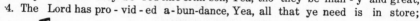

Come out from your ways of transgression, And has-ten to make Him your choice.
He's read - y to cleanse and to bless you, And save by His life - giv-ing Word.
Shall be blot-ted out by your Sav-iour, If you come to Him ere too late.
Then come and par-take of His boun - ty, And trust Him for grace ev - er-more.

Refrain

Oh, why should you wan-der in dark-ness? Oh, why should you lon-ger de - lay,

When Je - sus is read - y to save you, And keep you from sin ev - 'ry day?

436

In the Silent Midnight Watches

Behold, I stand at the door and knock.—REV. 3: 20

A. C. COXE

8. 5. 8. 5. D.

GEO. F. ROOT

Piano e marcato

1. In the si - lent mid - night watch-es, List— thy bos - om's door!
2. Death comes down with reck-less foot-steps, To the hall and hut;
3. Then 'tis time to stand en - treat-ing Christ to let thee in;

How it knock-eth, knock-eth, knock-eth, Knock-eth ev - er - more!
Think you death will tar - ry knock-ing, When the door is shut?
At the gate of heav - en beat-ing, Wail - ing for thy sin?

Say not 'tis thy puls - e's beat-ing, 'Tis thy heart of sin;
Je - sus wait-eth, wait - eth, wait-eth; But the door is fast;
Nay! a - las, thou guilt - y crea-ture! Hast thou, then, for - got?

'Tis thy Sav - iour knocks, and cri - eth, "Rise, and let Me in!"
Grieved, a-way thy Sav - iour go - eth, Death breaks in at last.
Je - sus wait-ed long to know thee, Now He knows thee not!

569 While Jesus Whispers to You

When Thou saidst, Seek ye my face, my heart said, Thy face, Lord, will I seek.—Ps. 27: 8

W. E. WITTER, 1878
and Mrs. C. M. ALEXANDER

COME, SINNER, COME 7. 4. 7. 4. D.

H. R. PALMER

1. While Je - sus whis - pers to you, Come, sin - ner, come!
2. Are you too, heav - y - la - den? Come, sin - ner, come!
3. Why will you lon - ger doubt Him? Come, sin - ner, come!
4. Far off you may have wan - dered, Come, sin - ner, come!
5. Oh, hear His ten - der plead - ing, Come, sin - ner, come!

While we are pray - ing for you, Come, sin - ner, come!
Je - sus will bear your bur - den, Come, sin - ner, come!
What will you do with - out Him? Come, sin - ner, come!
God's gifts you may have squan - dered, Come, sin - ner, come!
Come and re - ceive the bless - ing, Come, sin - ner, come!

Now is the time to own Him, Come, sin - ner, come!
Je - sus will not de - ceive you, Come, sin - ner, come!
For you His heart is yearn - ing, Come, sin - ner, come!
Cease now, your heart to hard - en, Come, sin - ner, come!
While Je - sus whis - pers to you, Come, sin - ner, come!

Now is the time to know Him, Come, sin - ner, come!
Je - sus will now re - ceive you, Come, sin - ner, come!
Why not to Him be turn - ing? Come, sin - ner, come!
Je - sus will free - ly par - don, Come, sin - ner, come!
While we are pray - ing for you, Come, sin - ner, come!

The Hem of His Garment

Thy faith hath made thee whole.— LK. 8: 48

570

G. F. R.

10. 6. 10. 6. Ref.

GEO F. ROOT

1. She on - ly touched the hem of His gar - ment As
2. She came in fear and trem - bling be - fore Him, She
3. He turned with "Daugh - ter, be of good com - fort, Thy

to His side she stole, A - mid the crowd that
knew her Lord had come; She felt that from Him
faith hath made thee whole;" And peace that pass - eth

gath - ered a - round Him, And straight-way she was whole.
vir - tue had healed her, The might - y deed was done.
all un - der - stand - ing With glad - ness filled her soul.

CHORUS

Oh, touch the hem of His gar - ment! And thou, too, shalt be free;

His sav - ing pow'r this ver - y hour Shall give new life to thee.

571 **Come to the Saviour Now**

I give unto them eternal life.—JN. 10: 28

JOHN M. WIGNER   6s. 8 l.   FREDERICK C. MAKER, 1881

1. Come to the Sav - iour now, He gen - tly call - eth thee;
2. Come to the Sav - iour now, Ye who have wan - dered far,
3. Come to the Sav - iour, all, What-e'er your bur - dens be;

In true re - pent - ance bow, Be - fore Him bend the knee:
Re - new your sol - emn vow, For His by right you are;
Hear now His lov - ing call, "Cast all your care on Me."

He wait - eth to be - stow Sal - va - tion, peace, and love,
Come, like poor wan - d'ring sheep Re - turn - ing to His fold;
Come, and for ev - 'ry grief In Je - sus you will find

True joy on earth be - low, A home in heav'n a - bove.
His arm will safe - ly keep, His love will ne'er grow cold.
A sure and safe re - lief, A lov - ing Friend, and kind.

Come, Ye Thankful People, Come

They joy before Thee according to the joy in harvest.—ISA. 9: 3

HENRY ALFORD, 1844   **ST. GEORGE'S (WINDSOR) 7. 7. 7. 7. D.**   GEORGE J. ELVEY, 1859

1. Come, ye thank-ful peo-ple, come, Raise the song of har-vest-home:
2. All the world is God's own field, Fruit un-to His praise to yield;
3. For the Lord our God shall come, And shall take His har-vest home;
4. E-ven so, Lord, quick-ly come To Thy fi-nal har-vest home;

All is safe-ly gath-ered in, Ere the win-ter storms be-gin;
Wheat and tares to-geth-er sown, Un-to joy or sor-row grown;
From His field shall in that day All of-fens-es purge a-way;
Gath-er Thou Thy peo-ple in, Free from sor-row, free from sin;

God, our Mak-er, doth pro-vide For our wants to be sup-plied:
First the blade, and then the ear, Then the full corn shall ap-pear;
Give His an-gels charge at last In the fire the tares to cast,
There for-ev-er pu-ri-fied, In Thy pres-ence to a-bide:

Come to God's own tem-ple, come, Raise the song of har-vest-home.
Lord of har-vest, grant that we Wholesome grain and pure may be.
But the fruit-ful ears to store In His gar-ner ev-er-more.
Come, with all Thine an-gels, come, Raise the glo-rious har-vest-home.

15

573

Angels Holy, High and Lowly

Praise ye the Lord from the heavens.—Ps. 148: 1

JOHN S. BLACKIE   WINDERMERE 8. 7. 8. 8. 7.   FREDERICK C. MAKER

1. An - gels ho - ly, High and low - ly, Sing the prais - es
2. Bond and free man, Land and sea man, Earth, with peo - ples
3. Praise Him ev - er, Boun - teous Giv - er; Praise Him, Fa - ther,

of the Lord! Earth and sky, all liv - ing na - ture, Man, the
wide - ly stored, Wan - d'rer lone o'er prai - ries am - ple, Full - voiced
Friend, and Lord! Each glad soul its free course wing - ing, Each glad

stamp of thy Cre - a - tor, Praise ye, praise ye, God the Lord!
choir, in cost - ly tem - ple, Praise ye, praise ye, God the Lord!
voice its free song sing - ing, Praise the great and might - y Lord!

574

Praise, O Praise Our God and King

Praise the name of the Lord your God, that hath dealt wondrously with you.—JOEL 2: 26

H. W. BAKER, 1861   SEYMOUR 7. 7. 7. 7.   Arr. from CARL VON WEBER, 1826

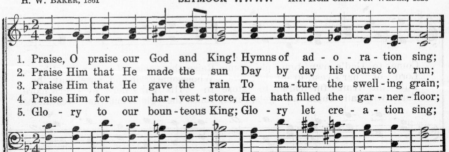

1. Praise, O praise our God and King! Hymns of ad - o - ra - tion sing;
2. Praise Him that He made the sun Day by day his course to run;
3. Praise Him that He gave the rain To ma - ture the swell - ing grain;
4. Praise Him for our har - vest - store, He hath filled the gar - ner - floor;
5. Glo - ry to our boun - teous King; Glo - ry let cre - a - tion sing;

Praise, O Praise Our God and King—Concluded

For His mer - cies still en - dure, Ev - er faith-ful, ev - er sure.
And the sil - ver moon by night, Shin - ing with her gen - tle light.
And hath bid the fer - tile field Of its pre - cious fruits to yield.
And for rich - er food than this, Pledge of ev - er - last - ing bliss.
Glo - ry to the Fa - ther, Son, And blest Spir - it, Three in One.

The God of Harvest Praise

575

Joy and gladness is taken from the plentiful field.—JER. 48: 33

JAMES MONTGOMERY, 1840   PERKINS 6. 6. 4. 6. 6. 6. 4.   E. A. PERKINS

1. The God of har - vest praise; In loud thanks - giv - ing raise
2. Yes, bless His ho - ly name, And pur - est thanks pro - claim
3. The God of har - vest praise; Hands, hearts, and voi - ces raise

Hand, heart and voice; The val - leys smile and sing, For - ests and
Thro' all the earth; To glo - ry in your lot Is come - ly,
With sweet ac - cord; From field to gar - ner throng, Bear - ing your

moun-tains ring; The plains their trib - ute bring; The streams re - joice.
but be not God's ben - e - fits for - got, A - midst your mirth.
sheaves a - long, And, in your har - vest song, Bless ye the Lord.

443

576 Sing to the Lord of Harvest

Thou crownest the year with Thy goodness.—Ps. 65: 11

GREENLAND 7. 6. 7. 6. D.

John S. B. Monsell, 1866

Arr. 1819, from
J. Michael Haydn

1. Sing to the Lord of har-vest, Sing songs of love and praise;
2. By Him the clouds drop fat-ness, The des-erts bloom and spring,
3. Heap on His sa-cred al-tar The gifts His good-ness gave,
4. To God the gra-cious Fa-ther, Who made us "ver-y good,"

With joy-ful hearts and voi-ces Your Al-le-lu-ias raise:
The hills leap up in glad-ness, The joy-ful val-leys sing:
The gold-en sheaves of har-vest, The souls He died to save:
To Christ, who, when we wan-dered, Re-stored us with His blood,

By Him the roll-ing sea-sons In fruit-ful or-der move;
He fill-eth with His full-ness All things with large in-crease,
Your hearts lay down be-fore Him, When at His feet ye fall,
And to the Ho-ly Spir-it, Who doth up-on us pour

Sing to the Lord of har-vest A song of hap-py love.
He crowns the year with good-ness, With plen-ty and with peace.
And with your lives a-dore Him, Who gave His life for all.
His bless-ed dews and sun-shine, Be praise for-ev-er-more.

We Plow the Fields

The eyes of all wait upon Thee, O Lord: and Thou givest them their meat in due season.—Ps. 145: 15

MATTHIAS CLAUDIUS, 1782   **WIR PFLÜGEN 7. 6. 7. 6. D. Ref.**   JOHANN A. P. SCHULZ

1. We plow the fields, and scat - ter The good seed on the land, But it is
2. He on - ly is the Mak - er Of all things near and far; He paints the
3. We thank Thee, then, O Fa - ther, For all things bright and good; The seed-time

fed and wa - tered By God's al-might-y hand; He sends the snow in
way-side flow - er, He lights the eve-ning star; The winds and waves o-
and the har - vest, Our life, our health, our food; Ac - cept the gift we

win - ter, The warmth to swell the grain, The breez-es, and the sun - shine,
bey Him; By Him the birds are fed; Much more to us the chil - dren,
of - fer For all Thy love im - parts, And, what Thou most de - sir - est,

REFRAIN

And soft re-fresh-ing rain;
He gives our dai - ly bread.   All good gifts a - round us Are sent from
Our hum - ble, thank-ful hearts.

heav'n a - bove; Then thank the Lord, O thank the Lord For all His love.

578 I Thank the Lord My Maker

Giving thanks alway for all things.—EPH. 5: 20

THOMAS MACKELLAR, 1844   WEBB 7. 6. 7. 6. D.   GEORGE J. WEBB, 1837

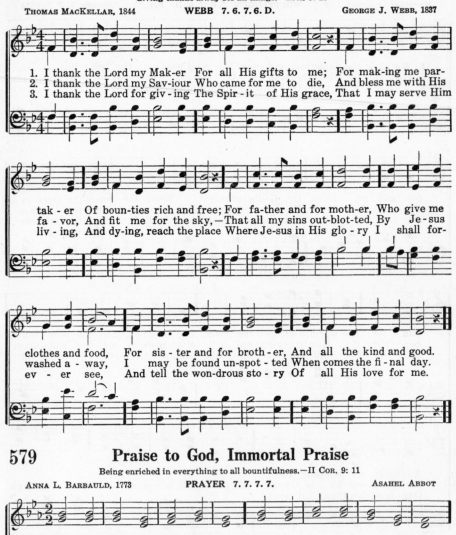

1. I thank the Lord my Mak-er For all His gifts to me; For mak-ing me par-
tak - er Of boun-ties rich and free; For fa-ther and for moth-er, Who give me
clothes and food, For sis - ter and for broth-er, And all the kind and good.

2. I thank the Lord my Sav-iour Who came for me to die, And bless me with His
fa - vor, And fit me for the sky,—That all my sins out-blot-ted, By Je-sus
washed a - way, I may be found un-spot-ted When comes the fi - nal day.

3. I thank the Lord for giv - ing The Spir-it of His grace, That I may serve Him
liv - ing, And dy-ing, reach the place Where Je-sus in His glo - ry I shall for-
ev - er see, And tell the won-drous sto - ry Of all His love for me.

579 Praise to God, Immortal Praise

Being enriched in everything to all bountifulness.—II COR. 9: 11

ANNA L. BARBAULD, 1773   PRAYER 7. 7. 7. 7.   ASAHEL ABBOT

1. Praise to God, im - mor - tal praise, For the love that crowns our days;
2. For the bless - ings of the field, For the stores the gar - dens yield,
3. Clouds that drop re - fresh - ing dews; Suns that ge - nial heat dif - fuse;
4. All that Spring with boun-teous hand, Scat-ters o'er the smil - ing land;
5. These, great God, to Thee we owe, Source whence all our bless-ings flow;

446

Praise to God, Immortal Praise—Concluded

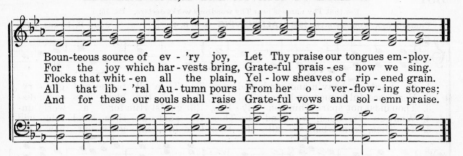

Boun-teous source of ev - 'ry joy, Let Thy praise our tongues em-ploy.
For the joy which har-vests bring, Grate-ful prais - es now we sing.
Flocks that whit - en all the plain, Yel - low sheaves of rip - ened grain.
All that lib - 'ral Au - tumn pours From her o - ver -flow-ing stores;
And for these our souls shall raise Grate-ful vows and sol - emn praise.

Praise, Lord, For Thee in Zion Waits

580

PSALM 65: 1

PARK STREET L. M.

HENRY F. LYTE, 1834   Arr. from FREDERICK M. A. VENUA, c. 1810

1. Praise, Lord, for Thee in Zi - on waits; Prayer shall be - siege Thy
2. How blest Thy saints! how safe - ly led! How sure - ly kept! how
3. The year is with Thy goodness crowned; Thy clouds drop wealth the
4. Lord, on our souls Thy Spir - it pour; The mor - al waste with-

tem - ple gates; All flesh shall to Thy throne re - pair, And find thro'
rich - ly fed! Sav - iour of all in earth and sea, How hap-py
world a - round; Thro' Thee the des - erts joy - ful sing, And na - ture
in re - store; O let Thy love our spring-tide be, And make us

Christ sal - va - tion there, And find thro' Christ sal - va - tion there.
they who rest in Thee, How hap - py they who rest in Thee.
smiles and owns her King, And na - ture smiles and owns her King.
all bear fruit to Thee, And make us all bear fruit to Thee. A - MEN.

581

O Lord of Heaven and Earth and Sea

For that Thy name is near Thy wondrous works declare.—Ps. 75: 1

CHRISTOPHER WORDSWORTH, 1863   **ALMSGIVING 8.8.8.4.**   JOHN B. DYKES, 1875

1. O Lord of heav'n and earth and sea, To Thee all praise and glo - ry
2. For peace-ful homes, and health-ful days, For all the bless - ings earth dis-
3. Thou didst not spare Thine on - ly Son, But gav'st Him for a world un-
4. What-ev - er, Lord, we lend to Thee, Re - paid a thou - sand - fold will
5. To Thee, from whom we all de - rive Our life, our gifts, our pow'r to

be! How shall we show our love to Thee, Who giv - est all?
plays, We owe Thee thank-ful - ness and praise, Who giv - est all.
done, And free - ly with that bless - ed One Thou giv - est all.
be; Then glad - ly will we give to Thee Who giv - est all.
give; O may we ev - er with Thee live, Who giv - est all!

582

For the Beauty of the Earth

The living God who giveth us richly all things to enjoy.—I TIM. 6: 17

FOLLIOTT S. PIERPOINT   **DIX 7s. 6 l.**   CONRAD KOCHER, 1838

1. For the beau - ty of the earth, For the beau - ty of the skies,
2. For the joy of hu - man love, Broth - er, sis - ter, par - ent, child,
3. For Thy Church, that ev - er - more Lift - eth ho - ly hands a - bove,
4. For Thy-self, best gift di - vine, To our race so free - ly giv'n;

For the love which from our birth O - ver and a - round us lies,—
Friends on earth, and friends a - bove; For all gen - tle thoughts and mild,
Of - f'ring up on ev - 'ry shore Its pure sac - ri - fice of love,—
For that great, great love of Thine, Peace on earth, and joy in heav'n,—

448

For the Beauty of the Earth—Concluded

Christ our God, to Thee we raise This our hymn of grate-ful praise.

God of Our Fathers

583

I thank Thee, and praise Thee, O Thou God of my fathers.—DAN. 2: 23

DANIEL C. ROBERTS, 1841—   PRO PATRIA 10s. 4 l.   H. W. PARKER

1. God of our fa-thers, whose al-might-y hand Leads forth in
2. Thy love di-vine hath led us in the past, In this free
3. From war's a-larms, from dead-ly pes-ti-lence, Be Thy strong
4. Re-fresh Thy peo-ple on their toil-some way; Lead us from

beau-ty all the star-ry band Of shin-ing worlds in splen-dor
land by Thee our lot is cast; Be Thou our Rul-er, Guard-ian,
arm our ev-er sure de-fense; Thy true re-lig-ion in our
night to nev-er-end-ing day; Fill all our lives with love and

thro' the skies, Our grate-ful songs be-fore Thy throne a-rise.
Guide and Stay, Thy Word our law, Thy paths our cho-sen way.
hearts in-crease; Thy boun-teous good-ness nour-ish us in peace.
grace di-vine; And glo-ry, laud and praise be ev-er Thine.

449

584

And Now, My Soul, Another Year

Here have we no continuing city.—HEB. 13: 14

S. BROWN, 1680–1732   MARKELL C. M.   ALDINE S. KIEFFER

1. And now, my soul, an - oth - er year Of thy short life is past;
2. Much of my hast - y life is gone, Nor will re - turn a - gain;
3. A - wake, my soul, with ut - most care Thy true con - di - tion learn;
4. Be - hold an - oth - er year be - gins; Set out a - fresh for heav'n;
5. De - vout - ly yield thy - self to God, And on His grace de - pend;

I can - not long con - tin - ue here, And this may be my last.
And swift my pass - ing mo - ments run, The few that yet re - main.
What are thy hopes? how sure? how fair? What is thy great con - cern?
Seek par - don for thy for - mer sins, In Christ so free - ly giv'n.
With zeal pur - sue the heav'n - ly road, Nor doubt a hap - py end.

585

For Thy Mercy and Thy Grace

God be merciful unto us, and bless us.—PS. 67: 1

HENRY DOWNTON, 1843   UNIVERSITY COLLEGE 7. 7. 7. 7.   Arr. from GOTTSCHALK

1. For Thy mer - cy and Thy grace, Faith-ful thro' an - oth - er year,
2. Lo! our sins on Thee we cast, Thee our per - fect sac - ri - fice,
3. In our weak-ness and dis - tress, Rock of strength, be Thou our stay;
4. Keep us faith - ful, keep us pure, Keep us ev - er - more Thine own,

Hear our song of thank - ful - ness; Je - sus, our Re - deem - er, hear.
And, for - get - ting all the past, Press to-wards our glo - rious prize.
In the path - less wil - der - ness Be our true and liv - ing way.
Help, O help us to en - dure; Fit us for the prom - ised crown.

At Thy Feet, Our God and Father

For His merciful kindness is great toward us.—Ps. 117: 2

JAMES D. BURNS, 1861 CRUCIFER 8. 7. 8. 7. D. HENRY SMART, 1867

1. At Thy feet, our God and Fa - ther, Who hath blessed us all our days,
2. Je - sus, for Thy love most ten - der, On the cross for sin - ners shown,
3. Ev - 'ry day will be the bright-er When Thy gra-cious face we see;

We with grate-ful hearts would gath-er, To be - gin the year with praise:
We would praise Thee, and sur - ren - der All our hearts to be Thine own:
Ev - 'ry bur - den will be light - er When we know it comes from Thee.

Praise for light so bright-ly shin - ing On our steps from heav'n a - bove;
With so blest a Friend pro - vid - ed, We up - on our way would go,
Spread Thy love's broad ban-ner o'er us, Give us strength to serve and wait,

Praise for mer-cies dai - ly twin - ing Round us gold - en cords of love.
Sure of be - ing safe - ly guid - ed, Guard-ed well from ev - 'ry foe.
Till the glo - ry breaks be - fore us Thro' the cit - y's o - pen gate.

587 Great God, We Sing That Mighty Hand

I will uphold Thee with the right hand of my righteousness.—ISA. 41: 10

PHILIP DODDRIDGE, Pub. 1755   WAREHAM L. M.   WILLIAM KNAPP, 1738

1. Great God, we sing that might-y hand By which sup-port-ed still we stand;
2. By day, at night, at home, a-broad, Still we are guard-ed by our God;
3. With grateful hearts the past we own; The fu-ture, all to us un-known,
4. In scenes ex-alt-ed or de-pressed, Be Thou our joy, and Thou our rest;

The ope-ning year Thy mer-cy shows—Let mer-cy crown it till it close.
By His in-ces-sant boun-ty fed, By His un-err-ing coun-sel led.
We to Thy guard-ian care com-mit, And, peaceful, leave be-fore Thy feet.
Thy good-ness all our hopes shall raise, A-dored thro' all our chang-ing days.

588 Now, Gracious Lord, Thine Arm Reveal

Remember, O Lord, Thy tender mercies.—Ps. 25: 6

JOHN NEWTON, 1779   EVENING TWILIGHT C. M.   Anon.

1. Now, gra-cious Lord, Thine arm re-veal, And make Thy glo-ry known;
2. From all the guilt and for-mer sin, May mer-cy set us free;
3. Send down Thy Spir-it from a-bove, That saints may love Thee more;
4. And when be-fore Thee we ap-pear In our e-ter-nal home,

Now let us all Thy pres-ence feel, And soft-en hearts of stone.
And let the year we now be-gin, Be-gin and end with Thee.
And sin-ners now may learn to love, Who nev-er loved be-fore.
May grow-ing num-bers wor-ship here, And praise Thee in our room.

Standing At the Portal

I will uphold thee with the right hand of my righteousness.—ISA. 41: 10

FRANCES R. HAVERGAL, 1873   ST. ALBANS 6.5. 12 l.   Arr. from F. JOSEPH HAYDN

1. Stand-ing at the por - tal Of the op'n-ing year, Words of com-fort meet us,
2. "I, the Lord, am with thee, Be thou not a - fraid; I will help and strengthen,
3. For the year be - fore us, O what rich sup-plies! For the poor and need - y
4. He will nev - er fail us, He will not for - sake; His e - ter - nal cov-enant,

Hush-ing ev - 'ry fear; Spo-ken thro' the si - lence By our Fa-ther's voice,
Be thou not dis-mayed. Yea, I will up - hold thee With My own right hand;
Liv-ing streams shall rise; For the sad and sin - ful Shall His grace a - bound;
He will nev - er break. Rest-ing on His prom-ise What have we to fear?

REFRAIN

Ten-der, strong and faithful, Mak-ing us re - joice.
Thou art called and cho-sen In My sight to stand." Onward, then, and fear not,
For the faint and fee - ble Perfect strength be found.
God is all - suf - fi - cient For the com-ing year.

Chil-dren of the day; For His word shall nev - er, Nev - er pass a - way.

590   **In Loud Exalted Strains**   DEDICATION

The King of glory shall come in.—Ps. 24: 7

UNITY 6. 6. 6. 6. 8. 8.

BENJAMIN FRANCIS, 1774.
     R. HUNTINGTON WOODMAN, 1895. Alt.

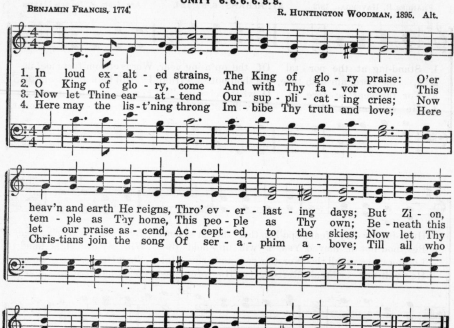

1. In loud ex-alt-ed strains, The King of glo-ry praise: O'er
2. O King of glo-ry, come And with Thy fa-vor crown This
3. Now let Thine ear at-tend Our sup-pli-cat-ing cries; Now
4. Here may the lis-t'ning throng Im-bibe Thy truth and love; Here

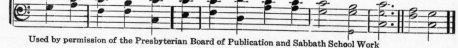

heav'n and earth He reigns, Thro' ev-er-last-ing days; But Zi-on,
tem-ple as Thy home, This peo-ple as Thy own; Be-neath this
let our praise as-cend, Ac-cept-ed, to the skies; Now let Thy
Chris-tians join the song Of ser-a-phim a-bove; Till all who

with His pres-ence blest, Is His de-light, His cho-sen rest.
roof vouch-safe to show How God can dwell with men be-low.
Gos-pel's joy-ful sound Spread its ce-les-tial in-fluence 'round.
hum-bly seek Thy face Re-joice in Thy a-bound-ing grace. A-MEN.

Used by permission of the Presbyterian Board of Publication and Sabbath School Work

591   **Thou, Whose Unmeasured Temple Stands**

Behold, heaven and heaven of heavens cannot contain Thee.—II CHRON. 6: 18

WILLIAM C. BRYANT, 1794-1878   **ST. MAGNUS. C. M.**   JEREMIAH CLARK, 1709

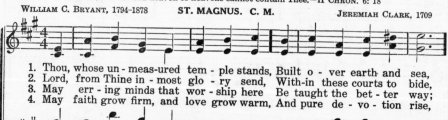

1. Thou, whose un-meas-ured tem-ple stands, Built o-ver earth and sea,
2. Lord, from Thine in-most glo-ry send, With-in these courts to bide,
3. May err-ing minds that wor-ship here Be taught the bet-ter way;
4. May faith grow firm, and love grow warm, And pure de-vo-tion rise,

Thou, Whose Unmeasured Temple Stands—Concluded

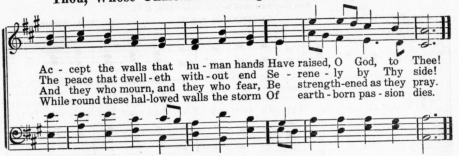

Ac - cept the walls that hu - man hands Have raised, O God, to Thee!
The peace that dwell-eth with-out end Se - rene - ly by Thy side!
And they who mourn, and they who fear, Be strength-ened as they pray.
While round these hal-lowed walls the storm Of earth - born pas - sion dies.

Founded On Thee 592

For other foundation can no man lay than that which is laid, which is Jesus Christ.—I COR. 3: 11

MENDON L. M.

SAMUEL F. SMITH, 1894

German Melody
Arr. by SAMUEL DYER, 1828

1. Found - ed on Thee, our on - ly Lord, On Thee, the
2. For Thee our wait - ing spir - its yearn, For Thee this
3. Come, with Thy Spir - it and Thy pow'r, The Con - qu'ror,
4. Ac - cept the work our hands have wrought; Ac - cept, O

ev - er - last - ing Rock, Thy Church shall stand as stands Thy
house of praise we rear; To Thee with long - ing hearts we
once the Cru - ci - fied; Our God, our Strength, our King, our
God, this earth - ly shrine; Be Thou our Rock, our Life, our

Word, Nor fear the storm, nor dread the shock.
turn; Come, fix Thy glo - rious pres - ence here.
Tow'r, Here plant Thy throne, and here a - bide.
Thought, And we, as liv - ing tem - ples, Thine. A - MEN.

593

O Our God, Who Doth Not Falter

MARRIAGE

And they two shall be one flesh.—Eph. 5: 31

LEVI MUMAW, 1926 LUCERNE 8. 7. 8. 7. T. A. WILLIS. 1876

1. O our God, who doth not fal-ter, Come and bless with gra-cious hand,
2. Join our hands and hearts in un-ion As Thou didst for us or-dain;
3. Thro' this life Thy hand doth lead us In Thy serv-ice, great or small;
4. When, O Lord, at Thy ap-pear-ing Thou shall meet Thy bride so fair;

As we stand be-fore this al-tar, Made sub-lime by Thy com-mand.
May our lives, in sweet com-mun-ion, All this world's vain hopes dis-dain.
With Thy heav'nly man-na feed us; Let Thy bless-ing hal-low all.
With the hosts Thy summons hear-ing, Then may we Thy glo-ry share. A-MEN.

594

O Perfect Love

That they may be made perfect in one.—Jn. 17: 23

DOROTHY F. GURNEY, 1883 SANDRINGHAM 11. 10. 11. 10. JOSEPH BARNBY

1. O per-fect Love, all hu-man tho't tran-scend-ing, Low-ly we
2. O per-fect Life, be Thou their full as-sur-ance Of ten-der
3. Grant them the joy which bright-ens earth-ly sor-row; Grant them the

kneel in prayer be-fore Thy throne, That theirs may be the love that knows no
char-i-ty and stead-fast faith, Of pa-tient hope, and qui-et, brave en-
peace which calms all earth-ly strife, And to life's day the glo-rious un-known

456

O Perfect Love—Concluded

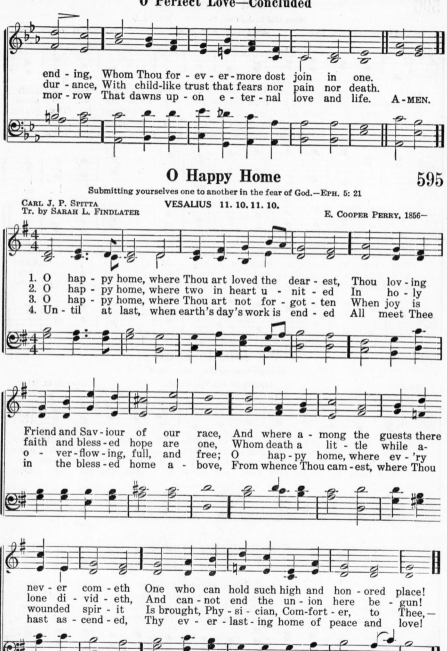

end - ing, Whom Thou for - ev - er - more dost join in one.
dur - ance, With child-like trust that fears nor pain nor death.
mor - row That dawns up - on e - ter - nal love and life. A - MEN.

O Happy Home 595

Submitting yourselves one to another in the fear of God.—EPH. 5: 21

CARL J. P. SPITTA   VESALIUS 11. 10. 11. 10.
Tr. by SARAH L. FINDLATER

E. COOPER PERRY, 1856—

1. O hap - py home, where Thou art loved the dear - est, Thou lov - ing
2. O hap - py home, where two in heart u - nit - ed In ho - ly
3. O hap - py home, where Thou art not for - got - ten When joy is
4. Un - til at last, when earth's day's work is end - ed All meet Thee

Friend and Sav - iour of our race, And where a - mong the guests there
faith and bless - ed hope are one, Whom death a lit - tle while a -
o - ver - flow - ing, full, and free; O hap - py home, where ev - 'ry
in the bless - ed home a - bove, From whence Thou cam - est, where Thou

nev - er com - eth One who can hold such high and hon - ored place!
lone di - vid - eth, And can - not end the un - ion here be - gun!
wounded spir - it Is brought, Phy - si - cian, Com - fort - er, to Thee,—
hast as - cend - ed, Thy ev - er - last - ing home of peace and love!

596

O God of Wisdom

What God hath joined together.—Mk. 10: 9

Menno M. Brubacher, 1926 **AMAMUS 8. 6. 8. 6.** Walter E. Yoder, 1926

1. O God of wis-dom, life and love, Thine is the bless-ed plan
2. These souls be-throthed be-fore Thee stand; Thy bless-ing we im-plore;
3. As they go forth up-on life's way, Sus-tain them by Thy grace;
4. May they with ho-ly lives a-dorn Thy doc-trines, Lord, and be
5. And when Thou, Lord, shalt come a-gain To gath-er home Thine own,

In ho-ly bonds of love to join The twain, cre-a-ted man.
U-nite Thou them in heart and hand, And guide them ev-er-more.
May they Thy ho-ly laws o-bey And live in joy and peace.
A-mid life's sun-shine and its storm True wit-ness-es for Thee.
May they, with du-ty no-bly done, Be blessed be-fore Thy throne.

597

We Join to Pray

Marriage is honorable.—Heb. 13: 4

Anon. **HAND IN HAND C. M.** Edward D. Naff

1. We join to pray, with wish-es kind, A bless-ing, Lord, from Thee,
2. We know that scenes not al-ways bright Must un-to them be giv'n;
3. Still hand in hand, their jour-ney thro', Joint pil-grims may they go;
4. May each in each still feed the flame Of pure and ho-ly love;

On those who now the bands have twined Which ne'er may bro-ken be.
But o-ver all give Thou the light Of love, and truth, and heav'n.
Min-gling their joys as help-ers true, And shar-ing ev-'ry woe.
In faith, and trust, and heart the same, The same their home a-bove.

Lead On, O King Eternal

I have given Him for a witness to the people, a leader and commander to the people.—Isa. 55: 4

ERNEST W. SHURTLEFF, 1888   7. 6. 7. 6. D.   UZZIAH C. BURNAP, 1895

1. Lead on, O King E-ter-nal, The day of march has come;
2. Lead on, O King E-ter-nal, Till sin's fierce war shall cease,
3. Lead on, O King E-ter-nal, We fol-low, not with fears;

Hence-forth in fields of con-quest Thy tents shall be our home:
And Ho-li-ness shall whis-per The sweet A-men of peace;
For glad-ness breaks like morn-ing Wher-e'er Thy face ap-pears;

Thro' days of prep-a-ra-tion Thy grace has made us strong,
For not with swords loud clash-ing, Nor roll of stir-ring drums,
Thy cross is lift-ed o'er us; We jour-ney in its light:

And now, O King E-ter-nal, We lift our bat-tle-song.
But deeds of love and mer-cy, The heav'n-ly king-dom comes.
The crown a-waits the con-quest; Lead on, O God of might.

Used by permission of the Presbyterian Board of Publication and Sabbath-School Work

599 Pour Out Thy Spirit From On High

Until the Spirit be poured upon us from on high.—Isa. 32: 15

JAMES MONTGOMERY, 1833 · HOLLEY L. M. GEORGE HEWS, 1835

1. Pour out Thy Spir - it from on high; Lord, Thine or -
2. With - in Thy tem - ple when they stand To teach the
3. Wis - dom and zeal and faith im - part, Firm - ness with
4. To watch and pray, and nev - er faint; By day and
5. Then, when their work is fin - ished here, In hum - ble

dain - ed serv - ants bless; Grac - es and gifts to
truth as taught by Thee, Sav - iour, like stars in
meek - ness, from a - bove, To bear Thy peo - ple
night strict guard to keep; To warn the sin - ner,
hope their charge re - sign, When the Chief Shep - herd

each sup - ply, And clothe them with Thy right - eous - ness.
Thy right hand The an - gels of the church - es be.
on their heart, And love the souls whom Thou dost love;
cheer the saint, Nour - ish Thy lambs, and feed Thy sheep;
shall ap - pear, O God, may they and we be Thine.

600 How Beauteous Are Their Feet

How beautiful upon the mountains are the feet of them that bring good tidings.—Isa. 52: 7

ISAAC WATTS, 1707 · ST. THOMAS S. M. G. F. HANDEL

1. How beau - teous are their feet Who stand on Zi - on's hill;
2. How charm - ing is their voice! How sweet their ti - dings are!
3. How hap - py are our ears, That hear this joy - ful sound,
4. How bless - ed are our eyes, That see this heav'n - ly light!
5. The watch - men join their voice, And tune - ful notes em - ploy;
6. The Lord makes bare His arm Thro' all the earth a - broad;

How Beauteous Are Their Feet—Concluded

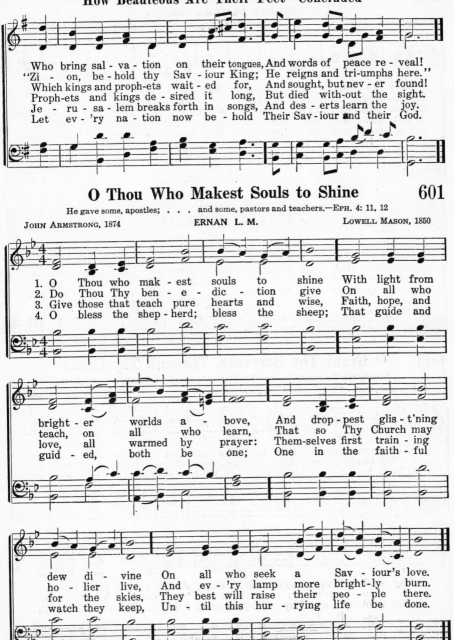

Who bring sal - va - tion on their tongues, And words of peace re - veal!
"Zi - on, be - hold thy Sav - iour King; He reigns and tri-umphs here."
Which kings and proph-ets wait - ed for, And sought, but nev - er found!
Proph-ets and kings de - sired it long, But died with-out the sight.
Je - ru - sa - lem breaks forth in songs, And des - erts learn the joy.
Let ev - 'ry na - tion now be - hold Their Sav-iour and their God.

O Thou Who Makest Souls to Shine 601

He gave some, apostles; . . . and some, pastors and teachers.—EPH. 4: 11, 12

JOHN ARMSTRONG, 1874   ERNAN L. M.   LOWELL MASON, 1850

1. O Thou who mak - est souls to shine With light from
2. Do Thou Thy ben - e - dic - tion give On all who
3. Give those that teach pure hearts and wise, Faith, hope, and
4. O bless the shep - herd; bless the sheep; That guide and

bright - er worlds a - bove, And drop-pest glis - t'ning
teach, on all who learn, That so Thy Church may
love, all warmed by prayer: Them-selves first train - ing
guid - ed, both be one; One in the faith - ful

dew di - vine On all who seek a Sav - iour's love.
ho - lier live, And ev - 'ry lamp more bright-ly burn.
for the skies, They best will raise their peo - ple there.
watch they keep, Un - til this hur - rying life be done.

602 And Are We Yet Alive

God who is rich in mercy.—EPH. 2: 4

CHARLES WESLEY

DENNIS S. M.

Arr. from HANS G. NAEGELI

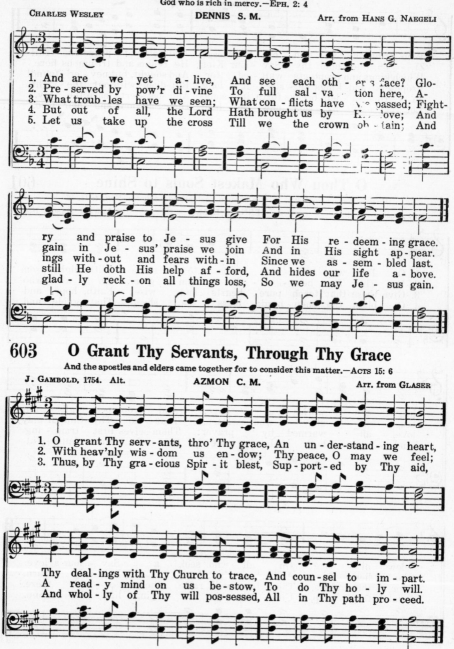

1. And are we yet a-live, And see each oth-er's face? Glo-
2. Pre-served by pow'r di-vine To full sal-va-tion here, A-
3. What troub-les have we seen; What con-flicts have we passed; Fight-
4. But out of all, the Lord Hath brought us by His love; And
5. Let us take up the cross Till we the crown ob-tain; And

ry and praise to Je-sus give For His re-deem-ing grace.
gain in Je-sus' praise we join And in His sight ap-pear.
ings with-out and fears with-in Since we as-sem-bled last.
still He doth His help af-ford, And hides our life a-bove.
glad-ly reck-on all things loss, So we may Je-sus gain.

603 O Grant Thy Servants, Through Thy Grace

And the apostles and elders came together for to consider this matter.—ACTS 15: 6

J. GAMBOLD, 1754. Alt.

AZMON C. M.

Arr. from GLASER

1. O grant Thy serv-ants, thro' Thy grace, An un-der-stand-ing heart,
2. With heav'nly wis-dom us en-dow; Thy peace, O may we feel;
3. Thus, by Thy gra-cious Spir-it blest, Sup-port-ed by Thy aid,

Thy deal-ings with Thy Church to trace, And coun-sel to im-part.
A read-y mind on us be-stow, To do Thy ho-ly will.
And whol-ly of Thy will pos-sessed, All in Thy path pro-ceed.

O God, Our Help

604

Lord, Thou hast been our dwelling place in all generations.—Ps. 90: 1

ISAAC WATTS, 1719   **ST. ANNE C. M.**   WILLIAM CROFT, 1708

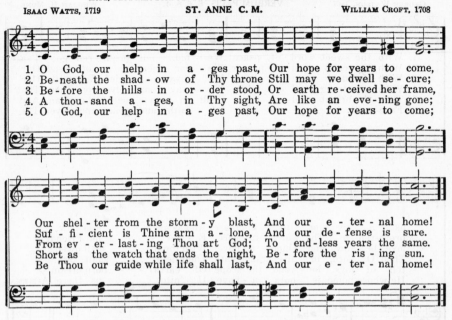

1. O God, our help in a - ges past, Our hope for years to come,
2. Be-neath the shad - ow of Thy throne Still may we dwell se - cure;
3. Be - fore the hills in or - der stood, Or earth re - ceived her frame,
4. A thou - sand a - ges, in Thy sight, Are like an eve - ning gone;
5. O God, our help in a - ges past, Our hope for years to come;

Our shel - ter from the storm - y blast, And our e - ter - nal home!
Suf - fi - cient is Thine arm a - lone, And our de - fense is sure.
From ev - er - last - ing Thou art God; To end - less years the same.
Short as the watch that ends the night, Be - fore the ris - ing sun.
Be Thou our guide while life shall last, And our e - ter - nal home!

Lord, Cause Thy Face On Us to Shine

605

Endeavoring to keep the unity of the Spirit in the bond of peace.—EPH: 4: 3

THOMAS COTTERILL, 1819   **HEBRON L. M.**   LOWELL MASON, 1830

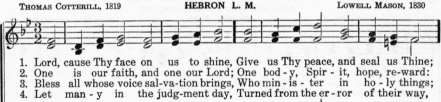

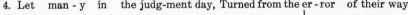

1. Lord, cause Thy face on us to shine, Give us Thy peace, and seal us Thine;
2. One is our faith, and one our Lord; One bod - y, Spir - it, hope, re - ward:
3. Bless all whose voice sal - va - tion brings, Who min - is - ter in ho - ly things;
4. Let man - y in the judg-ment day, Turned from the er - ror of their way,

Teach us to prize the means of grace, And love Thine earthly dwelling-place.
May we in one com - mun-ion be, One with each oth - er, one with Thee.
The eld-ers, pas-tors, dea-cons, bless; Clothe them with zeal and righteousness:
Their hope, their joy, their crown appear: Save those who preach and those who hear. AMEN.

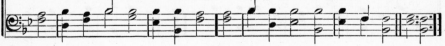

606

With the Sweet Word of Peace

The Lord of peace Himself give you peace always by all means.—II Thess. 3: 16

GEORGE WATSON, 1867   VERBUM PACIS 6. 6. 8. 4.   WILLIAM H. MONK

1. With the sweet word of peace We bid our breth-ren go; Peace
2. With the calm word of prayer We ear-nest-ly com-mend Our
3. With the dear word of love We give our brief fare-well; Our
4. With the strong word of faith We stay our-selves on Thee, That
5. Then the bright word of hope Shall on our part-ing gleam, And
6. Fare-well! in hope and love, In faith, and peace, and prayer; Till

as a riv-er to in-crease, And cease less flow.
breth-ren to Thy watch-ful care, E-ter-nal Friend!
love be-low, and Thine a-bove, With them shall dwell.
Thou, O Lord, in life and death, Their help shalt be;
tell of joys be-yond the scope Of earth-born dream.
He whose home is ours a-bove, U-nite us there. A-MEN.

607

Blest Be the Tie That Binds

Being knit together in love.—Col. 2: 2

JOHN FAWCETT, 1772   DENNIS S. M.   From HANS G. NAEGELI

1. Blest be the tie that binds Our hearts in Chris-tian love; The
2. Be-fore our Fa-ther's throne, We pour our ar-dent prayers; Our
3. We share our mu-tual woes, Our mu-tual bur-dens bear; And
4. When we a-sun-der part, It gives us keen-est pain; But

fel-low-ship of kin-dred minds Is like to that a-bove.
fears, our hopes, our aims are one, Our com-forts and our cares.
oft-en for each oth-er flows The sym-pa-thiz-ing tear.
we shall still be joined in heart, And hope to meet a-gain.

My Dearest Friends, In Bonds of Love

He that loveth his brother abideth in the light.—I Jn. 2: 10

Anon.   PARTING HAND L. M. D.   Jeremiah Ingalls, 1863

1. My dear-est friends, in bonds of love, Our hearts in sweet-est un - ion prove;
2. How sweet the hours have passed away, When we have met to sing and pray;
3. And since it is God's ho - ly will, We must be part-ed for a - while,
4. How oft I've seen the flow-ing tears, And heard you tell your hopes and fears;

Your friendship's like a draw - ing band, Yet we must take the part-ing hand.
How loath I've been to leave the place Where Je-sus shows His smil-ing face.
In sweet sub-mis-sion all in one, We'll say, "Our Fa-ther's will be done."
Your hearts with love have seemed to flame, Which makes me hope we'll meet a-gain.

Your pres-ence sweet, your un - ion dear, Your words de-light-ful to my ear;
Oh, could I stay with friends so kind, How would it cheer my struggling mind!
Dear fel - low-youth in Chris-tian ties, Who seek for man-sions in the skies,
Ye mourn-ing souls, in sad sur-prise, Je - sus re-mem-bers all your cries;

And when I see that we must part, You draw like chords a - round my heart.
But du - ty makes me un - der-stand That we must take the part-ing hand.
Fight on, you'll win the hap - py shore, Where parting hands are known no more.
Oh, taste His grace, in all that land We'll no more take the part-ing hand.

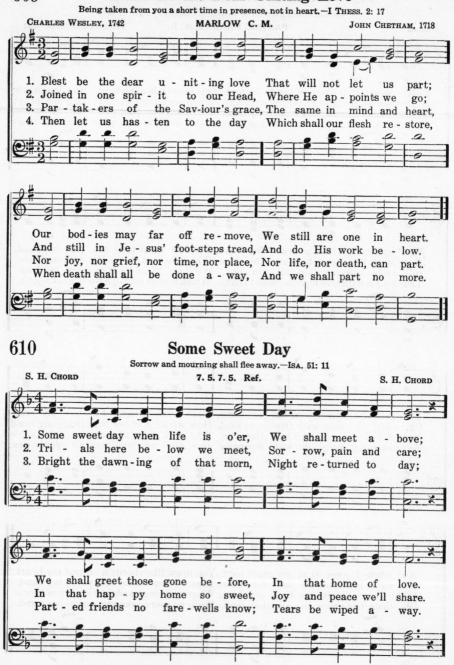

609

Blest Be the Dear Uniting Love

Being taken from you a short time in presence, not in heart.—I THESS. 2: 17

CHARLES WESLEY, 1742   MARLOW C. M.   JOHN CHETHAM, 1718

1. Blest be the dear u - nit - ing love That will not let us part;
2. Joined in one spir - it to our Head, Where He ap - points we go;
3. Par - tak - ers of the Sav-iour's grace, The same in mind and heart,
4. Then let us has - ten to the day Which shall our flesh re - store,

Our bod - ies may far off re - move, We still are one in heart.
And still in Je - sus' foot-steps tread, And do His work be - low.
Nor joy, nor grief, nor time, nor place, Nor life, nor death, can part.
When death shall all be done a - way, And we shall part no more.

610

Some Sweet Day

Sorrow and mourning shall flee away.—ISA. 51: 11

S. H. CHORD   7. 5. 7. 5. Ref.   S. H. CHORD

1. Some sweet day when life is o'er, We shall meet a - bove;
2. Tri - als here be - low we meet, Sor - row, pain and care;
3. Bright the dawn-ing of that morn, Night re - turned to day;

We shall greet those gone be - fore, In that home of love.
In that hap - py home so sweet, Joy and peace we'll share.
Part - ed friends no fare - wells know; Tears be wiped a - way.

Some Sweet Day—Concluded

REFRAIN

Some sweet day, some sweet day, Oh! that hap-py time will be, some sweet day.

Hail! Sweetest, Dearest Tie 611

Which hope we have as an anchor to the soul.—HEB. 6: 19

FAIR HAVEN C. M. D.

SUTTON
Slow

Scotch Air

1. Hail! sweet-est, dear-est tie that binds Our glow-ing hearts in one;
2. No lin-g'ring hope, no part-ing sigh, Our fu-ture meet-ing knows;

Hail! sa-cred hope, that tunes our minds To har-mo-ny di-vine:
There friendship beams from ev-'ry eye, And love im-mor-tal glows:

It is the hope, the bliss-ful hope Which Je-sus' grace has giv'n;
Oh, sa-cred hope, oh, bliss-ful hope Which Je-sus' grace has giv'n;

The hope, when days and years have passed, We all shall meet in heav'n.

612 **God Be With You**

Now, brethren, I commend you to God, and to the word of His grace.—ACTS 20: 32

J. E. RANKIN, 1882   9. 8. 8. 9. Ref.   W. G. TOMER, 1882

1. God be with you till we meet a - gain, By His counsels guide, up-hold you,
2. God be with you till we meet a - gain, 'Neath His wings protecting hide you,
3. God be with you till we meet a - gain, When life's perils thick confound you,
4. God be with you till we meet a - gain, Keep love's banner floating o'er you,

With His sheep se - cure-ly fold you: God be with you till we meet a - gain.
Dai - ly man-na still pro-vide you: God be with you till we meet a - gain.
Put His arms un - fail-ing round you: God be with you till we meet a - gain.
Smite death's threat'ning wave before you: God be with you till we meet a - gain.

REFRAIN

Till we meet, ... till we meet, Till we
Till we meet, till we meet,

meet at Je - sus' feet; Till we meet, ... till we
till we meet; Till we meet,

meet, God be with you till we meet a - gain.
till we meet,

Silently, They Pass Away

The spirit shall return unto God who gave it.—ECCL. 12: 7

10. 10. 10. 10. 8. 8.

C. E. LESLIE

613

1. Si - lent - ly, si - lent - ly, they pass a - way, Si - lent - ly,
2. Si - lent - ly, si - lent - ly, sweet is their sleep, Si - lent - ly,
3. Si - lent - ly, si - lent - ly, bur - y the dead, Si - lent - ly,
4. Si - lent - ly, si - lent - ly, lay them to rest, Si - lent - ly,

si - lent - ly, short is their stay; From earth to heav - en they've
si - lent - ly, for them we weep; Oh, how we mourn, and how
si - lent - ly, the soul has fled Up to our heav - en - ly
si - lent - ly, God thought it best A - loft in heav - en their

tak - en their flight, Far from all sor - row and pain and from night,
sad are our hearts, When from the bod - y the spir - it de - parts!
Fa - ther who gave, And through His great lov - ing kind - ness will save.
Sav - iour to meet, And all the sanc - ti - fied an - gels to greet.

To their Sav - iour who is call - ing, Call - ing, come home, Call - ing, come home.
But 'tis Je - sus who is call - ing, Call - ing, come home, Call - ing, come home.
For 'tis Je - sus who is call - ing, Call - ing, come home, Call - ing, come home.
So, 'tis Je - sus who is call - ing, Call - ing, come home, Call - ing, come home.

469

614 Teach Me the Measure of My Days

Lord, make me to know mine end, and the measure of my days.—Ps. 39: 4

ISAAC WATTS ST. FLAVIAN C. M. DAY'S Psalter

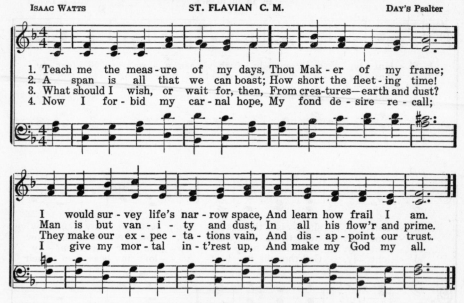

1. Teach me the meas-ure of my days, Thou Mak-er of my frame;
2. A span is all that we can boast; How short the fleet-ing time!
3. What should I wish, or wait for, then, From crea-tures—earth and dust?
4. Now I for-bid my car-nal hope, My fond de-sire re-call;

I would sur-vey life's nar-row space, And learn how frail I am.
Man is but van-i-ty and dust, In all his flow'r and prime.
They make our ex-pec-ta-tions vain, And dis-ap-point our trust.
I give my mor-tal in-t'rest up, And make my God my all.

615 It Is Not Death to Die

For me to live is Christ, and to die is gain.—PHIL. 1: 21

HENRI A. C. MALAN, 1832
Tr. by G. W. BETHUNE, 1847 GREENWOOD S. M. JOSEPH E. SWEETSER

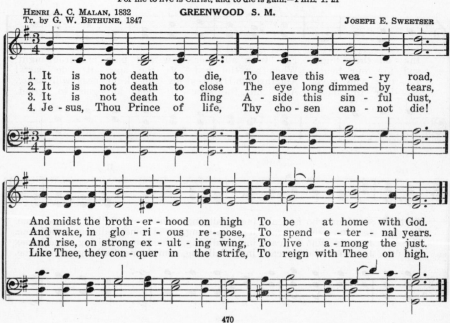

1. It is not death to die, To leave this wea-ry road,
2. It is not death to close The eye long dimmed by tears,
3. It is not death to fling A-side this sin-ful dust,
4. Je-sus, Thou Prince of life, Thy cho-sen can-not die!

And midst the broth-er-hood on high To be at home with God.
And wake, in glo-ri-ous re-pose, To spend e-ter-nal years.
And rise, on strong ex-ult-ing wing, To live a-mong the just.
Like Thee, they con-quer in the strife, To reign with Thee on high.

Why Should Our Tears in Sorrow Flow

That ye sorrow not, even as others which have no hope.—I THESS. 4: 13

WILLIAM H. BATHURST   **GREEN HILL C. M.**   ALBERT L. PEACE, 1885

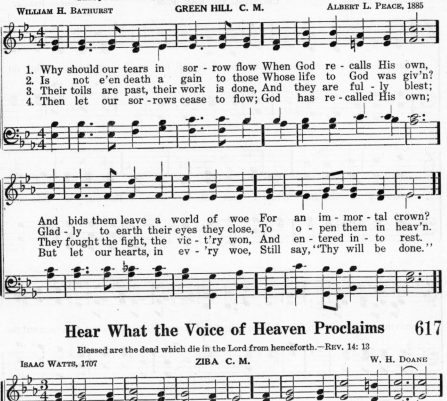

1. Why should our tears in sor - row flow When God re - calls His own,
2. Is not e'en death a gain to those Whose life to God was giv'n?
3. Their toils are past, their work is done, And they are ful - ly blest;
4. Then let our sor - rows cease to flow; God has re - called His own;

And bids them leave a world of woe For an im - mor - tal crown?
Glad - ly to earth their eyes they close, To o - pen them in heav'n.
They fought the fight, the vic - t'ry won, And en - tered in - to rest.
But let our hearts, in ev - 'ry woe, Still say, "Thy will be done."

Hear What the Voice of Heaven Proclaims

Blessed are the dead which die in the Lord from henceforth.—REV. 14: 13

ISAAC WATTS, 1707   **ZIBA C. M.**   W. H. DOANE

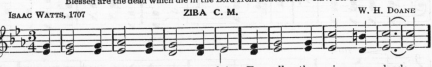

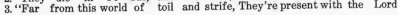

1. Hear what the voice from heav'n proclaims For all the pi - ous dead:
2. "They die in Je - sus, and are blest; How kind their slum - bers are!
3. "Far from this world of toil and strife, They're present with the Lord;

"Sweet is the sa - vor of their names, And soft their sleep - ing bed.
From suf - f'ring and from sin re - leased, They're freed from ev - 'ry snare.
The la - bors of their mor - tal life End in a large re - ward."

618 Sunset and Evening Star

And they shall see His face.—Rev. 22: 4, 5

ALFRED TENNYSON **CROSSING THE BAR P. M.** JOSEPH BARNBY

Sun - set and eve-ning star, And one clear call for me! And may there be no

moan-ing of the bar When I put out to sea, But such a tide as

moving seems a-sleep, Too full for sound and foam, When that which drew from out the

rall.

bound-less deep Turns a - gain home. Twi-light and eve-ning bell, And

home. Twi - - - light and eve-ning bell,

aft - er that the dark! And may there be no sad-ness of farewell When I em-bark;

Sunset and Evening Star—Concluded

cres — — — cen — — — do. rit.

For, tho' from out our bourne of time and place The flood may bear me far, ...

f

I hope to see my Pi - lot face to face When I have crossed the bar.

Servant of God, Well Done

619

Well done, thou good and faithful servant.—MATT. 25: 21

CHARLES WESLEY   VICTORY S. M.   H. A. WHITEHEAD

1. Serv - ant of God, well done!   Thy glo - rious war - fare's past;
2. With saints en - throned on high,   Thou dost Thy Lord pro - claim,
3. O hap - py, hap - py soul,   In ec - sta - sies of praise,
4. Re - deemed from earth and pain,   Ah! when shall we as - cend,

The bat - tle's fought, the race is won, And thou art crowned at last.
And still to God sal - va - tion cry, Sal - va - tion to the Lamb!
Long as e - ter - nal a - ges roll, Thou seest Thy Sav-iour's face.
And all in Je - sus' pres - ence reign With our trans - la - ted Friend?

620 My Latest Sun is Sinking Fast

I am now ready to be offered, and the time of my departure is at hand.—II Tim. 4: 6

JEFFERSON HASCALL, 1860   **LAND OF BEULAH C. M. Ref.**   WILLIAM B. BRADBURY

1. My lat-est sun is sink-ing fast, My race is near-ly run;
2. I know I'm nearing the ho-ly ranks Of friends and kin-dred dear,
3. I've al-most gained my heav'n-ly home, My spir-it loud-ly sings;
4. O bear my long-ing heart to Him Who bled and died for me;

My strong-est tri-als now are past, My tri-umph is be-gun.
For I brush the dews on Jor-dan's banks, The cross-ing must be near.
Thy ho-ly ones, be-hold, they come! I hear the noise of wings.
Whose blood now cleans-es from all sin, And gives me vic-to-ry.

CHORUS

O come, an-gel band, Come and a-round me stand; O,

bear me a-way on your snow-y wings To my im-mor-tal home: O,

bear me a-way on your snow-y wings To my im-mor-tal home.

Forever With the Lord

621

And so shall we ever be with the Lord.—I Thess. 4: 17

NEARER HOME S. M. D.

Isaac B. Woodbury, 1852
Arr. by Arthur S. Sullivan, 1874

James Montgomery, 1835

1. "For - ev - er with the Lord!" A - men, so let it be;
2. My Fa-ther's house on high, Home of my soul, how near,
3. For - ev - er with the Lord! Fa - ther, if 'tis Thy will,
4. So when my lat - est breath Shall rend the veil in twain,

Life from the dead is in that word, 'Tis im - mor - tal - i - ty:
At times, to faith's fore - see - ing eye, Thy gold - en gates ap - pear:
The prom - ise of that faith - ful word E'en here to me ful - fill:
By death I shall es - cape from death, And life e - ter - nal gain.

Here in the bod - y pent, Ab - sent from Him I roam,
Ah! then my spir - it faints To reach the land I love,
Be Thou at my right hand, Then can I nev - er fail;
Know - ing as I am known, How shall I love that word,

Yet night - ly pitch my mov - ing tent A day's march near - er home.
The bright in - her - it - ance of saints, Je - ru - sa - lem a - bove.
Up - hold Thou me, and I shall stand; Fight, and I must pre - vail.
And oft re - peat be - fore the throne, "For - ev - er with the Lord!"

622

Go to Thy Rest, Fair Child

I shall go to him, but he shall not return to me.—II SAM. 12: 23

LYDIA H. SIGOURNEY, 1791–1865   BURBER S. M.   J. H. TENNEY

Softly

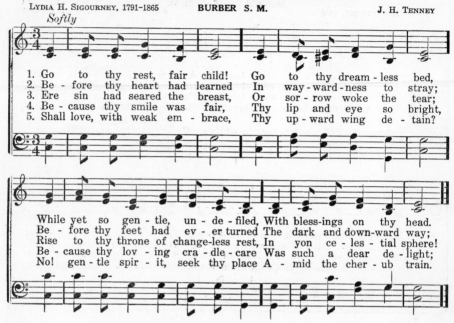

1. Go to thy rest, fair child! Go to thy dream-less bed,
2. Be-fore thy heart had learned In way-ward-ness to stray;
3. Ere sin had seared the breast, Or sor-row woke the tear;
4. Be-cause thy smile was fair, Thy lip and eye so bright,
5. Shall love, with weak em-brace, Thy up-ward wing de-tain?

While yet so gen-tle, un-de-filed, With bless-ings on thy head.
Be-fore thy feet had ev-er turned The dark and down-ward way;
Rise to thy throne of change-less rest, In yon ce-les-tial sphere!
Be-cause thy lov-ing cra-dle-care Was such a dear de-light;
No! gen-tle spir-it, seek thy place A-mid the cher-ub train.

623

Jesus, While Our Hearts Are Bleeding

The Lord gave, and the Lord hath taken away; blessed be the name of the Lord.—JOB. 1: 21

THOMAS HASTINGS, 1850   MOUNT VERNON 8. 7. 8. 7.   LOWELL MASON, 1833

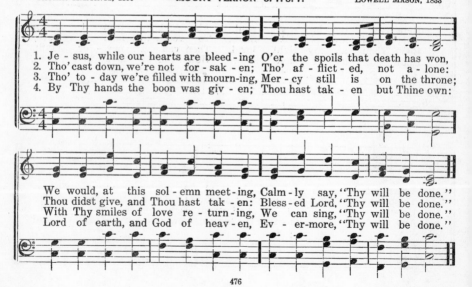

1. Je-sus, while our hearts are bleed-ing O'er the spoils that death has won,
2. Tho' cast down, we're not for-sak-en; Tho' af-flict-ed, not a-lone;
3. Tho' to-day we're filled with mourn-ing, Mer-cy still is on the throne;
4. By Thy hands the boon was giv-en; Thou hast tak-en but Thine own:

We would, at this sol-emn meet-ing, Calm-ly say, "Thy will be done."
Thou didst give, and Thou hast tak-en: Bless-ed Lord, "Thy will be done."
With Thy smiles of love re-turn-ing, We can sing, "Thy will be done."
Lord of earth, and God of heav-en, Ev-er-more, "Thy will be done."

Shall We Meet Beyond the River

624

And the remnant of the Lord shall return, and come to Zion with songs and everlasting joy upon their heads.—ISA. 35: 10

HORACE L. HASTINGS, 1858   **SHALL WE MEET 8. 7. 8. 7. Ref.**   ELIHU S. RICE, 1866

Moderato

1. Shall we meet be-yond the riv - er, Where the sur - ges cease to roll?
2. Shall we meet in that blest har-bor, When our storm - y voyage is o'er?
3. Shall we meet in yon-der cit - y, Where the tow'rs of crys-tal shine,
4. Shall we meet with Christ our Saviour, When He comes to claim His own?

Where in all the bright for - ev - er, Sor - row ne'er shall press the soul?
Shall we meet and cast the an-chor By the fair ce - les - tial shore?
Where the walls are all of jas - per, Built by work-man-ship di - vine?—
Shall we know His bless - ed fa - vor, And sit down up - on His throne?

CHORUS

Shall we meet, shall we meet, Shall we meet be - yond the riv - er?

Shall we meet be - yond the riv - er, Where the sur - ges cease to roll?

625

Sleep Thy Last Sleep

Them also which sleep in Jesus will God bring with Him.—I THESS. 4: 14

EDWARD A. DAYMAN, 1868   REQUIEM 4. 6. 4. 6. D.   JOSEPH BARNBY

1. Sleep thy last sleep, Free from care and sor - row; Rest, where none weep,
2. Life's dream is past, All its sin and sad - ness; Bright-ly at last
3. Tho' we may mourn Those in life the dear - est, They shall re - turn,

Till th' e - ter - nal mor - row; Tho' dark waves roll O'er the si - lent
Dawns a day of glad - ness: Un - der the sod, Earth, re - ceive our
Christ, when Thou ap-pear - est: Soon shall Thy voice Com - fort those now

riv - er, Thy faint-ing soul Je - sus can de - liv - er.
treas - ure, To rest in God, Wait-ing all His pleas - ure.
weep-ing, Bid - ding re - joice All in Je - sus sleep - ing. A-MEN.

626

For All Thy Saints

He being dead yet speaketh.—HEB. 11: 4

RICHARD MANT, 1837   CARLISLE S. M.   C. LOCKHART, 1745-1815

1. For all Thy saints, O Lord, Who strove in Thee to live,
2. For all Thy saints, O Lord, Ac - cept our thank - ful cry,
3. They all, in life and death, With Thee, their Lord, in view,
4. For this Thy name we bless, And hum - bly pray that we

For All Thy Saints—Concluded

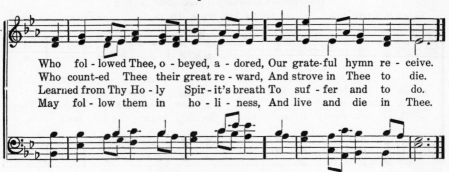

Who fol - lowed Thee, o - beyed, a - dored, Our grate-ful hymn re - ceive.
Who count-ed Thee their great re - ward, And strove in Thee to die.
Learned from Thy Ho - ly Spir - it's breath To suf - fer and to do.
May fol - low them in ho - li - ness, And live and die in Thee.

Heaven is My Home

627

And confessed that they were strangers and pilgrims on the earth.—HEB. 11: 13

6. 4. 6. 4. 6. 6. 6. 4.

LOWELL MASON, 1834

1. I'm but a stran - ger here, Heav'n is my home; Earth is a
2. What though the tem - pest rage, Heav'n is my home; Short is my
3. There at my Sav - iour's side, Heav'n is my home; I shall be

des - ert drear, Heav'n is my home. Dan - ger and sor - row stand
pil - grim-age, Heav'n is my home. Time's cold and win - try blast
glo - ri - fied, Heav'n is my home. There are the good and blest,

Round me on ev - 'ry hand; Heav'n is my fa - ther-land, Heav'n is my home.
Shall soon be o - ver-past; I shall reach home at last, Heav'n is my home.
Those I love most and best, There, too, I soon shall rest, Heav'n is my home.

628 I Will Sing You a Song

In my Father's house are many mansions.—JN. 14: 2

ELLEN H. GATES, 1865 HOME OF THE SOUL 12s. 9s. PHILIP PHILLIPS, 1865

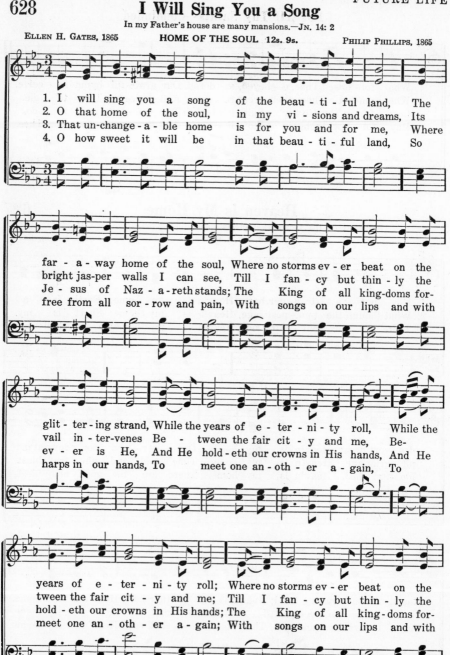

1. I will sing you a song of the beau - ti - ful land, The
2. O that home of the soul, in my vi - sions and dreams, Its
3. That un-change - a - ble home is for you and for me, Where
4. O how sweet it will be in that beau - ti - ful land, So

far - a - way home of the soul, Where no storms ev - er beat on the
bright jas-per walls I can see, Till I fan - cy but thin - ly the
Je - sus of Naz - a - reth stands; The King of all king-doms for-
free from all sor - row and pain, With songs on our lips and with

glit - ter - ing strand, While the years of e - ter - ni - ty roll, While the
vail in - ter-venes Be - tween the fair cit - y and me, Be-
ev - er is He, And He hold-eth our crowns in His hands, And He
harps in our hands, To meet one an - oth - er a - gain, To

years of e - ter - ni - ty roll; Where no storms ev - er beat on the
tween the fair cit - y and me; Till I fan - cy but thin - ly the
hold - eth our crowns in His hands; The King of all king - doms for-
meet one an - oth - er a - gain; With songs on our lips and with

I Will Sing You a Song—Concluded

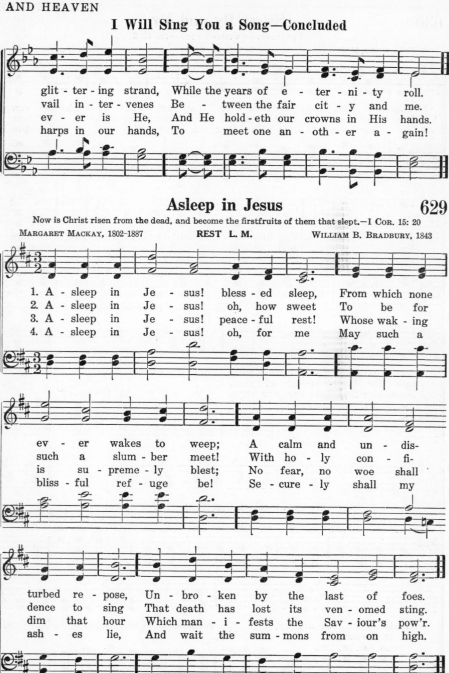

glit - ter - ing strand, While the years of e - ter - ni - ty roll.
vail in - ter - venes Be - tween the fair cit - y and me.
ev - er is He, And He hold - eth our crowns in His hands.
harps in our hands, To meet one an - oth - er a - gain!

Asleep in Jesus   629

Now is Christ risen from the dead, and become the firstfruits of them that slept.—I Cor. 15: 20

MARGARET MACKAY, 1802–1887   **REST L. M.**   WILLIAM B. BRADBURY, 1843

1. A - sleep in Je - sus! bless - ed sleep, From which none
2. A - sleep in Je - sus! oh, how sweet To be for
3. A - sleep in Je - sus! peace - ful rest! Whose wak - ing
4. A - sleep in Je - sus! oh, for me May such a

ev - er wakes to weep; A calm and un - dis-
such a slum - ber meet! With ho - ly con - fi-
is su - preme - ly blest; No fear, no woe shall
bliss - ful ref - uge be! Se - cure - ly shall my

turbed re - pose, Un - bro - ken by the last of foes.
dence to sing That death has lost its ven - omed sting.
dim that hour Which man - i - fests the Sav - iour's pow'r.
ash - es lie, And wait the sum - mons from on high.

481

630

Sweet By and By

I go to prepare a place for you.—Jn. 14: 2

S. F. Bennett, 1867   9. 9. 9. 9. Ref.   J. P. Webster, 1867

1. There's a land that is fair - er than day, And by faith we can see it a - far; For the Fa - ther waits o - ver the way, To pre - pare us a dwell-ing-place there.
2. We shall sing on that beau - ti - ful shore The me - lo - di - ous songs of the blest, And our spir - its shall sor - row no more, Not a sigh for the bless-ing of rest.
3. To our boun - ti - ful Fa - ther a - bove, We will of - fer the trib - ute of praise For the glo - ri - ous gift of His love, And the bless-ings that hal - low our days.

Chorus

In the sweet by and by, We shall meet on that beau - ti - ful shore; In the sweet by and by, We shall meet on that beau - ti - ful shore.

In the sweet by and by, In the sweet by and by,

There is a Land of Pure Delight

631

Thine eyes shall behold the land that is very far off.—Isa. 33: 17

ISAAC WATTS, 1707   **VARINA C. M. D.**   GEO. F. ROOT

1. There is a land of pure de-light, Where saints im-mor-tal reign;
2. Sweet fields be-yond the swell-ing flood Stand dressed in liv-ing green;
3. Oh, could we make our doubts re-move, Those gloom-y doubts that rise,

E-ter-nal day ex-cludes the night, And pleas-ures ban-ish pain.
So to the Jews old Ca-naan stood, While Jor-dan rolled be-tween.
And see the Ca-naan that we love, With un-be-cloud-ed eyes!

There ev-er-last-ing spring a-bides, And nev-er-with-'ring flow'rs;
But tim-'rous mor-tals start and shrink To cross this nar-row sea,
Could we but climb where Mo-ses stood, And view the land-scape o'er,

Death, like a nar-row sea, di-vides This heav'n-ly land from ours.
And lin-ger, trem-bling, on the brink, And fear to launch a-way.
Not Jor-dan's stream, nor death's cold flood, Should fright us from the shore.

632 **Sweet Rest in Heaven**

That they may rest from their labors.—Rev. 14: 13

SARAH C. LEATHERMAN   7. 6. 7. 6. Ref.   M. JANIE LEATHERMAN

1. Some days are dark and drear-y,.... And some are warm and bright;
2. Some-times our hearts are lone-ly, ... Oft - times the way seems hard,
3. Thus when this life is o - ver,.. When comes the time of rest,
4. We'll nev - er then grow wea - ry,... Our toil will all be o'er;
5. Yes, there we'll meet to - geth - er.... With loved ones gone be - fore;

And oft we feel so wea - ry,.... We're glad when comes the night.
But rest comes to us on - ly..... When we de - serve re - ward.
Our souls will rest for - ev - er..... In man-sions of the blest.
These days that are so drear - y...... Will troub - le us no more.
We'll rest and sing for - ev - er..... On that ce - les - tial shore.

REFRAIN

Our rest will soon be giv - en...... By Him who has con - trol;....

There's rest, sweet rest, in heav - en,.... Rest for the wea - ry soul....

484

Shall We Gather At the River

And he showed me a pure river of water of life.—REV. 22: 1

ROBERT LOWRY, 1864

8. 7. 8. 7. Ref.

ROBERT LOWRY

1. Shall we gath - er at the riv - er Where bright an - gel feet have trod;
2. On the mar - gin of the riv - er, Wash - ing up its sil - ver spray,
3. Ere we reach the shin-ing riv - er, Lay we ev - 'ry bur - den down;
4. Soon we'll gath-er at the riv - er, Soon our pil-grim-age will cease;

With its crys - tal tide for - ev - er Flow - ing by the throne of God?
We will walk and wor-ship ev - er, All the hap - py gold - en day.
Grace our spir - its will de - liv - er, And pro - vide a robe and crown.
Soon our hap - py hearts will quiv - er With the mel - o - dy of peace.

CHORUS

Yes, we'll gath-er at the riv - er, The beau-ti-ful, the beau-ti - ful riv - er,—

Gath - er with the saints at the riv - er, That flows by the throne of God.

634 I Love to Think of My Home Above

Set your affection on things above.—COL. 3: 2

LOUSIA E.   MY HOME ABOVE 9. 7. 9. 7. Ref.   CHAS. EDW. POLLOCK

1. I love to think of my home a-bove, In the glo-rious realms of light, Of the pearl-y gates and the gold-en streets, In that land where there is no night. Home, sweet home! Hap-py

2. I love to think of my home a-bove, Of that pure and ho-ly clime, Where the sor-rows of earth can nev-er come, But e-ter-nal joys will be mine.

3. I love to think of my home a-bove, Of the an-gel forms so bright, Of the bless-ed ones there a-round the throne, In the land of pure de-light. Home, sweet home! Home, sweet home!

REFRAIN

home, sweet home! Oh! say will you meet me there,
Home, sweet home! Happy home, sweet home!

In that home a-bove, where all is love, And joy be-yond com-pare?

My Heavenly Home is Bright and Fair
635

He looked for a city which hath foundations, whose builder and maker is God.—HEB. 11: 10

WILLIAM HUNTER, c. 1838   **I'M GOING HOME L. M. D.**   WILLIAM MILLER, 1854

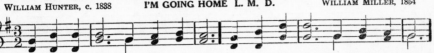

1. My heav'n-ly home is bright and fair, Nor pain, nor death can en - ter there;
2. My Fa-ther's house is built on high, Far, far a - bove the star-ry sky;
3. While here a stran-ger far from home, Af - flic-tion's waves may round me foam;
4. Let oth - ers seek a home be - low, Which flames devour, or waves o'er-flow:
5. Then fail the earth, let stars de - cline, And sun and moon re - fuse to shine,

Its glit-t'ring tow'rs the sun out-shine; That heav'nly man - sion shall be mine.
When from this earth-ly pris - on free, That heav'nly man - sion mine shall be.
Al - tho', like Laz - arus, sick and poor, My heav'nly man - sion is se - cure.
Be mine the hap - pier lot to own A heav'nly man - sion near the throne.
All na - ture sink and cease to be, That heav'nly man - sion stands for me.

REFRAIN

I'm go - ing home, I'm go - ing home, I'm go - ing home to die no more;

To die no more, to die no more, I'm go - ing home to die no more.

636 Often Weary and Worn

We which have believed do enter into rest.—HEB. 4: 3

W. F. COSNER   REST BY AND BY 12s 4l   CHAS. EDW. POLLOCK

1. Oft-en wea-ry and worn on the path-way be-low, When the bur-den is
2. You will not la-bor long for the Mas-ter be-low, Soon His call you will
3. Then, dear Saviour, I would not in sad-ness re-pine, Nor would here on a

heav-y, my heart throbs with woe; Oh, there comes a sweet whis-per to
hear, your free spir-it shall go To the light of His pres-ence in
bed of sweet ros-es re-cline; For a coun-try I seek where they

quell ev-'ry sigh, "Do not faint 'neath the load, there is rest by and by."
man-sions on high, Where the faith-ful re-pose; there is rest by and by.
nev-er-more die, And in Zi-on my home, there is rest by and by.

REFRAIN

There is rest   by and by,
There is rest by and by, there is rest by and by,   In the beau-ti-ful

cit-y there is rest by and by; Where the ran-somed shall live with the

Often Weary and Worn—Concluded

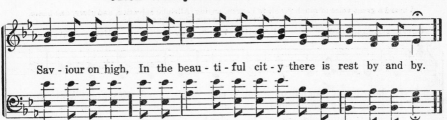

Sav - iour on high, In the beau - ti - ful cit - y there is rest by and by.

Oh, the Bliss of Loved Ones Resting 637

Blessed are they that do His commandments, that they may have right to the tree of life.—REV. 22: 14

JOHN S. COFFMAN ST. SYLVESTER 8. 7. 8. 7. 8. 7. Arr. from JOHN B. DYKES

1. Oh, the bliss of loved ones rest - ing By the crys-tal riv - er bright;
2. For this rest they longed and wait - ed, Heaven's glo - ry was the song;
3. May we not on earth sing with them, Echoing back their notes of praise?
4. Oh, the peace and rest in heav - en! Oh, the bliss of loved ones there!

'Neath the shade of trees im - mor - tal, Where no shad-ows dim the light!
Liv - ing faith now bids us hear them Sing-ing with the blood-washed throng;
Yes, but bless - ed hope in - spires us Heav'n's e - ter-nal songs to raise;
Love di - vine now bears us up - ward All their bless-ed-ness to share;

REFRAIN

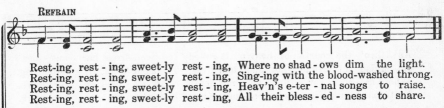

Rest-ing, rest - ing, sweet-ly rest - ing, Where no shad-ows dim the light.
Rest-ing, rest - ing, sweet-ly rest - ing, Sing-ing with the blood-washed throng.
Rest-ing, rest - ing, sweet-ly rest - ing, Heav'n's e - ter - nal songs to raise.
Rest-ing, rest - ing, sweet-ly rest - ing, All their bless - ed - ness to share.

638   I Heard a Sound of Voices

I heard a great voice of much people in heaven, saying, Alleluia; salvation, and glory, and honor,
and power, unto the Lord our God.—REV. 19: 1

GODFREY THRING, 1886   PATMOS 7. 6. 8. 6. D.   HENRY J. STORER, 1891

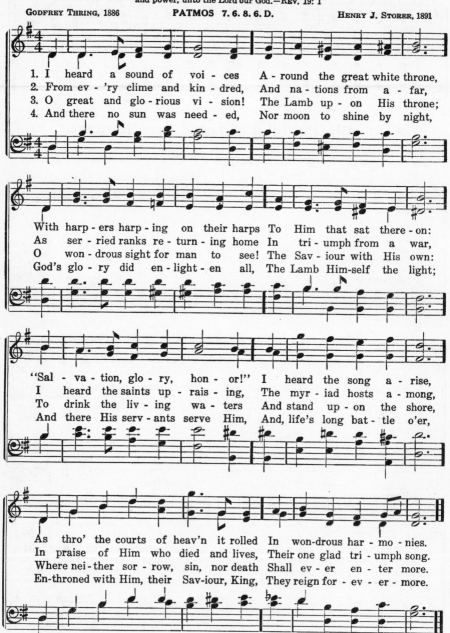

1. I heard a sound of voi - ces   A - round the great white throne,
2. From ev - 'ry clime and kin - dred,   And na - tions from a - far,
3. O great and glo - rious vi - sion!   The Lamb up - on His throne;
4. And there no sun was need - ed,   Nor moon to shine by night,

With harp - ers harp - ing on their harps To Him that sat there - on:
As ser - ried ranks re - turn - ing home In tri - umph from a war,
O won - drous sight for man to see! The Sav - iour with His own:
God's glo - ry did en - light - en all, The Lamb Him - self the light;

"Sal - va - tion, glo - ry, hon - or!" I heard the song a - rise,
I heard the saints up - rais - ing, The myr - iad hosts a - mong,
To drink the liv - ing wa - ters And stand up - on the shore,
And there His serv - ants serve Him, And, life's long bat - tle o'er,

As thro' the courts of heav'n it rolled In won - drous har - mo - nies.
In praise of Him who died and lives, Their one glad tri - umph song.
Where nei - ther sor - row, sin, nor death Shall ev - er en - ter more.
En - throned with Him, their Sav - iour, King, They reign for - ev - er - more.

490

O Paradise

To-day shalt thou be with me in paradise.—Lk. 23: 43

FREDERICK W. FABER, 1862   PARADISE 8. 6. 8. 6. Ref.   JOSEPH BARNBY, 1866

1. O   Par - a - dise! O   Par - a - dise! Who doth not crave for rest?
2. O   Par - a - dise! O   Par - a - dise! The world is grow - ing old;
3. O   Par - a - dise! O   Par - a - dise! I   want to sin   no more;
4. Lord Je - sus, King of Par - a - dise! O   keep me in Thy love,

Who would not seek the hap - py land Where they that loved are blest?
Who would not be   at rest and free Where love is nev - er cold?
I   want to be   as pure on earth As   on thy spot - less shore;
And guide me to   that hap - py land Of per - fect rest a - bove;

REFRAIN

Where loy - al hearts and true
Where loy - - - - al hearts and true Stand ev - er   in   the light,
       loy - al

All rap - ture thro' and thro', In God's most ho - ly sight. A-MEN.

640
Jerusalem, My Happy Home
The Holy City, New Jerusalem.—Rev. 21: 2

AURELIUS AUGUSTINE, 353–430   CANAAN C. M.   HENRY S. RUPP, 1826–1898

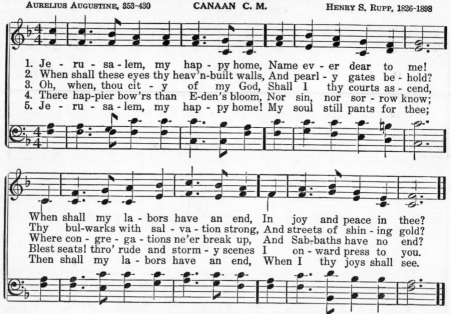

1. Je - ru - sa - lem, my hap - py home, Name ev - er dear to me!
2. When shall these eyes thy heav'n-built walls, And pearl - y gates be - hold?
3. Oh, when, thou cit - y of my God, Shall I thy courts as - cend,
4. There hap-pier bow'rs than E-den's bloom, Nor sin, nor sor - row know,
5. Je - ru - sa - lem, my hap - py home! My soul still pants for thee;

When shall my la - bors have an end, In joy and peace in thee?
Thy bul-warks with sal - va - tion strong, And streets of shin - ing gold?
Where con - gre - ga - tions ne'er break up, And Sab-baths have no end?
Blest seats! thro' rude and storm - y scenes I on - ward press to you.
Then shall my la - bors have an end, When I thy joys shall see.

641
There is No Night in Heaven
There shall be no night there.—Rev. 21: 25

CHARLES WESLEY   WOOLWICH S. M.   CHARLES E. KETTLE

1. There is no night in heav'n; In that blest world a - bove
2. There is no grief in heav'n; For life is one glad day;
3. There is no sin in heav'n; Be - hold that bless - ed throng—
4. There is no death in heav'n; For they who gain that shore

Work nev - er can bring wea - ri - ness, For work it - self is love.
And tears are of those for - mer things Which all have passed a - way.
All ho - ly is their spot - less robe, All ho - ly is their song.
Have won their im - mor - tal - i - ty, And they can die no more.

There's a Beautiful, Beautiful Land

And the city had no need of the sun, for the glory of God did lighten it.—Rev. 21: 23

HOME OF THE BLEST 9. 6. 9. 6. Ref.

H. B. Brenneman, 1883

Henry B. Brenneman

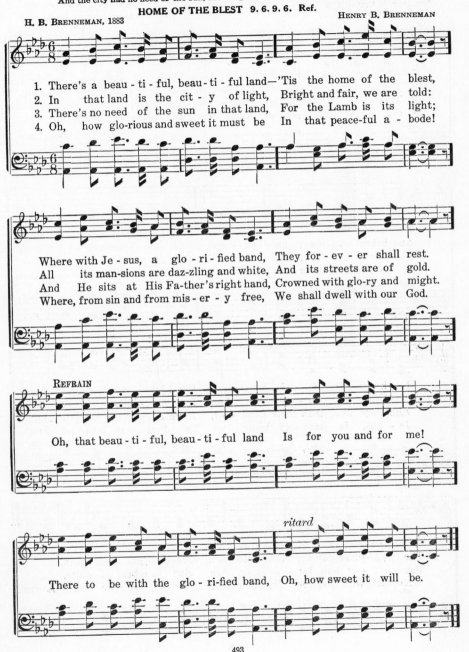

1. There's a beau - ti - ful, beau - ti - ful land—'Tis the home of the blest,
2. In that land is the cit - y of light, Bright and fair, we are told:
3. There's no need of the sun in that land, For the Lamb is its light;
4. Oh, how glo-rious and sweet it must be In that peace-ful a - bode!

Where with Je - sus, a glo - ri - fied band, They for - ev - er shall rest.
All its man-sions are daz-zling and white, And its streets are of gold.
And He sits at His Fa-ther's right hand, Crowned with glo-ry and might.
Where, from sin and from mis - er - y free, We shall dwell with our God.

REFRAIN

Oh, that beau - ti - ful, beau - ti - ful land Is for you and for me!

ritard

There to be with the glo - ri-fied band, Oh, how sweet it will be.

643
Jerusalem the Golden

And the city was pure gold.—REV. 21: 18

BERNARD of CLUNY, 1145
Tr. J. M. NEAL, 1845

EWING 7. 6. 7. 6. D.

ALEXANDER C. EWING, 1853

1. Je - ru - sa - lem the gold - en, With milk and hon - ey blest,
2. They stand, those halls of Si - on, All ju - bi - lant with song,
3. There, is the throne of Da - vid; And there, from care re - leased,
4. O sweet and bless - ed coun - try, The home of God's e - lect!

Be - neath thy con - tem - pla - tion Sink heart and voice op - prest;
And bright with many an an - gel, And all the mar - tyr throng:
The shout of them that tri - umph, The song of them that feast.
O sweet and bless - ed coun - try, That ea - ger hearts ex - pect!

I know not, O I know not, What joys a - wait us there;
The Prince is ev - er in them, The day - light is se - rene;
And they who, with their Lead - er, Have con-quered in the fight,
Je - sus, in mer - cy bring us To that dear land of rest!

What ra - dian - cy of glo - ry, What bliss be - yond com - pare.
The pas - tures of the bless - ed Are decked in glo - rious sheen.
For - ev - er and for - ev - er Are clad in robes of white.
Who art, with God the Fa - ther, And Spir - it, ev - er blest. A - MEN.

Praise God From Whom All Blessings Flow   644

REV. 5: 13

OLD HUNDRED L. M.

GUILLAUME FRANC, 1543
Genevan Psalter, 1551

THOMAS KEN, 1695

Praise God from whom all blessings flow, Praise Him all creatures here be-low,

Praise Him a-bove, ye heav'n-ly host, Praise Fa-ther, Son, and Ho-ly Ghost.

May the Grace of Christ Our Saviour   645

II COR. 13: 11-14

SARDIS 8. 7. 8. 7.

JOHN NEWTON, 1779

Arr. from LUDWIG VAN BEETHOVEN, 1805

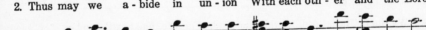

1. May the grace of Christ our Sav-iour, And the Fa-ther's boundless love,
2. Thus may we a-bide in un-ion With each oth-er and the Lord,

With the Ho-ly Spir-it's fa-vor, Rest up-on us from a-bove.
And pos-sess, in sweet com-mun-ion, Joys which earth can-not af-ford.   A-MEN.

646 **Gloria Patri**

EPH. 3: 21

Anon.

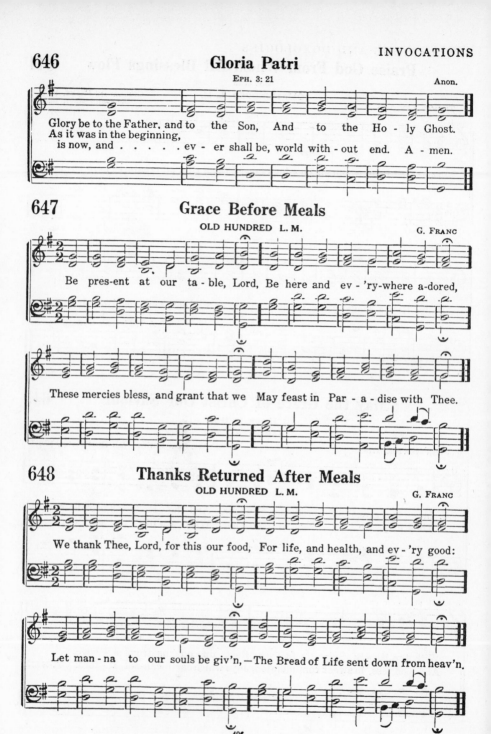

Glory be to the Father, and to the Son, And to the Ho - ly Ghost.
As it was in the beginning,
is now, and . . . . . ev - er shall be, world with - out end. A - men.

647 **Grace Before Meals**

OLD HUNDRED L. M.

G. FRANC

Be pres-ent at our ta - ble, Lord, Be here and ev - 'ry-where a-dored,

These mercies bless, and grant that we May feast in Par - a - dise with Thee.

648 **Thanks Returned After Meals**

OLD HUNDRED L. M.

G. FRANC

We thank Thee, Lord, for this our food, For life, and health, and ev - 'ry good:

Let man - na to our souls be giv'n, — The Bread of Life sent down from heav'n.

I Will Lift Up Mine Eyes

649

PSALM 121

B. C. BLODGETT

1 I will lift up mine eyes unto the mountains: from *whence* shall | my help | come ‖ My help cometh from the *Lord* | which made | heaven and | earth.

2 He will not suffer thy foot to be moved: He that *keep*eth thee | will not | slumber ‖ Behold He that keepeth *Is*rael shall | neither | slumber nor | sleep.

3 The Lord is thy keeper: the Lord is thy *shade* upon thy | right— | hand ‖ The sun shall not smite thee by *day* | nor the | moon by | night.

4 The Lord shall keep thee from all evil; *He* shall | keep thy | soul ‖ The Lord shall keep thy going out and thy coming in, from this time *forth* | and for | ever | more.

O Come, Let Us Sing

650

PSALM 95: 1-7; 96: 9

WILLIAM BOYCE, 1740

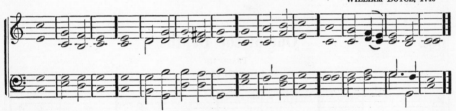

1 O come, let us *sing* | unto the | Lord ‖ let us heartily re*joice* in the | strength of | our sal | vation.

2 Let us come before His *pres*ence with | thanks — | giving ‖ and show our*selves* | glad in | Him with | psalms.

3 For the *Lord* is a | great — | God ‖ and a *great* | King a | bove all | gods.

4 In His hand are all the *cor*ners | of the | earth ‖ and the *strength* of the | hills is | His — | also.

5 The sea is *His* | and He | made it ‖ and His *hands* pre | pared the | dry — | land.

6 O come let us *wor*ship and | fall — | down ‖ and *kneel* be | fore the | Lord our | Maker.

7 For *He* is the | Lord our | God ‖ and we are the people of His pasture *and* the | sheep of | His — | hand.

8 O worship the *Lord* in the | beauty of | holiness ‖ let the whole *earth* | stand in | awe of | Him.

651   **O Be Joyful In the Lord**

PSALM 100

JUBILATE DEO   H. N. ALDRICH, 1647–1710

1 O be joyful in the *Lord* | all ye | lands: ‖ serve the Lord with gladness, and come be*fore* His | presence | with a | song.

2 Be ye sure that the *Lord* | He is | God; ‖ it is He that hath made us, and not we ourselves; we are His people, *and* the | sheep of | His — | pasture.

3 O go your way into His gates with thanksgiving, and *into* His | courts with | praise: ‖ be thankful unto *Him* and | speak good | of His | name.

4 For the Lord is gracious, His *mercy* is | ever | lasting; ‖ and His truth endureth from *gen*er | ation to | gener | ation.

5 Glory be to the *Father* | and to the | Son, ‖ *and* | to the | Holy | Ghost.

6 As it was in the beginning, is *now* and | ever | shall be, ‖ *world* — | without | end. A | MEN.

652   **Out of the Depths**

PSALM 130

DE PROFUNDIS   Unknown

1 Out of the depths have I cried unto *Thee* O | Lord: ‖ Lord, *hear* my | voice. ‖ Let Thine ears *be* at | tentive ‖ to the voice of my *suppli* | cations.

2 If Thou, Lord, shouldst *mark* in | iquities, ‖ O Lord, *who* shall | stand? ‖ But there is for*give*ness with | Thee, ‖ that Thou *may*est be | feared.

3 I wait for the Lord, my *soul* doth | wait; ‖ and in His *word* do I | hope. ‖ My soul waiteth for the Lord more than they that *watch* for the | morning: ‖ I say, more than they that *watch* for the | morning.

4 Let Israel *hope* in the | Lord; ‖ for with the Lord there is mercy, and with Him there is plen*teous* re | demption. ‖ And He shall redeem *Isra* | el ‖ from all *his* in | iquities.

Send Out Thy Light and Thy Truth

PSALM 43: 3

LUX FIAT

CHARLES F. GOUNOD

Send out Thy light and Thy truth, let them lead me; O, let them bring me to Thy ho - - ly hill. Send out Thy light and Thy truth, let them lead me; O, let them bring me to Thy ho - ly hill. O, let them lead me, O, let them lead me; O, let them bring me to Thy ho - ly hill. A - MEN.

654 Holy, Holy, Holy, Lord of Hosts

ISAIAH 6: 3

HOLY CITY

ALFRED R. GAUL

Ho - ly, Ho - - ly, Ho - ly, Lord of Hosts; Ho - ly,

Ho - - ly, Ho - ly is the Lord of Hosts. A - MEN.

655 The Lord Is In His Holy Temple

HABAKKUK 2: 20

E. O. EXCELL

The Lord is in His ho - ly tem - ple: Let all the

earth keep si - lence, keep si - lence be - fore... Him. A - MEN.

The Lord Bless Us and Keep Us 656

NUMBERS 6. 24–26
BENEDICTION

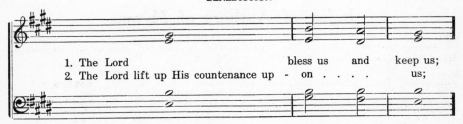

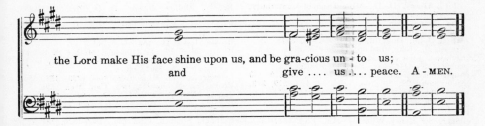

1. The Lord .... bless us and keep us;
2. The Lord lift up His countenance up - on .... us;

the Lord make His face shine upon us, and be gra-cious un - to us;
and .... give .... us .... peace. A - MEN.

The Lord's Prayer 657

MATTHEW 6: 9–13

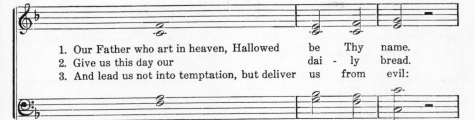

1. Our Father who art in heaven, Hallowed be Thy name.
2. Give us this day our .... dai - ly bread.
3. And lead us not into temptation, but deliver us from evil:

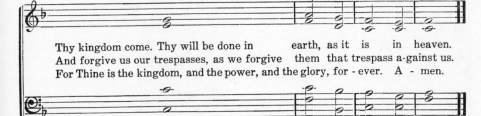

Thy kingdom come. Thy will be done in earth, as it is in heaven.
And forgive us our trespasses, as we forgive them that trespass a-gainst us.
For Thine is the kingdom, and the power, and the glory, for - ever. A - men.

TYPOGRAPHY BY ANDERSON BROS.
117 W. HARRISON ST., CHICAGO

Index of Authors of Hymns

Abbreviations: Am., American; Can., Canadian; Dea., Deacon; Eng., English; Ger., German; Ir., Irish; Men., Mennonite Church; Min., Minister; Sc., Scotch;

Adams, Mrs. Sarah, (Flower) Eng., 1805-1848, 369
Addison, Joseph M. A. Eng. 1672-1719, 9, 31
Alexander, Mrs. Cecil Frances, Ir. 1823-1895, 106, 473
Alexander, Mrs. C. M., 569
Alexander, James Waddell, Am. 1804-1859, 121
Alford, Henry, D. D., Min., Dean of Canterbury, Author, 1810-1871, 142, 245, 572
Allen, James, Min. Eng. 1734-1804, 43, 71,
Anderson, Mrs. G. W., 1819——, 507
Argyll, John, Duke of, Sc. 1845-1914, 393
Armstrong, John, Bishop, 1813-1856, 601
Atchison, John Bush, Min. Am. 1840-1882, 556
Auber, Mrs. Harriett, Eng. 1773-1862, 158
Augustine, Aurelius, Bishop of H'ppo, 353-430, 640
Anonymous, 33, 50, 100, 138, 172, 183, 219, 273, 285, 302, 316, 327, 344, 366, 442, 444, 456, 540, 597, 608, 613, 627, 646, 647, 648, 654

Baker, Sir Henry Williams, Min. Eng. 1821-1877, 44, 253, 482, 574
Bakewell, John, Min. Eng. 1721-1819, 65
Barbauld, Mrs. Anna Laetetia, Nee Aiken, Eng. 1743-1825, 579
Barber, Mary A. S., 1840——, 421
Baring-Gould, Sabine, M. A., Min. Eng. 1834-1924, 216, 493
Barnard, Mrs. Charlotte, 411
Barton, Bernard, Bank Clerk, Eng. Poet, 1784-1849, 239, 443
Bathurst, W'lliam Hiley, Min. Eng. 1796-1877, 149, 461, 616
Baxter, Mrs. Lydia, Am. 1809-1874, 486, 538
Bennet, S. Fillmore, Am. 1836-1898, 630
Bernard of Clairvaux, Gallican, Abbott of Burgundy, 1091-1153, 78, 86, 121
Bernard of Cluny, Fr., 12th Century, 643
Bethune, George Washington, D. D., Min., 83, 615
Bickersteth, Edward Henry, D. D., Bishop, Eng. 1825-1906, 317, 358, 455
Biegle, H. B., 257
Billhorn Peter P., Am. Evangelist, Singer, 1861—, 257
Birks, Canon Thomas Rawson, Eng. 1810-1883, 191
Blackall, Chr'stopher Ruby, Am. 1830——, 525
Blackie, John Stuart, Prof. of Greek, Sc., 1809-1895, 573
Blacklock, Thomas, Sc. 1721-1791, 13
Blachford, Ambrose M., Min. Eng., 1842——, 212
Bliss, Philip Paul, Am. Evangelist, Singer, 1838-1876, 236, 255, 469, 515, 534, 558
Bode, John Ernest, M. A., Min. Eng., 1816-1874, 363
Bonar, Horatius, D. D., Min. Sc., 1808-1889, 41, 148, 254, 267, 312, 364, 382, 428, 449, 499, 529, 559
Bonar, Mrs. Jane G., (Mrs. Horatius) Sc., 1821-1884, 301
Booth, Ballington, Eng. Am., 1859——, 481
Borthwick, Jane, Sc., 1813-1897, 426
Bowly, Mary P., 324
Bowr'ng, Sir John, LL. D., Eng., 1792-1872, 450

Brady, Nicholas, Min. Eng., 1659-1726, 355
Breck, Mrs. Frank A., 143
Brenneman, Henry B., Dea. Men., b. 1831, Fairfield, O., d. 1887, Elkhart, Ind., 642
Bridane, Jaques, Min. Gallican, 1701-1767, 112
Bridges, Matthew, Eng. Ang., 1800-1894, 137, 141, 322
Brooks, Phillips, Bishop, D. D., Am. 1835-1893, 91
Brooks, Stopford Augustus, Min. Ir., 1832-1918, 114
Brown, Jessie H., 1661——, 243
Brown, Mrs. Phoebe Hinsdale, Mother of Samuel Brown, P'oneer American Missionary to Japan, 1783-1861, 440
Browne, Simon, Min. Eng., 1660-1732, 155, 584
Brubacher, Menno M., Dea. Can. Men., 596
Bruce, Michael, Sc. 1746-1767, 287, 480
Bryant, William Cullen, Am. Poet and Author, 1794-1878, 591
Bulfinch, Stephen, Min. Am., 1809-1870, 181
Bullock, Dean William, Can., 1798-1874, 171
Burleigh, William Henry, Am., 1812-1871, 402
Burns, James Drummond, Min. Sc., 1823-1864, 215, 586
Burton, John Jr., Dea. Eng., 1803-1877, 231
Byler, Elsie, Am. Men. (1911), 19

Campbell, Margaret C., 1827-1841, 8
Canitz, Frederick R. L. von, Ger. Privy Counselor, 1654-1699, 199
Cary, Miss Phoebe, Am. Poet, 1824-1871, 310
Cawood, John, M. A., Min. Eng., 1775-1852, 98
Cennick, John, Min. Surveyor, Evangelist, Eng., 1718-1765, 144, 347
Chord, S. H., 610
Clark, Emily V., (1891), 512
Clark, W. H., 67
Claudius, Matthias, Ger. Author, 1740-1815, 577
Cleator, Alice Jean, 399
Clement of Alexandria, 170-220, 55
Clephane, Miss Elizabeth Cecil'a, Sc., 1830-1869, 108
Codner, Mrs. Elizabeth Harrison, Eng. Mildmay Protestant Mission, 1835——, 532
Coffman, John S.. Men. Evangelist, b. 1848, Va., d. 1899, Elkhart, Ind., 561, 637
Coffman, Samuel Frederick, Bishop, Men., 1872-——, 167, 323, 325, 330
Coghill, Anna Louisa, (Walker) Can., 1836-1907, 502
Coll'ns, Henry A., M. A., Min. Eng., 1830——, 435
Conder, Josiah, Eng. Author and Publisher, 1789-1855, 63, 314, 414
Cosner, W. F., 636
Cotterill, Thomas, Min. Eng., 1779-1823, 605
Cousin, Annie Ross, Sc., 1824-1926, 377
Cowper, William, Eng. Poet, 1731-1800, 169, 367, 396
Coxe, Arthur Cleveland, D. D., LL. D., Bishop, Am., 1818-1896, 88, 336, 568
Craig, R. J., Min., 338
Crewdson, Mrs. Jane (Fox), Eng., 1809-1863, 282

502

INDEX OF AUTHORS OF HYMNS

503

17

Index of Composers of Tunes

Abbreviations: Am., American; Eng., English; Ger., German; Ir., Irish; Men., Mennonite; Min., Minister.

INDEX OF COMPOSERS OF TUNES

507

INDEX OF COMPOSERS OF TUNES

Index of Scripture Texts

INDEX OF SCRIPTURE TEXTS

Metrical Index of Tunes

512

514

Index of Tunes

INDEX OF TUNES

Subject Index of Hymns

518

SUBJECT INDEX OF HYMNS

519

SUBJECT INDEX OF HYMNS

·SUBJECT INDEX OF HYMNS

SUBJECT INDEX OF HYMNS

523

SUBJECT INDEX OF HYMNS

524

SUBJECT INDEX OF HYMNS

SUBJECT INDEX OF HYMNS

527

SUBJECT INDEX OF HYMNS

528

SUBJECT INDEX OF HYMNS

529

Index of First Lines and Titles

Titles in caps; first lines in small type

INDEX OF FIRST LINES AND TITLES

531

INDEX OF FIRST LINES AND TITLES

INDEX OF FIRST LINES AND TITLES

INDEX OF FIRST LINES AND TITLES

INDEX OF FIRST LINES AND TITLES